Everyday Mathematics®

The University of Chicago School Mathematics Project

Teacher's Guide to Activities

Pre-Kindergarten Pre-K

Mc Graw Hill Wright Group

The McGraw·Hill Companies

Everyday Mathematics

The University of Chicago School Mathematics Project (UCSMP)

Max Bell, Director, UCSMP Elementary Materials Component; Director, *Everyday Mathematics* First Edition
James McBride, Director, *Everyday Mathematics* Second Edition
Andy Isaacs, Director, *Everyday Mathematics* Third Edition
Amy Dillard, Associate Director, *Everyday Mathematics* Third Edition

Authors

Deborah Arron Leslie, Ann E. Audrain, Jean Bell,

Max Bell, Jeanine O'Nan Brownell

Third Edition Early Childhood Team Leaders

Deborah Arron Leslie, David W. Beer

Technical Art
Diana Barrie

Editorial Assistant
Patrick Carroll

Consultant
Arthur J. Baroody

Mathematics and Technology Advisor
James Flanders

Contributors
Dorothy Freedman, Margaret Krulee

Field Test Director
David W. Beer

Illustrator Credits
Deborah Melmon, Elizabeth Allen

Photo Credits
©Brand X Pictures/Fotosearch, p. 2; ©1989 Jan Brett, used by permission of G.P. Putnam's Sons, p. 11, 150; ©Dorling Kindersley/Getty Images, cover *right*; Ed-Imaging, p. xxvii, 104, 105, 276; ©Fotosearch, LLC, p. 97 *right*; ©Cadence Gamache, p. xix, xxxii, 167; cover and back photograph by Sharon Hoogstraten, courtesy of Dave Wyman; ©iStock International Inc., p. xxi, 19, 328, 329; ©Jupitermedia Corporation, p. 97 *left*; ©Ken O'Donoghue, p. xxiii, 19; ©JoLin/Shutterstock, Inc., p. 329; ©Shutterstock, Inc., cover *top;* Julie Vogel, p.324.

www.WrightGroup.com

 **Wright Group**

Printed in the United States of America.

Send all inquiries to:
Wright Group/McGraw-Hill
P.O. Box 812960
Chicago, IL 60681

ISBN 978-0-07-604509-9
MHID 0-07-604509-9

2 3 4 5 6 7 8 9 CPS 13 12 11 10 09 08 07

The University of Chicago School Mathematics Project (UCSMP)

Acknowledgments

The first edition of *Everyday Mathematics* was made possible by sustained support over several years from the GTE Corporation and the National Science Foundation; additional help came from the Amoco Foundation through its support of the University of Chicago School Mathematics Project (UCSMP). Earlier projects supported by the National Science Foundation, the National Institute of Education, and the Benton Foundation provided us with insights into the surprising capabilities of young children.

Development of the second edition of *Everyday Mathematics* was funded by the Everyday Learning Corporation and the authors; development of this third edition was supported by Wright Group/McGraw-Hill, the University of Chicago, and the authors.

For all three editions, many University of Chicago and UCSMP colleagues have been helpful. For this third edition, Deborah Arron Leslie, David W. Beer, Rachel Malpass McCall, Cheryl G. Moran, Mary Ellen Dairyko, Amy Dillard, Noreen Winningham, and Ann McCarty formed a committee that provided invaluable guidance on many key issues. We also acknowledge dedicated and resourceful assistance on production and technical tasks by many people at the University of Chicago and at Wright Group/McGraw-Hill.

Over the years that UCSMP has been working in schools, feedback and advice from teachers willing to take risks in trying development versions of our materials have been essential and enormously helpful. There are too many such teachers to list, but their contributions are gratefully acknowledged.

Andy Isaacs
Director, Third Edition

James McBride
Director, Second Edition

Max Bell
Director, First Edition

Contents

Everyday Mathematics®

A Mission to Improve School Mathematics

"We, our funders, and our users, believe strongly that even the best curricula of decades ago are not adequate for today's youth."

University of Chicago School Mathematics Project

The University of Chicago School Mathematics Project

Everyday Mathematics was developed by the University of Chicago School Mathematics Project (UCSMP) in order to enable children in elementary grades to learn more mathematical content and become life-long mathematical thinkers.

◆ The National Science Foundation, Amoco, GTE, and other leading corporations supported the project through substantial, long-term funding.

◆ A strong partnership was developed among researchers, mathematics educators, classroom teachers, students, and administrators.

◆ A consistent, core author team at the University of Chicago School Mathematics Project collaborated on all grade levels to provide a cohesive and well-articulated Pre-K through Grade 6 curriculum.

Research Foundation

Everyday Mathematics begins with the premise that students can, and must, learn more mathematics than has been expected from them in the past. This premise is based on research the UCSMP author team undertook prior to writing the curriculum. Following are some major findings of this research:

◆ The typical U.S. mathematics curriculum is arithmetic-driven, slow-paced with isolated instruction, and broad, without depth of content.

◆ International studies show that U.S. students learn much less mathematics than students in other countries.

◆ Children are capable of learning more mathematics in a richer curriculum.

◆ All children can be successful mathematical thinkers.

◆ Mathematics is meaningful to children when it is varied, rich, and rooted in real-world problems and applications.

Instructional Design

The *Everyday Mathematics* instructional design was carefully crafted to capitalize on student interest and maximize student learning.

◆ High expectations for all students
◆ Concepts and skills developed over time and in a wide variety of contexts
◆ Balance among mathematical strands
◆ Dynamic applications
◆ Multiple methods and strategies for problem solving
◆ Concrete modeling as a pathway to abstract understanding
◆ Collaborative learning in partner and small-group activities
◆ Cross-curricular applications and connections
◆ Built-in professional development for teachers

Everyday Mathematics®

Meeting Standards, Achieving Results

The *Everyday Mathematics* program is celebrating 20 years of research and development. The program offers schools results unmatched by any other elementary mathematics program.

Research, Validation, Results

As part of the research for *Everyday Mathematics,* the authors at the University of Chicago School Mathematics Project examined successful curricula from around the world, researched how children learn mathematics, and studied the actual use of mathematics by people in their everyday lives. The results of this research were used to establish the scope and sequence for the mathematical content of the *Everyday Mathematics* program.

Field Testing

The program was written and field tested one grade at a time. Field tests gathered information from classroom teachers and students in three main areas: teacher use of materials, student response to materials, and student achievement. Based on teacher and student feedback, the authors revised the curriculum before *Everyday Mathematics* was published.

Learner Verification

The best way to show effectiveness of a program is to study it over time. Several independent research studies have been conducted which provide evidence for the effectiveness of *Everyday Mathematics.* For example, *Everyday Mathematics* was the focus of a five-year longitudinal study conducted by researchers at Northwestern University. Reports from this study and others are available through the University of Chicago School Mathematics Project or Wright Group/McGraw-Hill

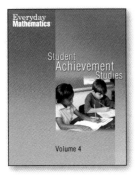

Volume 4

Volume 5

Tri-State Student Achievement Study

The ARC Center, a National Science Foundation (NSF) project, located at the Consortium for Mathematics and Its Applications (COMAP), studied the effects of standards-based mathematics programs on student performance on state-mandated standardized tests in Massachusetts, Illinois, and Washington.

The findings in this report are based on the records of over 78,000 students: 39,701 who had used the *Everyday Mathematics* curriculum for at least two years, and 38,481 students from comparison schools. The students were carefully matched by reading level, socioeconomic status, and other variables.

Results showed that the average scores of students in the *Everyday Mathematics* schools were consistently higher than the average scores of students in the comparison schools. The results hold across different state-mandated tests and across topics ranging from computation, measurement, and geometry to algebra, problem-solving, and making connections. (A complete report is available from COMAP or Wright Group/McGraw-Hill.)

Closing the Gap

Many districts using the *Everyday Mathematics* program have helped minority students close any previously experienced achievement gap, while maintaining achievement growth in all other student categories. This helps schools and districts meet adequate yearly progress set forth by No Child Left Behind legislation. District information is available by contacting Wright Group/McGraw-Hill.

Everyday Mathematics®

Rigorous Mathematics

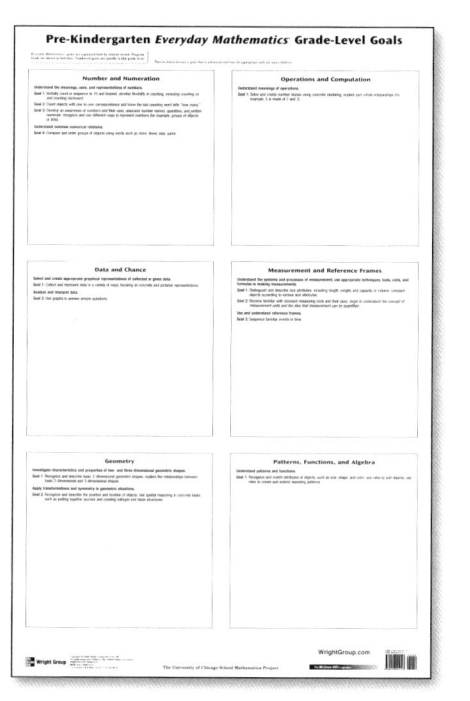

Program Goals and Grade-Level Goals

Everyday Mathematics structures content into Grade-Level Goals and Program Goals. Grade-Level Goals are then organized by content strand and are carefully articulated across the grades. The content in each grade provides all children with a balanced mathematics curriculum that is rich in real-world problem-solving opportunities. The success of this approach to teaching mathematics is evident in children's improved scores on standardized tests.

Number and Numeration
- Understand the meanings, uses, and representations of numbers
- Understand equivalent names for numbers
- Understand common numerical relations

Operations and Computation
- Compute accurately
- Make reasonable estimates
- Understand meanings of operations

Data and Chance
- Select and create appropriate graphical representations of collected or given data
- Analyze and interpret data
- Understand and apply basic concepts of probability

Measurement and Reference Frames
- Understand the systems and processes of measurement; use appropriate techniques, tools, units, and formulas in making measurements
- Use and understand reference frames

Geometry
- Investigate characteristics and properties of two- and three-dimensional geometric shapes
- Apply transformations and symmetry in geometric situations

Patterns, Functions, and Algebra
- Understand patterns and functions
- Use algebraic notation to represent and analyze situations and structures

Everyday Mathematics

Components at a Glance

The table below shows core materials that are used on a regular basis throughout *Pre-Kindergarten Everyday Mathematics.*

PRE-KINDERGARTEN MATERIALS

Teacher's Guide to Activities
Easy-to-follow classroom activities and ongoing daily routines, as well as a section about math in all areas of the Pre-K classroom.

Math Masters
Blackline masters for activities, routines, Family Connections, and games.

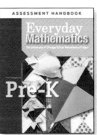

Assessment Handbook
Pre-Kindergarten-specific handbook that provides ideas for ongoing and periodic assessment. Includes blackline masters for tracking progress.

Resources for the Pre-Kindergarten Classroom
Contains curriculum support materials including optional theme-based activities; lists of books, games, songs, masters, software; and ideas for family letters.

Minute Math® Contains brief activities for transition times and for spare moments throughout the day.

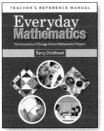

Teacher's Reference Manual
Contains comprehensive background information about mathematical content and program management for Early Childhood.

Mathematics at Home Books
Engaging activities for children to do at home with their families.

TECHNOLOGY COMPONENT

Sing Everyday! Songs to accompany many activities in the *Teacher's Guide to Activities.*

Everyday Mathematics®

Planning and Instructional Support

Pre-Kindergarten *Everyday Mathematics* organizes content into eight topics. Each Topic Opener provides an overview of the content for the section. Also included is support for ongoing learning and practice, assessment, and differentiated instruction. Topic Openers are useful for planning and advance preparation.

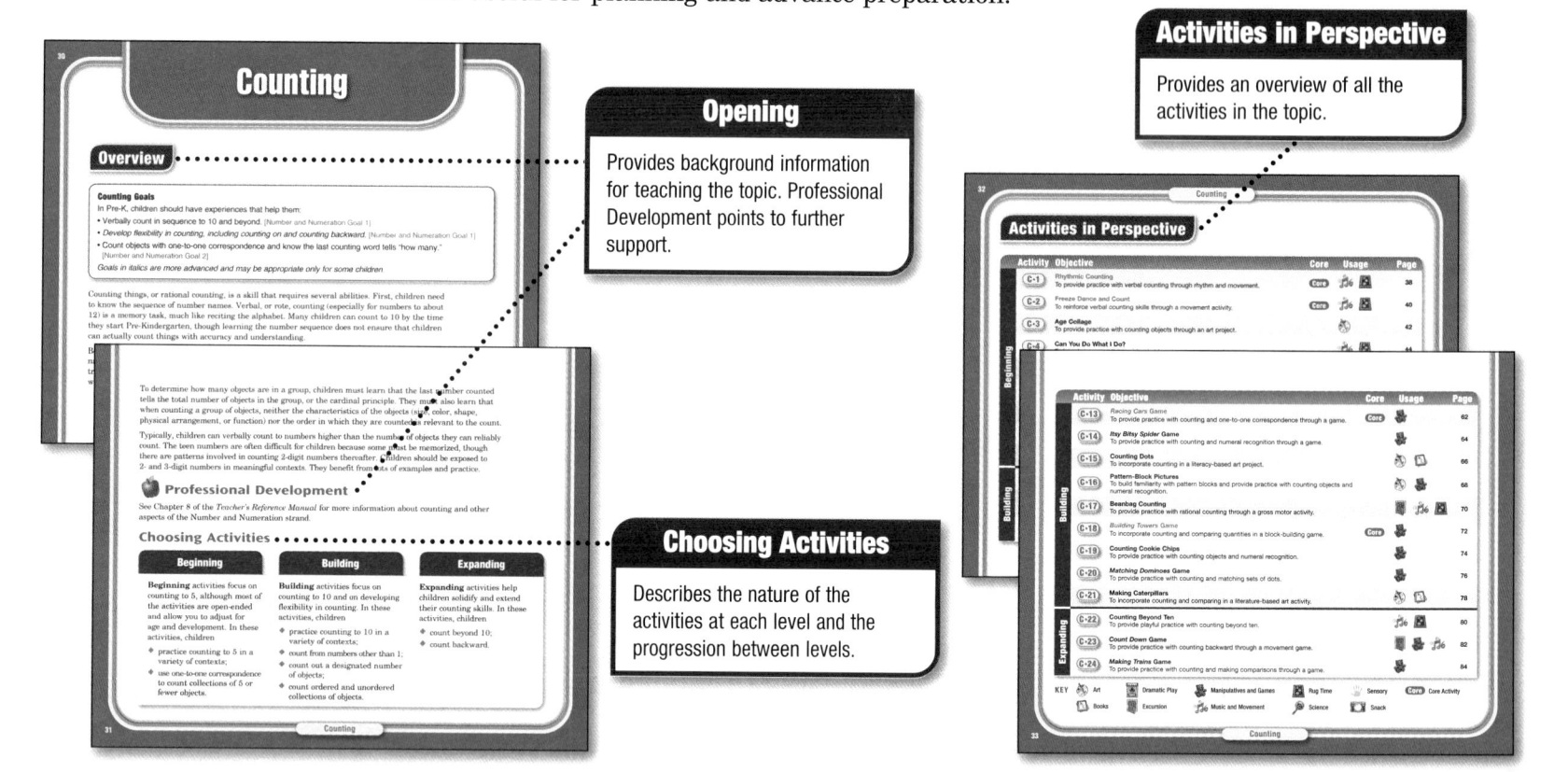

Activities in Perspective

Provides an overview of all the activities in the topic.

Opening

Provides background information for teaching the topic. Professional Development points to further support.

Choosing Activities

Describes the nature of the activities at each level and the progression between levels.

Differentiated Instruction

Offers adaptations for a wide-range of pre-school classrooms.

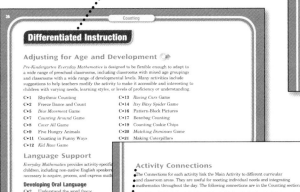

Teaching Resources

Highlights home activities. Also, provides extra teaching ideas using games, songs, poems, books, technology, and *Minute Math*.

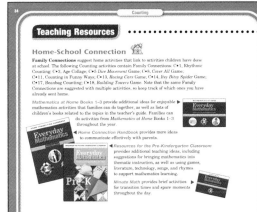

Ongoing Assessment

Includes opportunities to assess progress toward Grade-Level Goals.

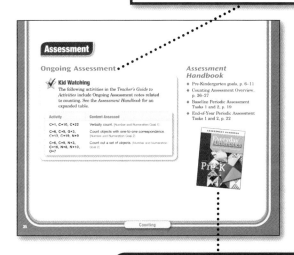

Assessment Support

Includes Assessment Masters and additional uses of the *Assessment Handbook*.

Activity Connections

Summarizes links from the Main Activity to different curricular and classroom areas.

Everyday Mathematics®

Instructional Plan

Activity Support

▶ **Main Activity**　　　　▶ **Connections**

Topic Indicator

Describes the main mathematical topic for the activity. Pre-K *Everyday Mathematics* is organized into eight mathematical topics: Counting, Number Concepts, Operations, Graphing, Measurement, Shapes, Position and Spatial Relationships, and Patterns and Sorting.

Core Activity

Identified here in this symbol. Of 118 activities, fifty-two are labeled as Core.

Main Activities

Main instruction for the activity.

Number Concepts

N•6　Comparing in Trays

◎ **Objective**　To provide concrete experiences with comparing quantities.

Core Activity

Key Mathematics Concepts and Skills
- Count dots on a die. [Number and Numeration Goal 2]
- Visually compare two sets of objects. [Number and Numeration Goal 4]
- Use terms such as *more, less, fewer,* and *same* to describe comparisons. [Number and Numeration Goal 4]

Other Skills Cooperation, Pretending and Role Play

Terms to Use more, less, fewer, same amount

Materials ice-cube trays or egg cartons; masking tape or marker; counters; dot dice; small and large toy animals and paper plates (optional)

▶ **Main Activity**　　Whole Group　✔Small Group　✔Partners　✔Center

Have partners sit side-by-side with an ice-cube tray or egg carton between them. Place the tray vertically between the children, so that each child has his or her own column of cups. Mark the start at the bottom edge of the tray with masking tape or a marker.

Children take turns rolling a die. They say the number, count out that number of counters, and put one counter in each cup on their side of the tray. (Be sure children start filling cups from the bottom of the tray.) After each partner has had a turn, they compare the number of counters on each side of the tray. Encourage children to use comparison words such as *more, less, fewer,* and *same.* Children clear the tray before they roll and compare again.

Planning Tip If you do not have ice-cube trays or egg cartons, you can use masking tape to divide a cookie sheet or cafeteria tray into 12 sections.

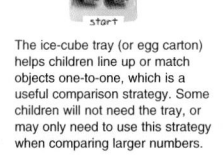

start

The ice-cube tray (or egg carton) helps children line up or match objects one-to-one, which is a useful comparison strategy. Some children will not need the tray, or may only need to use this strategy when comparing larger numbers.

To add interest, you may want to allow children to "feed" the counters to stuffed animals after each round. Provide two toy animals (one larger than the other) and two paper plates. After each round, the child with more counters feeds them to the larger animal, and the child with fewer counters feeds them to the smaller animal. Children make a food pile for each animal and add counters with each turn.

Adjusting for Age and Development

For some children, you may want to begin with dice having 1–3 dots, then expand to numbers 4–6.

Ongoing Assessment: Kid Watching

You can use this activity to informally assess children's ability to visually compare sets of objects and describe the comparisons using words such as *more, fewer, less,* and *same.*

Connections

Snack Connection Give each child a small handful (6 or less of each) of two different types of small snacks (pretzels and raisins, for example). Have them line up each type of snack side by side so they can compare which type they have more of. You may need to help children arrange the items side by side. Provide trays or egg cartons for children who need them.

Mathematics Connection Have a small group of 3–4 children each roll a dot die. Children line up the dice in order from the least to the most dots. Dice with the same number of dots can be stacked.

105 | **Beginning**

Connections
Suggestions for connecting the activity to different curricular and classroom areas.

Level Indicator
Describes whether the difficulty is Beginning, Building, or Expanding.

ELL

Developing Oral Language

This activity will help children develop their understanding of the words *more, less, fewer,* and *same amount.* You can enhance children's learning by modeling the use of comparative language. For example: *You have more because all of your cups are full and she has an empty cup. Yours both go up this high, so you have the same amount.*

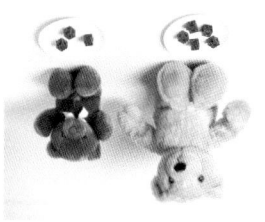

Children may want to "feed" the larger set to the larger bear and the smaller set to the smaller bear.

Everyday Mathematics®

Assessment

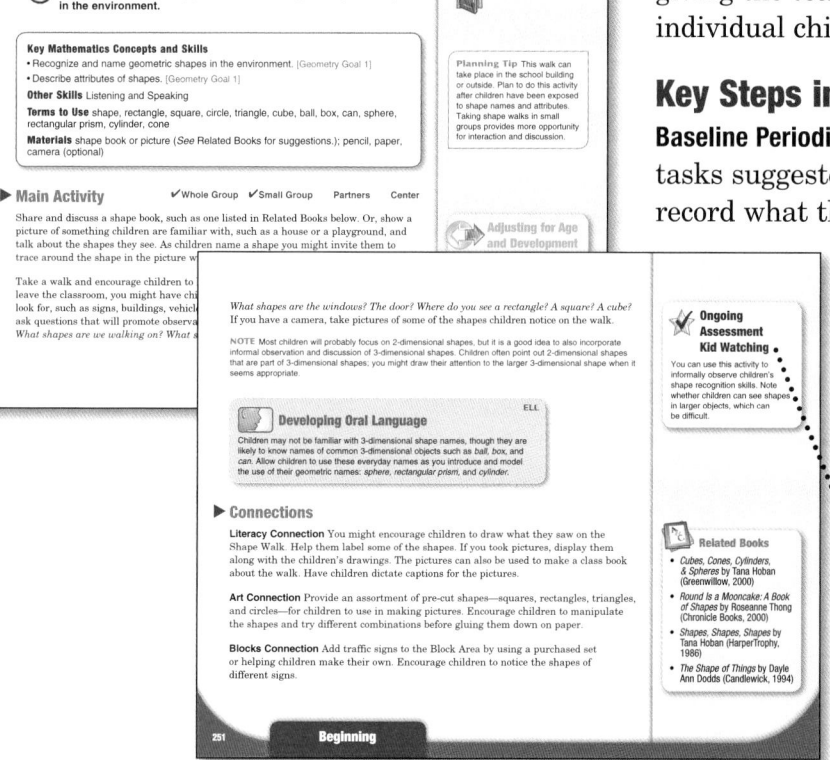

In *Everyday Mathematics,* assessment is like a motion picture revealing the development of each child's mathematical understanding over time, giving the teacher useful feedback about the instructional needs of both individual children and the class as a whole.

Key Steps in Assessment

Baseline Periodic Assessment At the beginning of the year, use the baseline tasks suggested in the *Assessment Handbook* to help you observe and record what the kids understand and can do.

Ongoing Assessment Observe children as they do the activities to assess their skills and understanding. Kid-watching opportunities are highlighted in many of the activities. These can be found either in the margins or the main text column.

End-of-year Periodic Assessment Use the end-of-the year tasks suggested in the *Assessment Handbook* to help you determine how children have progressed.

Kid Watching

Notes suggest how to use kid-watching to effectively adapt instruction and monitor children's progress.

Types of Assessment

The *Assessment Handbook* provides ideas and tools for creating a complete picture of each child's progress and making assessment and instruction more manageable, productive, and exciting. Samples of assessment recording tools offered in the *Assessment Handbook* are pictured below.

◆ **Ongoing Assessment** Informal kid-watching and anecdotal record keeping, as well as samples of children's work

◆ **Periodic Assessment** Baseline and end-of-year assessment activities

Class Checklists

Provided for Ongoing Assessment, Baseline, and End-of-Year assessments.

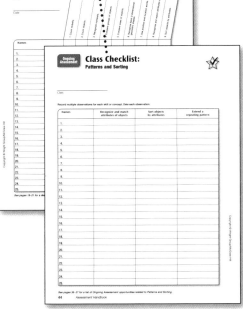

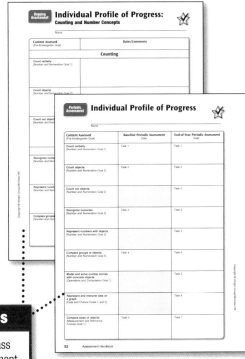

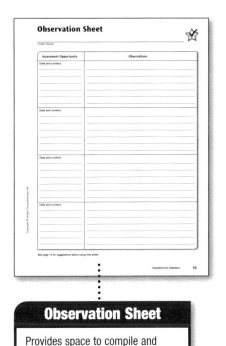

Individual Profiles of Progress

Can be used in tandem with, or instead of, Class Checklists. Provided for both Ongoing Assessment and Periodic Assessment.

Observation Sheet

Provides space to compile and organize individual data for any concept or skill.

Contents

Activity	Title	Page	Core Activity	Usage									
				Art	Books	Dramatic Play	Excursion	Manipulatives and Games	Music and Movement	Rug Time	Science	Sensory	Snack
Position and Spatial Relationships Topic Opener		266											
R◆1	Teddy Bear Positions	274	Core						●	●			
R◆2	Face Collage	276		●									
R◆3	Pattern-Block Puzzles I	278	Core					●					
R◆4	Where, Oh Where Has My Little Dog Gone?	280				●			●	●			
R◆5	Obstacle Course	282	Core				●		●	●			
R◆6	Pattern-Block Puzzles II	284						●					
R◆7	Treasure Map	286				●	●						
Patterns and Sorting Topic Opener		288											
P◆1	Attribute Match	296	Core					●		●			
P◆2	Movement Patterns	298	Core						●	●			
P◆3	Officer, Officer Game	300	Core			●		●		●			
P◆4	Color Patterns	302	Core					●					
P◆5	Sorting Objects	304	Core					●					
P◆6	Sorting Leaves	306					●					●	
P◆7	Exploration of Pattern Blocks	308	Core					●					

Welcome to *Everyday Mathematics*®, the elementary school mathematics curriculum developed by the University of Chicago School Mathematics Project (UCSMP). *Everyday Mathematics* offers you and your children a broad, rich, and balanced experience in mathematics.

Pre-Kindergarten Everyday Mathematics emphasizes the following content strands, skills, and concepts:

◆ **Number and Numeration** Verbal counting up to and beyond 10; rational counting with one-to-one correspondence; representing numbers; comparing sets and numbers; numeral recognition.

◆ **Operations and Computation** Exploring the meaning of addition and subtraction; developing and using concrete strategies to solve addition and subtraction problems.

◆ **Data and Chance** Collecting and organizing data; creating and analyzing concrete and pictorial graphs; exploring basic probability concepts through games and real-life events.

◆ **Measurement and Reference Frames** Distinguishing and describing size attributes; comparing length, weight, and capacity or volume; becoming familiar with nonstandard and standard measuring tools and their uses; sequencing familiar events in time.

◆ **Geometry** Exploring 2-dimensional and 3-dimensional shapes; recognizing and describing the position and location of objects; developing spatial reasoning.

◆ **Patterns, Functions, and Algebra** Recognizing and matching attributes of objects; using rules to sort by attributes, extend and create patterns, and play games; exploring visual, rhythmic, sound, and movement patterns.

Throughout *Everyday Mathematics,* emphasis is placed on:

◆ a realistic approach to problem solving in everyday situations, other applications, and purely mathematical contexts.

◆ frequent and distributed practice of basic skills through ongoing routines and mathematical games.

◆ an instructional approach that revisits topics regularly to ensure full concept development and long-term retention of learning.

◆ activities that explore a wide variety of mathematical content and offer opportunities for children to apply their skills and understanding to geometry, measurement, and algebra.

During your first year, you will become increasingly comfortable with the content, components, and strategies of *Pre-Kindergarten Everyday Mathematics.* You and your class will experience mathematical processes as a part of everyday work and play. These processes will gradually shape children's ways of thinking about mathematics and will foster the development of mathematical intuition and understanding. By the end of the year, we think you will agree that the rewards are worth the effort.

Have an exciting year!

Professional Preparation

Components for *Pre-Kindergarten Everyday Mathematics*

Go to...	When you need...	
Teacher's Guide to Activities	• Mathematics All Around • Ongoing Daily Routines	• Beginning, Building, and Expanding Activities • Topic support information
Early Childhood Teacher's Reference Manual	• Background on mathematical content	• Ideas for curriculum and classroom management in early childhood classrooms (Pre-K and K)
Assessment Handbook	• Suggestions for ongoing and periodic assessment	• Overview of the *Everyday Mathematics* assessment philosophy and tools and techniques for assessment
Minute Math® (Pre-K)	• Quick mathematics activities and problems to use during transition times or spare moments in the day	
Resources for the Pre-Kindergarten Classroom	• Family letters and ideas for class newsletters • Optional theme-based activities and masters • Songs, rhymes, and finger plays	• Lists of books, software, games, and other optional materials to support the Pre-Kindergarten program
Content-by-Strand Poster	• Skills organized by content strand and level of difficulty	
Early Childhood Home Connection Handbook	• Home-school communication for Pre-K and K	
Math Masters	• Blackline masters for routines, activities, games, and Family Connections	
Mathematics at Home Books 1–3	• A variety of activities that children can do over the course of the school year with their families	

Suggested Reading and Other Preparation

In order to prepare for effective classroom and curriculum management, we suggest the following before you teach *Pre-Kindergarten Everyday Mathematics* for the first time.

Review each component in your **Classroom Resource Package,** using the table on page xxvi as a guide.

Prepare to initiate the **Ongoing Daily Routines.** These will require some planning and setup before the first day, in order to begin them at the start of school.

Read the **Mathematics All Around** section, beginning on page 2, to help you become aware of the mathematics going on all around as your children work and play at school. It may also help you set up your classroom to promote children's natural mathematics explorations.

Read the **Topic Opener** for each topic, focusing on the Overview section and the Activities in Perspective tables. Pay particular attention to the **Beginning** activities in each topic and note which of these activities are **Core** activities. Choose several activities to use during the first few weeks of school.

Photocopy the **Introductory Family Letter** on page 69 of *Resources for the Pre-Kindergarten Classroom* to distribute to children's families early in the school year.

Review the **Baseline assessment tasks** on pages 19–21 in the *Assessment Handbook* and consider when and how you will administer these tasks.

Find an easily accessible location for your Pre-Kindergarten *Minute Math* book.

Set up your **Math Center.** Organize a variety of manipulatives so they are easy for children to access and maintain in good order. Add and rotate materials frequently.

Consult the manipulatives list on page xxxiii to determine what you have and what you will need.

Peruse the various sections in ***Resources for the Pre-Kindergarten Classroom***. If you do an All about Me theme early in the school year, be sure to read the activities in the All about Me Theme, in the Theme Activities section.

Read the **Management Guide** (Chapters 1–7) in the *Early Childhood Teacher's Reference Manual* for tips for getting started with the Pre-Kindergarten program.

At the beginning of the year, include counters, connecting cubes, sorting materials, games, and puzzles in your Math Center. Add new materials as they are introduced.

The following pages introduce instructional procedures and suggestions for implementing *Pre-Kindergarten Everyday Mathematics.*

Mathematics All Around

Young children naturally explore mathematics all the time as they interact with materials, with each other, and with their surroundings. The Mathematics All Around section of the *Teacher's Guide to Activities* acknowledges and builds on this important, but informal, mathematics learning by helping you

- set up an environment that promotes purposeful, spontaneous mathematics activities, and
- respond to these activities in ways that promote continued exploration, reflection, and learning.

This section is important because it helps provide an appropriate balance between child-initiated explorations and the teacher-initiated activities that are detailed in the remainder of the *Teacher's Guide to Activities.* Both types of experiences are important to maximize children's engagement and learning in mathematics.

Ongoing Daily Routines

In *Everyday Mathematics,* children learn a great deal of mathematics through daily routines. Through the routines, mathematical concepts are reinforced on a daily basis and children become aware of how mathematics pervades our everyday lives. The introduction on pages 24 and 25 explains the philosophy behind the routines and suggests tips for implementing the routines.

NOTE The routines in *Pre-Kindergarten Everyday Mathematics* are
- Attendance (pages 26–27)
- Linear Calendar (pages 28–29).
Plan to initiate both routines at the beginning of the year.

Activities

There are 118 Activities in the *Teacher's Guide to Activities,* which are grouped into **eight mathematical topics**. These topics are not "units" that you should work through from beginning to end. Rather, choose and intersperse activities from all of the topic areas over the course of the year, in response to the interests and needs of your children and classroom. You may find it beneficial to cluster several activities from a single topic together, but keep in mind that children learn best when activities and topics are revisited and reinforced over time.

Within each Topic, there are **three levels of activities: Beginning, Building, and Expanding.** The age, experience, and skill levels of your children will help you determine how much time to spend on the Beginning activities before moving on to the Building, and then to the Expanding activities for a particular topic. Classrooms with very young children may spend most of their time on the Beginning and Building activities and never do the Expanding activities, which is fine. Classrooms with older preschoolers may move quickly through the Beginning activities and spend most of their time on Building and Expanding activities. If you have children for more than one year, you might wait and use many of the Building and Expanding activities during the second year of their program. In all cases, use your children as your guide for determining your path and pace through the activities. (Keep in mind that children may require a different pace for different topics.) The program is intentionally flexible to adapt to a wide range of classrooms.

There are fifty-two activities designated as **Core Activities.** Teachers with very limited time or who would like more guidance about how to move through the program can provide a rich mathematics experience using only the core activities, especially if they are repeated and varied over the course of the year. All of the core activities are either Beginning or Building activities; none are in the Expanding category.

There is also useful information in the **Topic Openers** to help you choose activities. Each Topic Opener provides information about how children learn and progress through the important concepts and skills in that topic and summarizes the activities in each level.

NOTE The eight mathematical topics in the *Teacher's Guide to Activities* are

- Counting
- Number Concepts
- Operations
- Graphing
- Measurement
- Shapes
- Position and Spatial Relationships
- Patterns and Sorting.

Activities: Format and Features

Each activity in *Pre-Kindergarten Everyday Mathematics* includes a Main Activity and Connections. The diagram highlights important features of the Pre-Kindergarten activities. Note that most of the features relate to the Main Activity, rather than the Connections.

Activity Number and Title Activity C-2 refers to the 2nd activity in the Counting Topic. The Activity title describes the content of the Main Activity.

Objective This is the teacher's purpose for teaching the Main Activity.

Organizer Box This feature contains information for doing the Main Activity.

- **Key Mathematics Concepts and Skills** describe the key mathematical content of the activity. Each is linked to a Pre-Kindergarten Goal. The **Other Skills** describe nonmathematical skills that children will develop and use during the activity.
- **Terms to Use** consists of mathematical words that teachers should use informally in the course of conducting the activity.
- The **Materials** list includes materials needed to do the Main Activity. Additional materials, not listed, may be needed for the Connections.

Main Activity The main activity includes the key content.

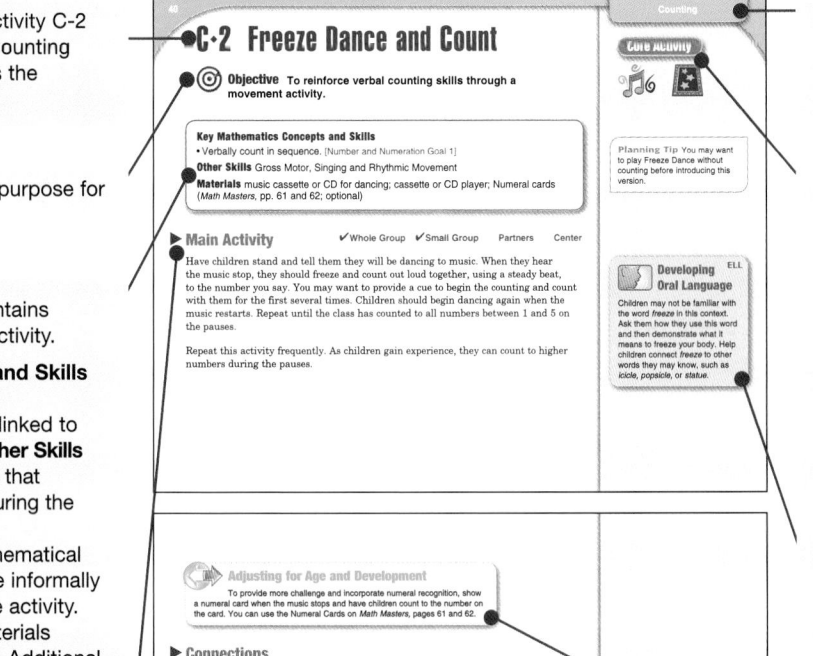

Topic The colored borders at the top and bottom of the activity and the tab at the top right correspond to the Topic for the activity. Each topic is color-coded.

Core Activity and Usage Icons Core activities are indicated with a label next to the title. The usage icons indicate the type of activity, such as a Rug Time activity, an Art activity, or an Excursion. The usage icons include Art, Books, Dramatic Play, Excursion, Manipulatives and Games, Music and Movement, Rug Time, Science, Sensory, and Snack.

Developing Oral Language These notes highlight opportunities to use the activity to build children's language and communication skills. While these suggestions may be particularly useful for English Language Learners, they are often relevant for many other children as well, since all young children are just learning mathematical language.

Adjusting for Age and Development These notes suggest ways to modify an activity to make it accessible and interesting to children with varying needs, learning styles, or levels of proficiency or understanding.

Grouping Suggestions Most activities include more than one grouping suggestion, allowing teachers to decide how to implement the Main Activity. Sometimes an activity calls for multiple grouping suggestions, such as when the activity begins with a Whole Group introduction, then continues in Small Groups or at a Center. *Small Group* is defined as 3 to 6 children working with adult help. *Center* implies materials at a Center where children generally work independently.

Ongoing Assessment Notes These notes highlight opportunities to use the activity for informal assessment.

Connections These suggestions are additional ways for children to explore the content of the Main Activity. Connections often focus on a different curricular area or another area of the classroom. Teachers can pick and choose from the Connections to integrate mathematics into all areas of the pre-kindergarten classroom and curriculum and to help meet the needs of individual children. Connections also include Family Connections, which suggest ways for children to explore the content at home. Teachers in full-time programs will probably be able to use more Connections than teachers in part-time programs, although all teachers will find many Connections that fit into their classroom schedule and help them integrate more mathematics into their daily activities.

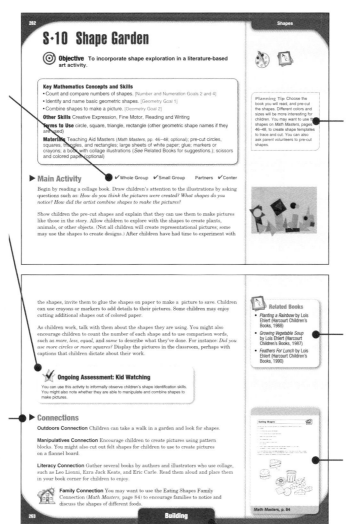

Planning Tip This includes advance preparation information. These suggestions often relate to materials, scheduling, or space issues.

Related Books This suggests mathematical and other books that complement the main activity.

Math Masters If an activity calls for blackline masters from the *Math Masters* book, minis of one or more of the masters are usually included in the margin.

Level The tab at the bottom of the activity indicates whether the activity is Beginning, Building, or Expanding.

Assessment

Everyday Mathematics supports a balanced approach to assessment, one that provides information both for guiding instruction and for evaluating student understanding. Assessment takes place on an ongoing, informal basis as children do the activities. There are also suggestions for periodic assessment tasks at the beginning and end of the year. Refer to the *Assessment Handbook* and the Topic Openers in the *Teacher's Guide to Activities* for detailed information regarding assessment.

Differentiation

Everyday Mathematics has been designed to accommodate a wide range of student backgrounds and abilities. The program also includes many tools and suggestions to help teachers differentiate instruction to meet children's diverse needs. Refer to the Adjusting for Age and Development suggestions in the activities themselves, the Management Guide in the *Early Childhood Teacher's Reference Manual,* and the Topic Openers in the *Teacher's Guide to Activities* for detailed information about differentiation.

Providing for Home-School Connections

Comprehensive and consistent home-school communication is essential for successful implementation of *Everyday Mathematics.* The *Home Connection Handbook* has many suggestions and tools that can help you introduce families to the *Everyday Mathematics* curriculum. In addition, the Family Letters and newsletter ideas in *Resources for the Pre-Kindergarten Classroom,* the Family Connections in *Math Masters,* and the *Mathematics at Home* Books facilitate ongoing communication and engage parents as partners in their children's learning.

Manipulatives for *Pre-Kindergarten Everyday Mathematics*

The table below lists the materials that are used on a regular basis throughout *Pre-Kindergarten Everyday Mathematics*. Select activities call for additional materials that you or children can bring in at the appropriate time.

Item	Quantity	Item	Quantity
Connecting cubes	2 pkg (200 total)	Measuring cups, dry	1 set of 4
Counters, chips	1 set (450 total)	Measuring cups, liquid	1 set of 3
Counters, panda bear	1 set (80 total)	Meter stick	1
Counting sticks	1 pkg (1000 total)	Pan balance	2
Dice, blank	1 pkg (16 total)	Pattern blocks	1 set (250 total)
Dice, dot	2 pkg (24 total)	Tape measure, 30 m, 100'	1
Dice, dot, large foam	1 pair	Timer	1
Dominoes, double-6	2 sets (110 total)	Transparent spinners	1 pkg (5 total)
Inch cubes	10 pkg (100 total)		

Additional Valuable Classroom Resources

- Geoboards
- Rubber bands
- Rulers
- Straws
- Buttons
- Various materials for sorting
- Sorting trays

All of the items are available from Wright Group/McGraw-Hill. They may be purchased either as a comprehensive classroom manipulatives kit or by individual components. The manipulatives kit provides appropriate quantities for a class of 25 and comes packaged in durable plastic tubs with labels.

Mathematics All Around

Young children spontaneously explore mathematics all the time as they interact with materials, with each other, and with their surroundings. They count and sort, notice and describe shapes and patterns, estimate and compare sizes, and wonder about the numbers they see all around them. These mathematical observations and developing concepts and skills are important tools that children use as they explore and make sense of their world.

Children learn a great deal from their self-chosen interests and activities. This part of the *Teacher's Guide to Activities* is intended to help you become more aware of the mathematics that naturally occurs as children work and play at school. By recognizing what children are already doing with mathematics, you will be better equipped to respond to their spontaneous mathematical activities in ways that foster continued exploration and learning. Sometimes the best response involves simply watching what a child is doing, without intervening at all; sometimes it means engaging the child in conversation or asking a thought-provoking question; sometimes it means drawing other children in, or, if the child is receptive, building on or extending the activity. Of course, it is important not to squelch children's self-initiated work or play with an abundance of questions, instructions, or teacher-directed tasks.

By pointing out various ways that young children use mathematics every day, this part of the teacher's guide may also help you consider ways to set up your classroom environment to promote children's natural mathematics explorations.

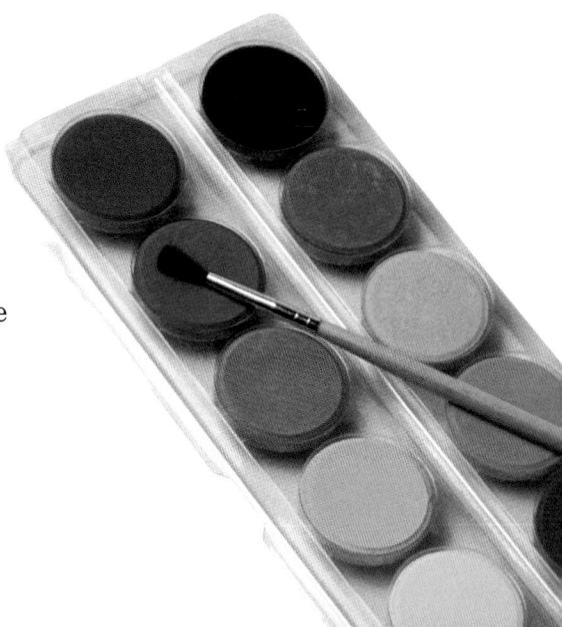

Keep in mind that this first part of the teacher's guide focuses on ***child-initiated*** activities and explorations. Each section in this part of the guide also cross-references several related activities that teachers might initiate. Those activities are detailed in the Activities section, beginning on page 30.

Art and Mathematics

▶ Introduction

There are numerous connections between art and mathematics. Shapes, patterns, size, scale, and symmetry are just some of the concepts that are important in both areas. For children who are drawn to art or craft activities, the list that follows may provide ideas for embedding mathematical learning into their work in the Art Center. Similarly, it may help you find ways to bring new children to the Art Center by capitalizing on their interests in counting, patterns, measurement, or other mathematical concepts. Both the art and the mathematics will be more meaningful to children if they emerge from children's own creativity, thinking, and exploration, so avoid art projects that require all children to follow the same rules or produce identical products.

The bulleted items that follow describe things young children do naturally in their artistic explorations. The list is intended to help you recognize opportunities for observing and encouraging children's mathematics explorations within the context of their artwork.

▶ Counting and Number Concepts

- When creating artwork, children often **think about quantity**. *How many beads should I use for my necklace? I want to glue 4 candles on my cake.* Encourage **counting and comparing** with questions such as: *How many trees did you make? Are there more trees or more flowers?*

- Children may need to **count** when collecting materials for projects. For example, you might direct them to take 5 toothpicks and 5 marshmallows.

▶ Measurement

- Children **explore measurement and make size comparisons** as a necessary part of many art activities. *I need a big piece of paper to make my whole family. This yarn was too short to fit over my head.*

- When working on projects, such as making chains or stringing beads, encourage children to **think about how the sizes will change** if they join their chains or bead strings together.

▶Shapes and Position and Spatial Relationships

- Children often use geometric shapes in their artwork. You can help children **recognize and identify geometric shapes** by describing parts of children's artwork and encouraging children to **use shape names** in their descriptions. *The house is made with a square and a triangle.*

- If children have a hard time getting started with drawing or creating an art project, ask them to **think about the shapes they might use**. *What shape do you want the jack-o'-lantern's eyes to be?*

- Children **use position words** to describe their artwork. *I drew myself* between *my mom and my dad. The sun is* at the top *of the paper.*

▶Patterns and Sorting

- Children often spontaneously **create patterns** as a part of art projects, especially if multiple colors, textures, or materials are available for them to use. Encourage children's patterning by pointing out and describing the patterns they create.

- Children will often **group objects and materials** when doing artwork. They might separate children and grownups in a drawing, or use only shiny buttons for a collage. By commenting on what they are doing, you help them make connections to sorting and classifying.

These Main Activities include art. Also, look for many Art Connections.

Blocks and Mathematics

▶ Introduction

Mathematics is an integral part of block play, and children's mathematical learning in the block area is deep and lasting because it develops over time through repeated, concrete experiences. As children build, they have first-hand experiences with 3-dimensional shapes and important spatial relationship concepts. They experiment with height, weight, and balance as they work to make stable structures; at the same time, they explore shape, symmetry, and patterns as they make structures look the way they want them to look.

In the block area, children get immediate feedback in their efforts to problem-solve: They can see the garage is not big enough for the cars, for example. Building encourages children to think flexibly and mathematically to solve this type of problem. If they run out of one size block, they may discover that two or three different blocks can be put together to fill the space. Similarly, by manipulating the blocks as they build, they learn that they can position the blocks in different ways to get different effects.

The bulleted items that follow describe things young children do naturally as they work and play in the Block Center. The list is intended to help you recognize opportunities to facilitate or encourage children's mathematics explorations in the context of their play.

▶ Counting and Number Concepts

- Children **count and compare quantities** as they build. *This side has 6 blocks and this one only has 4; I have to find 2 more blocks before I can add the roof.*

- Children often **use numbers** to label their buildings with addresses, floor numbers, or other information.

▶ Measurement

- Children often **measure and compare** their buildings using both standard and nonstandard measurement tools and units. *My skyscraper is almost as tall as you! This garage comes up to my knees. Our castle is as long as 4 rulers!*

- Children **discover the importance of weight** in building, since their structures will fall if they are top-heavy!

▶ Shapes and Position and Spatial Relationships

- Children **develop familiarity with 3-dimensional shapes** as they build with blocks and talk about the blocks they are using. They also **notice and describe 2-dimensional shapes** that make up the faces of the 3-dimensional blocks. As they manipulate blocks, children come to understand that rotating or repositioning objects does not change their shape— an important concept in geometry.

- Children also **explore relationships between shapes** as they find different ways to combine blocks that produce the same shapes and/or sizes.

- Children naturally use **position words** to describe how they are building or to collaborate with other builders. *Put that one on top. I'm putting the round block* next to *the door.*

▶ Patterns and Sorting

- Children often naturally **incorporate symmetry** and **patterns** into their buildings. *Both sides of my castle are the same. I used 2 short blocks, then 1 long one, then 2 more short blocks, then 1 long one ... .*

- Children **sort according to size and shape** as they put blocks away, if shelves are organized for blocks to be stored in this way.

- Children may **group blocks** and build with just one type for a building or section of a building. *I used the long blocks for the tall building and the short blocks for the small one.*

These Main Activities incorporate blocks. Also, look for many Blocks Connections.

Building Activity	Page
Building Towers Game (C◆18) **Core**	72
Bear Stories: Joining (O◆4) **Core**	146
Bear Stories: Taking Away (O◆5) **Core**	148

Expanding Activity	Page
"How Many More?" Game (O◆9)	156
Comparing Heights of Block Buildings (M◆14)	228

Books and Mathematics

▶ Introduction

Connecting mathematics to children's literature is a meaningful way to integrate math in the classroom. Books provide a natural context to discuss and reason about mathematical ideas. Many of the literacy activities you already do also support mathematical learning. For example:

- **Predicting:** Children use number, shape, color, and language patterns to predict what will happen next in a story.

- **Sequencing:** Children sequence story events using words such as *first, second, third, next,* and *last*.

- **Comparing/Contrasting:** Children compare books by the same author or on the same topic and identify elements that are the same and different.

Many books directly address counting, patterns, sequencing, comparison, shapes, and other mathematical ideas, though there is math to be found in just about every book.

Exploring mathematics through books can take many forms. You will choose to read particular books aloud to the whole class. Children can look at these and other books in the book corner or classroom library. Label a basket or shelf for "math" books. Also plan to include books that children make.

NOTE *Resources for the Pre-Kindergarten Classroom* includes an extensive list of children's books that highlight math, organized by mathematical topic. In addition, many activities in the Activities section of this guide suggest Related Books that complement the activities.

Children's literature, as well as their story dictation, may cover a range of mathematical concepts, such as time (*A long, long time ago…*), size (*Once there was a VERY big dinosaur…*), and quantity (*The ogre had 100 brothers and sisters!*). Add materials to your Drawing and Writing Center that support the mathematics that might emerge from children's writing or story dictation. In addition to providing a range of math-related books,

Kids' Menu

hot dog $1.50

pizza $1.75

french fries $1.20

you might want to post a number chart, provide number stencils or stamps, and rotate thematic materials with numbers such as phone books, maps, restaurant menus, and so on.

The bulleted items that follow describe connections between mathematics and books. Often, children will discover these on their own or with peers as you share books with the class or as they explore books independently in the classroom and create their own books and stories. At times, you may want to ask questions to encourage children to "read" the math in books.

▶ Counting and Number Concepts

- Children **notice numbers** represented in stories such as *Goldilocks and the Three Bears* and *Ten in the Bed*. Show children how to play Numbers I Spy with books: *I spy with my little eyes 3 bowls of porridge.*

- Retelling stories with flannel-board cutouts or puppets requires **counting and one-to-one matching.**

- Children often need to **count** when dramatizing a story. *How many people do we need to be bears? How many bowls (spoons, chairs, beds) do we need?*

- Counting books support children in **thinking and talking about numbers.** Children may be interested in **creating their own counting books or number books** for the classroom library.

- Children may **notice page numbers** in books. They may also enjoy **numbering the pages** in books they create. You might ask a child to find a particular page number or count how many pages are in a book.

- Children often **include numbers and quantities** in their dictated stories.

▶ Measurement

- Children **make sense of measures of time**—day/night, seasons, years, a long time ago, and so on—when listening to, retelling, or sequencing a story.

- Children **compare and describe** the sizes of different books. *My book is bigger than yours. This book is heavier than that one. That book has lots of pages! This book is too tall for the shelf.*

- Children may **compare and describe the relative sizes** of characters or pictures in books. They may notice that objects that are far away appear smaller in the illustrations than objects that are close.

- Children may **notice and compare the lengths of words or the sizes of letters** in books.

▶ Shapes and Position and Spatial Relationships

- Children may **notice and identify shapes** as they look at book illustrations. They might trace a picture with their fingers or try to copy it in their artwork.

- Shape books support children in **thinking and talking about geometric shapes.** Encourage children to **find shapes in their environment** that match those in a book and to describe the similarities between the shapes.

- As children learn the conventions of print, they begin to **track print from left to right and top to bottom.**

- Children begin to **notice the shapes of letters and numbers** as they look at books and eventually try to write letters and numbers. You may want to ask questions such as the following: *Which letters (or numbers) have straight lines? Which letters (or numbers) have curved lines? Which letters (or numbers) have both? How is an* A *like a triangle? How is an* O *like a circle?*

▶ Patterns and Sorting

- Children **use language and picture patterns** to "read" predictable books. They often **use or extend language patterns** from books in their own stories.

- Organizing and maintaining a classroom library requires **sorting and classifying.** Invite children to help you organize books by genre or author. On a field trip to the public library or bookstore, draw children's attention to how books are sorted on the shelves.

These Main Activities incorporate books. Also see the Literacy Connections and the Related Books listed in the activities.

Dramatic Play and Mathematics

▶ Introduction

There are many ways in which mathematics is integrated into the Dramatic Play Center. One-to-one correspondence, number sense, sorting, measurement, size, and scale are pervasive as children set the table, play store or restaurant, dress up, pretend to cook, and engage in other imaginary play. Rotate and add materials that will help children extend the mathematics that might emerge from their play.

The bulleted items that follow describe things young children do naturally as they play in the Dramatic Play Center. The list is intended to help you recognize opportunities to observe and facilitate children's mathematics explorations in the context of their play.

▶ Counting and Number Concepts

- Children often use **one-to-one correspondence** when setting the table or serving food. *If there are 3 chairs, how many plates do I need?* They also **count and compare numbers** of objects as they play. *How many more cups do we need?*

- Many items in the Dramatic Play Center (telephones, keyboards, cash registers, cereal boxes, and so on) engage children in **recognizing, identifying, and using numbers.** Talk with children about the numbers they notice.

- Children naturally **use ordinal numbers** as they organize their play. *I get to do the cash register first. What should we add to the pot next? You can be last.*

▶ Measurement

- Children **explore measurement concepts and vocabulary** as they pretend to cook. *I added 7 cups of salt to my soup. Bring me 2 pounds of potatoes!* Include math tools in the Dramatic Play Center, such as measuring cups and spoons.

- Children also **incorporate time concepts and language** in imaginary play. *Time for bed! It's 7 o'clock. Let's pretend it's next year and be kindergarteners.*

- Children **compare and describe sizes** of objects as they play. *I need a bigger piece of pizza. Which dress is longest? These shoes are too small.*

- Children might **use play money** in a pretend store. They might also **make, buy, and sell** tickets for carnivals or shows.

▶ Position and Spatial Relationships

- Children **describe the position and relationships** of objects and children. *Sit next to me! Put the soup on the table. Go under the bridge.*

▶ Patterns and Sorting

- Children may **sort and categorize** materials in the Dramatic Play Center: for example, all the dress-up clothes in one box or everything for a picnic grouped together. Clean-up may require sorting, depending on how the Center is organized.

- Children often **sort or group** themselves as part of imaginary play. *All the princesses stand here and all the knights go over there.*

The following Main Activities incorporate role-playing. Also, see Dramatic Play Connections.

Music and Movement and Mathematics

▶ Introduction

Music and movement are integral parts of the preschool classroom. As children sing and act out counting songs, play instruments in rhythmic patterns, and dance or move in various ways, they naturally use and reinforce many mathematical concepts. After you introduce songs and games, children will sing them on their own and come up with their own variations. Gather clues to children's developing mathematical understandings by watching how children participate in and extend these activities.

The bulleted items that follow describe ways mathematics emerges in the classroom as children sing and move. The list is intended to help you recognize opportunities to facilitate children's mathematics explorations in the context of music and movement activities. *Resources for the Pre-Kindergarten Classroom* and the *Sing Everyday!* CD provide words for many children's songs, chants, and finger plays that highlight math. Also, look for many Music and Movement Connections.

▶ Counting and Number Concepts

- When singing counting songs, children **practice verbal counting** forward and backward.

- Children **use their fingers to show numbers** in songs, correlating the number they sing with the number of fingers they show.

- Children use **one-to-one correspondence** as they match steps or other movements to words in songs or game directions.

▶ Operations

- In many familiar children's songs, children **experience simple addition and subtraction** as they add or take away one thing for each verse.

▶ Measurement

- Children **experience and discuss durations of time** as they sing songs of different lengths. *Let's start with 10 ducks. That will take a really long time!* They are also mindful of time as they wait for a turn to add a verse or do a movement.

- Children **experience and describe aspects of time and speed** as they sing slow and fast songs and songs where the tempo changes. Incorporating slow and fast movements makes the experience more concrete.

- Children **explore and compare lengths** as they do various movements in songs or movement games. *Now make big jumps. Now change to tiny jumps. Simon Says take one giant step forward.*

▶ Position and Spatial Relationships

- Children **model spatial relationships** with many movement activities. *Put your hand on top of your head, stand back to back.*

▶ Patterns and Sorting

- Children **follow and extend patterns** as part of many songs.

- Children **create new patterns** as they sing original versions of familiar songs. Instead of "Head, Shoulders, Knees and Toes" children may do "Tummy, Ankles, Legs, and Feet."

▶ Sorting and Classifying

- Many songs encourage children to **classify.** For example, when singing "Aiken Drum" you might suggest that children only add parts that are food.

- In many songs, children **use attributes** to follow directions or form groups. *If you're wearing red, touch your head.*

These Main Activities incorporate music and/or movement.

Outdoors and Mathematics

▶ Introduction

Mathematics opportunities are abundant during outside time. They emerge naturally from children's games and gross motor play, as well as from their interactions with nature. Listen carefully during recess to hear children exploring mathematical concepts spontaneously: *How many jumps? How high did it bounce? Let's dig a deep hole!*

The bulleted items that follow describe activities young children do outside all the time. The list is intended to help you recognize opportunities for observing and encouraging children's natural explorations of mathematics during outside time.

▶ Counting and Number Concepts

- Children **count** all sorts of things—jumps, ball bounces, swings, steps on the ladder, wheels on the tricycle, rungs on the monkey bar, people in line, paces around the edge of the playground, clouds, flowers, birds, and so on.

- Children **compare numbers** of objects. *I went across 4 rungs; last time I only did 2.*

- Many outdoor rules rely on **counting**. For example: How many children are allowed on the climber? How many minutes on the riding toys? How many pushes on the swing?

▶ Measurement

- Children **investigate and compare linear measurements,** such as height, length, or distance. *Which slide is longer? I'm swinging higher than the trees!* At this age, direct measurement comparisons are most appropriate. But, some children may also be interested in thinking of ways to **use nonstandard measurement units and techniques,** such as the number of steps from one end of the field to another or cutting a string to match the length of the slide. You might also bring out standard measuring tools, such as a tape measure, for children to experiment with.

- Children **think and talk about measures of time and speed.** *How long did it take to cross the field? How many minutes until we go inside? I ran very fast!*

Shapes and Position and Spatial Relationships

- Children **notice shapes** in their environments. *The ball is round (a sphere); the slide and ladder look like a triangle from the side.*

- Children can use sidewalk chalk to **draw shapes** on the ground. They might also draw paths or shapes on which to ride bikes or riding toys.

- Children may **notice and interpret shapes** on traffic signs as they use riding toys: an octagonal stop sign, an arrow showing which way to go, a triangular yield sign to indicate where they need to move slowly.

- Children **describe the position** of birds, insects, people, or objects: *on* the bridge, *in* the tunnel, *down* the slide, *up* in the sky, or *under* the leaf.

- Children can also use sidewalk chalk to **explore position and spatial relationships.** *Draw the starting line in front of the slide. Draw a little circle inside the big one.*

Patterns and Sorting

- Children may **notice and describe patterns** in their play, such as a swing going back and forth or a ball bouncing up and down.

- Children may also **notice and describe patterns** in nature or their surroundings, such as color patterns on flowers, markings on animals, bird calls, and brick arrangements.

- Child nature collectors often **sort** their rock, leaf, or other collections. *The big ones go here and the little ones go there.*

- Children **sort and classify** other types of objects, such as different types of swings or balls.

These Main Activities can be done outdoors. Also, look for many Outdoors Connections.

Science and Mathematics

▶ Introduction

Science and mathematics are closely linked, as both focus on understanding and describing objects and events in the natural and physical environment. Science provides a meaningful context in which children can apply their developing mathematics skills, such as sorting a collection of rocks to learn more about their attributes and origins; noticing patterns in the natural world; figuring out how long it takes for a ball to roll down a ramp; and measuring how long the ramp is.

Young children are natural scientists, curious and observant as they make sense of their world. As children look closely at the things that interest them, many of their observations have a mathematical component, such as size, shape, or quantity.

The bulleted items that follow describe things children do naturally as they explore science. The list is intended to help you recognize opportunities to facilitate or encourage children's mathematics explorations in the context of their scientific endeavors.

▶ Counting and Number Concepts

- Children **count** nature collections, such as acorns, rocks, or leaves. *I have 8 rocks. 5 of my leaves are dried up.*

- Children **count and compare** as they make observations. *This spider has 8 legs; that ant only has 6. My flower has 6 petals and 4 leaves.*

▶ Measurement

- Children **measure height, length, and weight,** and **compare and describe measurements.** *Do you think the big shell is heavier than these 2 small shells? How much do you think our plant has grown since Monday?*

- Children **think about time concepts** as they observe and describe events and change. *The tree lost its leaves during the winter. My plant grew this much in 2 days. I want to count how long it takes for the rock to fall to the ground.*

- Children **estimate** as they work with materials. *I think I will need two cups to hold all the sand. I'm going to need a longer pole for my plant.*

▶Shapes

- Children **notice and describe shapes and symmetry** when they look at things closely. *There's a circle in the middle of the flower. The bird's beak looks like a triangle. The wings of the butterfly match each other.*

▶Patterns and Sorting

- Children **notice and describe patterns** in nature and in physical phenomena: for example, striped animal markings, or the back and forth of a moving swing or vibrating rubber band.

- Children **sort (and re-sort)** natural and man-made objects according to different attributes. Sorting encourages children to look closely and notice details.

- Children also **group and categorize** animals by various attributes. *Does it have 2, 4, or more legs? Is it covered by fur, feathers, or bare skin?*

These Main Activities incorporate science. Also, look for many Science Connections.

Beginning Activity	Page
Sorting Leaves (P◆6)	306

Building Activity	Page
Exploration of the Pan Balance (M◆6) **Core**	210
Exploration of Capacity (M◆10) **Core**	218
Exploration of Standard Measuring Tools (M◆12) **Core**	222
Classroom Cooking (M◆13) **Core**	224
Snake Patterns (P◆12)	318

Expanding Activity	Page
Graphing Weather (G◆10)	190
Comparing Weights (M◆15)	230

Sensory Table and Mathematics

▶ Introduction

There are many ways in which children may explore mathematics with sand, water, rice, or other materials at the sensory table. As they dig holes, fill and empty containers, and experiment with various materials, children count, measure, compare sizes, and explore shape and position concepts. Include materials such as measuring cups, spoons, and containers of various sizes and shapes that will help children extend the mathematics that emerges from their play.

The bulleted items that follow describe things children do naturally as they play at the sensory table. The list is intended to help you recognize opportunities to facilitate or encourage children's mathematical explorations in this context.

▶ Counting and Number Concepts

- Children may **count and compare** how many scoops it takes to fill different containers.

- Children might **count** objects that they bury (or objects that they find buried) in the sand, rice, dirt, or other material.

- Children may need to **count** as they collaborate to build a sand castle or make a batch of sand pies. *I already made 2 windows on this side. We need 4 more pies for the bakery!*

▶ Measurement

- Children **explore measurement** as they fill and empty different containers, including measuring cups and spoons.

- Children might **order** the cups or spoons by size. If you have a nesting set, children often enjoy figuring out how they stack or fit inside each other.

- Children may **compare capacities** by pouring material from one container to another and noting which holds more. Containers of different sizes and shapes can prompt interesting discoveries. *The water overflowed when I poured it into this cup!*

Children **explore weight** as they notice the difference in the weights of filled and empty cups. They may also **compare and describe the weights** of different materials. *A cup of sand is heavier than a cup of water!*

▶ Shapes and Position and Spatial Relationships

- Children **develop familiarity with 3-dimensional shapes** as they sculpt with wet sand.

- Children might **describe and compare shapes** of different containers. *My container is tall and skinny. Mine has a square hole at the top. That one looks like a giant soup can.*

- Children will naturally **use position words** to describe their explorations at the sensory table. *The rock is* under *the water. This cup fits* inside *that one. Pour some more* on top.

▶ Patterns and Sorting

- Children will often naturally **group objects and materials** at the sensory table. They might group objects that sink or float, or objects that work well for digging, pouring, or other tasks.

These Main Activities can be done either in the sensory table or by using sensory materials. Also, look for many Sensory Table Connections.

Snack and Meal Times and Mathematics

▶ Introduction

Preparing food and eating together provide many meaningful opportunities for children to practice and use their developing mathematical skills. There is immediate feedback as children decide whether there is enough food (napkins, juice, and so on) and try to give everyone the same amount. When children cook, it is often necessary for them to read numbers on a recipe, count and measure ingredients, and keep track of time in order to get successful results.

The bulleted items that follow describe the variety of ways children naturally use mathematics as they prepare and serve food, set the table, and eat together. By allowing and encouraging children to help with snack and meal times, you can provide many valuable opportunities to explore numbers and mathematical concepts. A Snack Helper or similar job is a useful addition to a classroom job chart.

▶ Counting and Number Concepts

- Children **count** crackers, cups, napkins, and so on.

- Children **compare** the number of children with the number of cups or napkins and **use counting and one-to-one correspondence** to give each child one cup or napkin. *20 children are in school today; I need 20 cups. Now I'll pass them out.* If children do not have enough, they **figure out how many more** they need.

- Children **problem-solve** to figure out how much each child should get and how to share equally. *If I put one cracker on each napkin there are some left over; what should I do with the extras?* They also **explore the idea of *equal*** as they think about whether amounts are the same.

- Children **explore parts of a whole (fractions)** when they divide crackers or share a bunch of grapes. They may even use the word *half*.

▶ Graphing

- Children often informally **collect and analyze data** at snack or meal times. *If you have an apple, hold it up. Raise your hand if you like raisins.*

- Snack and meal times may spark other authentic reasons to **gather and record data.** *How many people want chocolate and how many want vanilla? Should we make apple bread or banana bread?*

▶ Measurement

- Children **explore and use measuring tools** when they cook. *Are all the cups the same size? Does it make a difference if the cup is full or only partially full?*

- Children may also **explore time concepts** when cooking. *The recipe says it has to bake for an hour. Let's set the timer.*

- Children **describe the sizes** of various items. *Should we use the big plates or the small ones? I got a tiny apple.*

- Children **compare** quantities of food or drink. *I have more juice because my cup is higher. No fair! You got more raisins. Is one big cookie the same as two little cookies?*

▶ Shapes and Position and Spatial Relationships

- Children **notice and describe shapes** during snack and meal times. *I have a round cookie on a square napkin. Let's sit at the rectangular table.* Children often enjoy **creating shapes** with food. *When I take a bite out of my cookie it looks like a moon. I made a cheese triangle!*

- Children naturally **use position words** during snack and mealtimes. *I put the cup on the napkin. My juice is inside my cup. Come sit next to me.*

▶ Patterns and Sorting

- Children **notice and describe patterns** as they set the table or prepare to eat. *Every bowl has a spoon next to it. The tablecloth has a striped pattern.*

- Children may also **create and continue patterns** as they eat. *I'm taking a drink of milk, then a bite of sandwich and then a bite of carrot. Then I'll do it again.*

- Children often **sort or group** food items when preparing or eating snacks or meals. *The fruit goes on the blue plate and the crackers go on the green plate. My healthy food is on my napkin, and my treats are in my lunch box.*

These Main Activities involve food. Also, look for many Snack Connections.

Beginning Activity	Page
"Take-Away" Songs (O♦2) Core	142

Building Activity	Page
Planning a Snack (G♦8)	186
Classroom Cooking (M♦13) Core	224

Ongoing Daily Routines

Pre-Kindergarten Everyday Mathematics includes two ongoing daily routines: the Attendance and Linear Calendar routines. These routines help teachers integrate mathematics into the daily life of the classroom and allow children to use their emerging mathematics skills in ways that are meaningful for them and for classroom functioning.

The Pre-Kindergarten routines are brief and engaging for children, so they are enjoyable and manageable additions to classroom meeting times, even for very young children. The program suggests many flexible options for implementing the routines to make them compatible with a variety of classroom structures, setups, and schedules. Read through the Attendance and Linear Calendar routines before the first day of school,

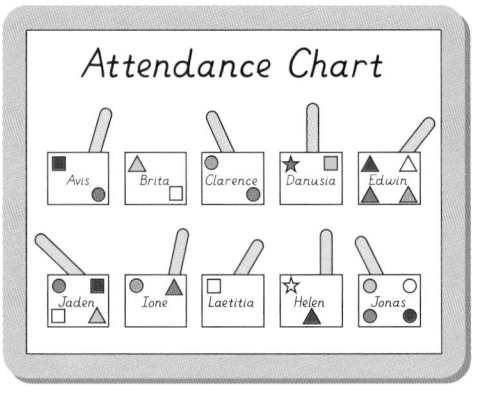

so you can introduce them as early as your schedule permits. As you introduce and implement the routines, keep in mind the following:

▷ It's best to start the routines early and let children "grow into" them at their own pace. Don't worry if children need support or don't fully understand the routines from the beginning; they will become increasingly comfortable with them over time.

▷ Although the routines are written as separate activities, it works well to do parts of them together during a class meeting at the beginning of the school day.

▷ Be flexible and responsive to the needs and interests of your children when deciding how much time to spend on each routine, as well as which parts of the routines to focus on each day or at different times in the year.

▷ You can differentiate by offering varying levels of support and posing different kinds of questions while doing the routines, depending on individual children's comfort levels and understanding.

▷ The routines include suggestions for adding complexity as the school year progresses. You will know best whether these ideas are appropriate for your class and, if so, at what point they should be introduced.

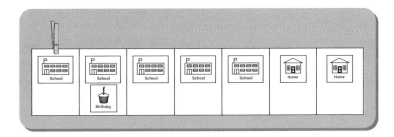

ROUTINE 1

Attendance Routine

▶ Purpose

Children practice counting, collecting data, and problem solving as they track daily attendance and use the data for real-life purposes.

Supporting Pre-Kindergarten Goals

• Count and compare the number of children absent and present. [Number and Numeration Goals 2 and 4]

• Create a daily record of children who are absent and present. [Data and Chance Goal 1]

• Answer questions based on an attendance chart. [Data and Chance Goal 2]

Materials

Pocket Chart

☐ posterboard

☐ paper pockets

☐ small index cards or craft sticks

Sign-in Grid

☐ large sheet(s) of paper

☐ pencil or wipe-off marker

T Chart

☐ posterboard

☐ index cards (cut in half)

☐ material to attach cards to chart (reusable adhesive, magnets, clips)

For all charts

☐ small photo of each child or stickers (optional)

▶ Making a Chart

Add an "Attendance Helper" to your Job Chart or classroom helper routine, and consider the following suggestions as you create a system for recording daily attendance.

NOTE In each case, you might want to add a small photo of each child (or stickers the child selects) next to his or her name on the chart and/or card.

Pocket Chart Create a chart with each child's name on a pocket. Collect a set of cards or craft sticks for children to place in their pockets when they arrive at school. (The cards or sticks do not need to have children's names on them.) If you have two classes, use a double-sided laminated chart— one side per class.

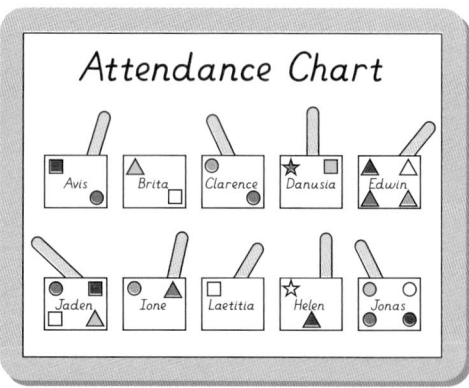

T Chart Create Present and Absent columns on laminated posterboard. Write children's names on cards for children to place in the appropriate column. Prepare a system for attaching the cards to the chart.

Present		Absent	
Carla	🙂	Rebecca	🐻
Aimee	🙂	Sybill	🙂
John	🙂		
David	🙂		
Erik	🙂		

Monday	
Debbie	X
Jeanine	
Patrick	
David	✓
Ann	Ann
Dorothy	D

Sign-in Chart Create a chart on a large piece of paper. Write children's names along the left side and the day of the week at the top. Leave room for children to "sign in" next to their names with a line, an *X,* or letters from their names. You can use a new sheet each day, or you can laminate the chart to make it reusable. (Change the day of the week and erase children's writing each day.)

▶ Taking Attendance

Model for children how to use the attendance system to "sign-in" when they arrive at school. Initially, many children will need help with this. At a class meeting, help the Attendance Helper use the chart to report the number of children absent and present. Then he or she can verify the present number by counting the number of children in class. This is easiest if children are seated in a circle, so the Helper can move around, counting aloud and pointing to each child. Encourage children to compare the counted number with the record on the chart to see the connection.

Help children apply the attendance information in meaningful ways: *How many cups do we need for juice today? How many empty chairs will we have?*

Moving Forward

▶ Gaining Independence

Over the course of the year, children will become more independent about signing in. You might gradually add to the Attendance Helper's responsibilities by having him or her remind children to sign in, count and report the information on the chart with less help, and perhaps record the number of children who are present and absent. Over time, you can also use the attendance information to ask questions such as: *Are there more girls or more boys at school today? If Delilah leaves early, how many children will still be here? If Marcos and Julian come later, how many will be present? Absent?*

As the year goes on, you may not need much group time for the routine, since children will use and understand the attendance chart more independently.

Linear Calendar Routine

▶ Purpose

Children use a simple calendar to track time, distinguish home and school days, and record special events. The linear calendar introduced in this routine is very meaningful for young children and lays groundwork for understanding the more complicated traditional grid calendar.

Supporting Pre-Kindergarten Goals

• Count home days and school days. [Number and Numeration Goal 2]

• Use a simple calendar to sequence home and school days and special events. [Measurement and Reference Frames Goal 3]

Materials

☐ Teaching Masters (*Math Masters*, pp. 4 and 5)

☐ long sheet(s) of construction paper or chart paper

☐ material to attach pictures to calendar (tape, magnets, reusable adhesive, clips)

☐ clothespin

▶ Setting up the Calendar

Add a "Calendar Helper" to your Job Chart or Classroom Helper routine. Copy and cut numerous home and school symbols from *Math Masters,* page 4, as well as special-event symbols from *Math Masters,* page 5. Cut long strips of construction paper or chart paper to serve as 1-week calendar strips. If desired, you can cut and laminate one strip to reuse each week.

Each week you will use a long strip of paper divided into 7 side-by-side spaces to represent the days of the week, and add a home or school symbol to the appropriate spaces to represent home or school days. Clip a clothespin to the first space on the calendar strip and hang the strip in your meeting area where children will be able to reach it.

NOTE Some teachers use copies of a photograph of their school on the calendar, instead of the school symbol from the master. You can personalize or add other symbols as well.

▶ Using the Calendar

At the beginning of each week, add the home and school symbols, as well as any applicable special-event symbols, to the linear calendar strip. Children will understand the calendar best if you begin the strip with the first "school day" of the week and put the weekend "home days" together at the end of the strip. Each day, look at the calendar during your class meeting and have the Calendar Helper move the clothespin to that day's space. (If you have only one class, you might have the Calendar Helper cross out or shade the day's space.) Ask questions such as: *How many days until our next home day? Are there any special events coming up? How many days away are they? Is tomorrow a school day or a home day? How many school days do we have this week? How many days are left in the week?*

NOTE Over long school breaks you may want to send home a strip of paper marked with the number of days the children will be out of school. Children can count and mark off the days until school begins again.

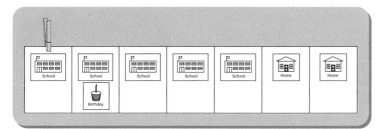

If desired, you can tape the week-long strips together into a longer horizontal strip or place them in rows to simulate a more traditional grid calendar.

Moving Forward

▶ Adding Complexity

As the year progresses, you may want to have children construct the calendar day-by-day. In this case, the Calendar Helper adds the appropriate symbol for the day. On the day before a weekend or other home days, the Calendar Helper can add those symbols, too. Later in the year you might want to add labels for the days of the week to the linear calendar. Some teachers incorporate a song into their calendar routine. The song "Today Is Monday" is included on the Sing Everyday! CD.

If your class seems ready, the New Year might be a good time to introduce the class to a traditional grid calendar that displays the days of the week and the dates. If you move to a grid calendar, help children make the transition by continuing to use the home and school symbols from the linear calendar.

Links to the Future

Many children are confused or overwhelmed by the organization of a grid calendar and the concept of months, days, and dates, so don't expect children to master this format yet. Children will have many experiences to learn about months, days of the week, and numeric dates in Kindergarten and First Grade.

NOTE See Graphing Weather, page 190, for an activity in which children graph daily weather information for a month. This activity can be incorporated into your calendar routine later in the school year, if desired.

Counting

Overview

> **Counting Goals**
>
> In Pre-K, children should have experiences that help them:
> - Verbally count in sequence to 10 and beyond. [Number and Numeration Goal 1]
> - *Develop flexibility in counting, including counting on and counting backward.* [Number and Numeration Goal 1]
> - Count objects with one-to-one correspondence and know the last counting word tells "how many." [Number and Numeration Goal 2]
>
> *Goals in italics are more advanced and may be appropriate only for some children.*

Counting things, or rational counting, is a skill that requires several abilities. First, children need to know the sequence of number names. Verbal, or rote, counting (especially for numbers to about 12) is a memory task, much like reciting the alphabet. Many children can count to 10 by the time they start Pre-Kindergarten, though learning the number sequence does not ensure that children can actually count things with accuracy and understanding.

Beyond knowing the number names in sequence, rational counting requires linking a single number name to one object at a time, or one-to-one correspondence. To count correctly, children have to keep track of those objects already counted, making sure not to count any twice. Initially children do best when they have fewer than five items to count and the objects are arranged in a straight line.

To determine how many objects are in a group, children must learn that the last number counted tells the total number of objects in the group, or the cardinal principle. They must also learn that when counting a group of objects, neither the characteristics of the objects (size, color, shape, physical arrangement, or function) nor the order in which they are counted is relevant to the count.

Typically, children can verbally count to numbers higher than the number of objects they can reliably count. The teen numbers are often difficult for children because some must be memorized, though there are patterns involved in counting 2-digit numbers thereafter. Children should be exposed to 2- and 3-digit numbers in meaningful contexts. They benefit from lots of examples and practice.

 Professional Development

See Chapter 8 of the *Teacher's Reference Manual* for more information about counting and other aspects of the Number and Numeration strand.

Choosing Activities

Beginning	Building	Expanding
Beginning activities focus on counting to 5, although most of the activities are open-ended and allow you to adjust for age and development. In these activities, children ◆ practice counting to 5 in a variety of contexts; ◆ use one-to-one correspondence to count collections of 5 or fewer objects.	**Building** activities focus on counting to 10 and on developing flexibility in counting. In these activities, children ◆ practice counting to 10 in a variety of contexts; ◆ count from numbers other than 1; ◆ count out a designated number of objects; ◆ count ordered and unordered collections of objects.	**Expanding** activities help children solidify and extend their counting skills. In these activities, children ◆ count beyond 10; ◆ count backward.

Activities in Perspective

	Activity	Objective	Core	Usage		Page
Beginning	C·1	**Rhythmic Counting** To provide practice with verbal counting through rhythm and movement.	Core	🎵 🟦		38
	C·2	Freeze Dance and Count To reinforce verbal counting skills through a movement activity.	Core	🎵 🟦		40
	C·3	**Age Collage** To provide practice with counting objects through an art project.		🎨		42
	C·4	**Can You Do What I Do?** To introduce a counting activity that incorporates movement.		🎵 🟦		44
	C·5	*Dice Movement* Game To reinforce one-to-one counting through a movement game.	Core	🧸 🎵 🟦		46
	C·6	**Searching for Bears** To provide practice with rational counting through a search-and-find activity.		📘 🖼️		48
	C·7	*Counting Around* Game To provide practice with verbal counting through a game.		🧸 🟦		50
	C·8	*Cover All* Game To provide practice with counting and one-to-one correspondence through a game.	Core	🧸		52
	C·9	**Five Hungry Animals** To provide practice with counting and numeral recognition through a role-playing activity.		🖼️ 🧸		54
Building	C·10	**Counting Songs to Ten** To provide practice with verbal counting to 10 through counting songs.		🎵 🟦		56
	C·11	Counting in Funny Ways To provide playful practice with verbal counting, including starting at numbers other than 1.	Core	🎵 🟦		58
	C·12	*Kid Race* Game To provide practice with counting and one-to-one correspondence through a game.		 		60

KEY

Art   Dramatic Play   Manipulatives and Games   Rug Time   Sensory   Core Core Activity

Books   Excursion   Music and Movement   Science   Snack

Counting

Teaching Resources

Home-School Connection

Family Connections suggest home activities that link to activities children have done at school. The following Counting activities contain Family Connections: C◆1, Rhythmic Counting; C◆3, Age Collage; C◆5 *Dice Movement* Game; C◆8, *Cover All* Game; C◆11, Counting in Funny Ways; C◆13, *Racing Cars* Game; C◆14, *Itsy Bitsy Spider* Game; C◆17, Beanbag Counting; C◆18, *Building Towers* Game. Note that the same Family Connections are suggested with multiple activities, so keep track of which ones you have already sent home.

Mathematics at Home Books 1–3 provide additional ideas for enjoyable ▶ mathematics activities that families can do together, as well as lists of children's books related to the topics in the teacher's guide. Families can do activities from *Mathematics at Home* Books 1–3 throughout the year.

◀ *Home Connection Handbook* provides more ideas to communicate effectively with parents.

◀ *Resources for the Pre-Kindergarten Classroom* provides additional teaching ideas, including suggestions for bringing mathematics into thematic instruction, as well as using games, literature, technology, songs, and rhymes to support mathematics learning.

Minute Math provides brief activities ▶ for transition times and spare moments throughout the day.

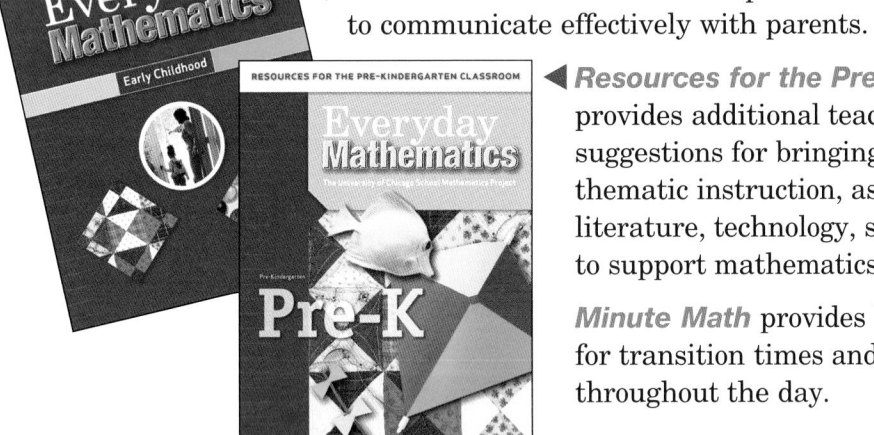

Assessment

Ongoing Assessment

 ### Kid Watching

The following activities in the *Teacher's Guide to Activities* include Ongoing Assessment notes related to counting. See the *Assessment Handbook* for an expanded table.

Activity	Content Assessed
C✦1, C✦10, C✦22	Verbally count. [Number and Numeration Goal 1]
C✦8, C✦9, G✦3, C✦13, C✦19, N✦9	Count objects with one-to-one correspondence. [Number and Numeration Goal 2]
C✦6, C✦9, N✦3, C✦16, N✦8, N✦10, O✦7	Count out a set of objects. [Number and Numeration Goal 2]

Assessment Handbook

- Pre-Kindergarten goals, p. 6–11
- Counting Assessment Overview, p. 26–27
- Baseline Periodic Assessment Tasks 1 and 2, p. 19
- End-of-Year Periodic Assessment Tasks 1 and 2, p. 22

ASSESSMENT HANDBOOK

Everyday Mathematics

The University of Chicago School Mathematics Project

Pre-Kindergarten

Pre-K

Differentiated Instruction

Adjusting for Age and Development

Pre-Kindergarten Everyday Mathematics is designed to be flexible enough to adapt to a wide range of preschool classrooms, including classrooms with mixed age groupings and classrooms with a wide range of developmental levels. Many activities include suggestions to help teachers modify the activity to make it accessible and interesting to children with varying needs, learning styles, or levels of proficiency or understanding.

C♦1	Rhythmic Counting	**C♦13**	*Racing Cars* Game
C♦2	Freeze Dance and Count	**C♦14**	*Itsy Bitsy Spider* Game
C♦5	*Dice Movement* Game	**C♦16**	Pattern-Block Pictures
C♦7	*Counting Around* Game	**C♦17**	Beanbag Counting
C♦8	*Cover All* Game	**C♦19**	Counting Cookie Chips
C♦9	Five Hungry Animals	**C♦20**	*Matching Dominoes* Game
C♦11	Counting in Funny Ways	**C♦21**	Making Caterpillars
C♦12	*Kid Race* Game	**C♦23**	*Count Down* Game

Language Support

Everyday Mathematics provides activity-specific suggestions to help all children, including non-native English speakers, develop the language necessary to acquire, process, and express mathematical ideas.

Developing Oral Language

C♦2   Understand the word *freeze*.

C♦16   Practice position words and pattern-block shape names.

Language & Vocabulary

Informally use these terms that are related to counting.

all	less
some	fewer
how many	same number
more	

Activity Connections

The Connections for each activity link the Main Activity to different curricular and classroom areas. They are useful for meeting individual needs and integrating mathematics throughout the day. The following connections are in the Counting section.

Art

C♦5 *Dice Movement* Game
C♦8 *Cover All* Game
C♦10 Counting Songs to Ten
C♦14 *Itsy Bitsy Spider* Game
C♦15 Counting Dots
C♦16 Pattern-Block Pictures
C♦21 Making Caterpillars
C♦23 *Count Down* Game

Blocks

C♦13 *Racing Cars* Game
C♦18 *Building Towers* Game

Dramatic Play

C♦3 Age Collage
C♦9 Five Hungry Animals
C♦19 Counting Cookie Chips

Family Connections

See Home-School Connection on page 34.

Games

C♦4 Can You Do What I Do?
C♦7 *Counting Around* Game
C♦8 *Cover All* Game

C♦11 Counting in Funny Ways
C♦20 *Matching Dominoes* Game
C♦24 *Making Trains* Game

Listening Center

C♦1 Rhythmic Counting

Literacy

C♦9 Five Hungry Animals
C♦11 Counting in Funny Ways
C♦16 Pattern-Block Pictures
C♦22 Counting Beyond Ten
C♦23 *Count Down* Game

Manipulatives

C♦20 *Matching Dominoes* Game

Mathematics

C♦15 Counting Dots
C♦17 Beanbag Counting

Music and Movement

C♦1 Rhythmic Counting
C♦2 Freeze Dance and Count
C♦4 Can You Do What I Do?
C♦5 *Dice Movement* Game
C♦6 Searching for Bears

C♦7 *Counting Around* Game
C♦12 *Kid Race* Game
C♦17 Beanbag Counting
C♦18 *Building Towers* Game
C♦22 Counting Beyond Ten
C♦23 *Count Down* Game

Outdoors

C♦2 Freeze Dance and Count
C♦9 Five Hungry Animals
C♦10 Counting Songs to Ten
C♦12 *Kid Race* Game

Science

C♦13 *Racing Cars* Game
C♦21 Making Caterpillars

Sensory Table

C♦6 Searching for Bears

Snack

C♦3 Age Collage
C♦6 Searching for Bears
C♦8 *Cover All* Game
C♦19 Counting Cookie Chips
C♦20 *Matching Dominoes* Game

C·1 Rhythmic Counting

Objective To provide practice with verbal counting through rhythm and movement.

Key Mathematics Concepts and Skills

• Verbally count in sequence. [Number and Numeration Goal 1]

• Match movements to count words with one-to-one correspondence. [Number and Numeration Goal 2]

Other Skills Singing and Rhythmic Movement

Materials none

▶ Main Activity   ✔Whole Group ✔Small Group ☐ Partners ☐ Center

Invite children to join you in counting from 1 to 5. Ask: *Can you clap to 5? Try doing one clap for each count. Can you jump to 5? Try doing one jump for each count. Can you count with a low, slow voice to 5?* Continue giving one specific movement or tone of voice for each counting beat: whispering, twisting, using a high squeaky voice, or counting slowly. Be creative! Encourage children to share ideas for movements, rhythms, or voice tones to use while counting.

NOTE You can use this activity to get and hold children's attention during transitions. You may want to end with a whisper or soft voice before beginning the next activity.

Adjusting for Age and Development

When children are ready, have them count to higher numbers. When they can go beyond 10, they can change movements or rhythms with each "decade." They might clap from 1 to 9, whisper from 10 to 19, and jump from 20 to 29. Play Follow the Leader to change the counting motion or rhythm.

Ongoing Assessment: Kid Watching

You can use this activity to assess children's verbal counting skills. Note whether children seem to follow others to sustain the count or whether they are already independent counters. How high are they comfortable counting?

▶ Connections

Listening Center Connection Put recordings of counting songs or finger plays in your listening center and encourage children to sing and count along. See *Resources for the Pre-Kindergarten Classroom* for song suggestions. You can make recordings of the class singing the songs.

Music and Movement Connection Chant and act out the song "One Frog Goes Hop," which is featured on the Sing Everyday! CD.

> *One little frog goes HOP.*
> *Along comes another and they just can't stop,*
> *So TWO little frogs go HOP, HOP.*
> *Along comes another and they just can't stop,*
> *(Continue for THREE and FOUR.)*
> *So FIVE little frogs go HOP, HOP, HOP, HOP, HOP.*
> *They all got tired so they had to STOP.*

 Family Connection You may want to use the Fun with Counting Family Connection (*Math Masters*, page 72) to encourage families to count together at home.

 **Links to the Future**

Counting activities in the Beginning section go up to 5. Counting activities in the Building section of the *Teacher's Guide to Activities* go up to 10. Counting activities in the Expanding section go beyond 10. However, all of the counting activities can be adapted to the level and needs of children in your class.

Math Masters, p. 72

C·2 Freeze Dance and Count

 Objective To reinforce verbal counting skills through a movement activity.

Key Mathematics Concepts and Skills

• Verbally count in sequence. [Number and Numeration Goal 1]

Other Skills Gross Motor, Singing and Rhythmic Movement

Materials music cassette or CD for dancing; cassette or CD player; Numeral cards (*Math Masters*, pp. 61 and 62; optional)

Planning Tip You may want to play Freeze Dance without counting before introducing this version.

▶ Main Activity

☑ Whole Group   ☑ Small Group   ☐ Partners   ☐ Center

Have children stand and tell them they will be dancing to music. When they hear the music stop, they should freeze and count out loud together, using a steady beat, to the number you say. You may want to provide a cue to begin the counting and count with them for the first several times. Children should begin dancing again when the music restarts. Repeat until the class has counted to all numbers between 1 and 5 on the pauses.

Repeat this activity frequently. As children gain experience, they can count to higher numbers during the pauses.

 **Developing Oral Language** ELL

Children may not be familiar with the word *freeze* in this context. Ask them how they use this word and then demonstrate what it means to freeze your body. Help children connect *freeze* to other words they may know, such as *icicle, popsicle,* or *statue.*

To provide more challenge and incorporate numeral recognition, show a numeral card when the music stops and have children count to the number on the card. You can use the Numeral Cards on *Math Masters,* pages 61 and 62.

▶ Connections

Music and Movement Connection Sing and have children act out favorite counting songs. See *Resources for the Pre-Kindergarten Classroom* for suggestions. Children can also practice counting to the tune of familiar songs.

Outdoors Connection Children may enjoy learning how to play Freeze Tag during outdoors time. You might encourage them to count to see how long they stay frozen.

C·3 Age Collage

Objective To provide practice with counting objects through an art project.

Key Mathematics Concepts and Skills

- Count out a specified number of objects. [Number and Numeration Goal 2]
- Associate number names and quantities. [Number and Numeration Goal 3]
- Represent numbers with groups of objects. [Number and Numeration Goal 3]

Other Skills Creative Expression, Fine Motor

Materials collage materials (such as pompons, buttons, beads, fabric, foam, tissue paper, feathers); paper; glue; paint or markers; trays or plates; paper bags (optional)

Planning Tip Collect a variety of collage materials. Collect enough for each child to choose 3, 4, or 5 of each type, according to his or her age. Set up a table with each type of material on a tray or plate. Plan to do this activity after children have some experience with collage materials and making collages.

▶ Main Activity

☐ Whole Group   ✔ Small Group   ☐ Partners   ☐ Center

Gather children in a circle to sing "How Old Are You Now?" (Sing to the tune of "Happy Birthday.") Give each child a turn to say his or her age. You may want a list of ages or birthdays for reference. After the song, tell children they will each create a collage that shows his or her age.

NOTE You may want to do this activity in conjunction with a child's birthday. See Age Graph, page 174, for another activity related to children's ages.

A "4" age collage

A "5" age collage

Show children the materials that you set up and explain that they should take the number of each kind of material that matches how old they are. For example, a four-year-old might select 4 buttons, 4 beads, and 4 feathers. Provide children with paper bags to collect their collage materials, or allow them to return to the materials table multiple times. Some children might have difficulty counting out the correct number of each material, so count with children as needed. Have children glue the collage materials onto their papers. They may also want to decorate their age collages with paint or markers.

You might want to have children help you sort the collages by age and display them.

▶ Connections

Snack Connection Provide birthday candles at snack time. Each child can take the number of candles that matches his or her age and put them in a soft food, such as a muffin or a banana.

Dramatic Play Connection Suggest that children host a birthday party for a teddy bear or class pet. Children can make invitations and decorations, "bake" a cake, and add the correct number of candles.

 Family Connection You may want to use the Birthday Counting Family Connection (*Math Masters,* page 73) to encourage families to incorporate counting into their birthday celebrations.

Related Books

- *Bunny Cakes* by Rosemary Wells (Viking Juvenile, 1999)
- *Carl's Birthday* by Alexandra Day (Farrar, Straus and Giroux, 1995)
- *What Comes in 2's, 3's, and 4's?* by Suzanne Aker (Aladdin, 1992)

Birthday Counting

Birthdays provide an excellent opportunity to count and learn about numbers. As you prepare for family celebrations, you can find many pleasurable counting experiences to share with your child:

- Count the number of people coming to the party.
- Set the table with the right number of napkins, cups, and utensils.
- Count candles for the cake.
- Make a card or birthday banner. (*Grandma is 60!* or *Happy 1st Birthday!*)

As you celebrate birthdays together, talk about the ages of people in your family. Ask questions like "How old will you be on your next birthday?" or "Which cousin is older?" Informal conversations like this help children use numbers in ways that have meaning for them.

Math Masters, p. 73

Beginning

C•4 Can You Do What I Do?

🎯 **Objective** To introduce a counting activity that incorporates movement.

Key Mathematics Concepts and Skills

• Verbally count in sequence. [Number and Numeration Goal 1]

• Count movements with one-to-one correspondence. [Number and Numeration Goal 2]

Other Skills Singing and Rhythmic Movement

Materials none

▶ Main Activity

☑ Whole Group ☑ Small Group ☐ Partners ☐ Center

Teach children the rhyme "Can You Do What I Do?" (See below and listen to the Sing Everyday! CD.) Each time you chant the rhyme, pick a number and a movement for the group to follow. For example, tap your head 3 times or clap your hands 5 times. Make sure that you count as you model the movement, so children know how many times to do the motion. Then, counting aloud in unison, children do the movement the correct number of times. Repeat with different numbers and movements.

> *Can you do what I do?*
> *Follow, follow me.*
> *Can you do what I do?*
> *Follow, follow _____ (me or child's name).*

If desired, you can add a line to the rhyme: *Can you do it very _____? (slow, fast, loud, soft, high, low,* and so on).

When children are familiar with the activity, give them turns to choose and model a number and movement for the group to follow.

▶ Connections

Music Connection Add musical instruments to the activity. Children can follow by doing the correct number of beats (shakes, taps, rings, and so on) instead of doing body movements. Encourage children to explore tempo by playing faster and slower.

Game Connection Play Simon Says in small groups. Use numbers in the directions, such as *Simon says, jump 2 times*. When children are familiar with the game, they can take turns being Simon.

C·5 *Dice Movement* Game

Objective To reinforce one-to-one counting through a movement game.

Key Mathematics Concepts and Skills

- Count dots on a die. [Number and Numeration Goal 2]
- Count movements with one-to-one correspondence. [Number and Numeration Goal 2]

Other Skills Cooperation, Gross Motor

Materials Game Masters (*Math Masters,* pp. 50 and 51); an oversized dot die; blank dice or cubes to make customized dice (optional)

▶ **Main Activity**   ✔Whole Group ✔Small Group ☐ Partners ✔Center

Show one of the movement cards to the players. Then ask a child to roll a large die, count the number of dots, and announce the number. All players should then do the activity on the card that number of times. For example, if the picture shows someone clapping and a 3 is rolled, children would clap three times. Repeat the activity, giving each player a chance to pick the activity card and roll and read the die. After children have learned the game, place the materials in a Center for children to play together.

Adjusting for Age and Development

For a simpler game, make a die with fewer dots. For a challenge, use two dice, each marked on two sides with 1, 2, or 3 dots, and have children count the total number of dots to determine how many times to do each action.

Planning Tip Photocopy the Movement Cards (*Math Masters,* pages 50 and 51) and cut apart the pictures. If possible, mount the pictures on large index cards and/or laminate them to make them more durable. You can make additional movement cards using photographs or drawings. You can make an extra-large die by adding dots—with stickers or permanent marker—to a large wooden or foam cube. Also see the Art Connection for another way to make large dice.

▶ Connections

Music and Movement Connection The class can sing and move to "Children Work with Hammers," which is featured on the Sing Everyday! CD. Children should sit with their legs extended.

> *Children work with one hammer,* (Hammer with one fist on leg.)
> *One hammer, one hammer.*
> *Children work with one hammer,*
> *Then they work with two.*
> *Children work with two hammers,* (Hammer with two fists on legs.) …
> *Children work with three hammers,* (Hammer with two fists and one leg moving up and down.) …
> *Children work with four hammers,* (Hammer with two fists and both legs.) …
> *Children work with five hammers,* (Hammer with two fists, both legs, and nod head.)
> *Five hammers, five hammers.*
> *Children work with five hammers,*
> *Then they go to sleep.* (Say line slowly and put head on hands, as if asleep.)

Art Connection Children can make their own dice using two half-pint milk cartons with the tops cut off. Show children how to fit the cartons into one another to make a single cube. Provide paper, markers, or stickers for children to add dots. Children can take the dice home to play *Dice Movement* or other games.

Family Connection You might want to use the Playing Games Family Connection (*Math Masters,* page 74) to encourage families to play games together at home. You can also create a "game bag" with a die and a copy of the Movement Card masters so children can play *Dice Movement* with their families.

NOTE Games provide important practice for children throughout the program. Many teachers create game bags containing game materials and directions that children can "check out" to play at home.

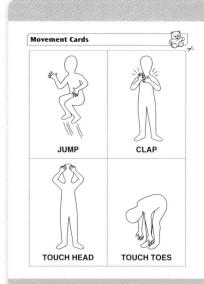

Math Masters, p. 50

Math Masters, p. 74

C·7 Counting Around Game

 Objective To provide practice with verbal counting through a game.

Key Mathematics Concepts and Skills

• Verbally count in sequence. [Number and Numeration Goal 1]

Other Skills Cooperation, Listening and Speaking

Materials beanbag (optional)

▶ Main Activity   ✔Whole Group ✔Small Group ☐ Partners ☐ Center

Have children stand in a circle. Start with everyone counting in unison to five and giving a clap as they say "five." Repeat several times, starting over with 1 and clapping on 5 each time.

When children seem comfortable repeating the choral count from 1 to 5, tell them they are going to play a counting game. Explain that this time they will count around the circle: a child will begin by saying "one," the next child will say "two," the next child "three," and so on in order. To help children keep track of who says the next number, it may be helpful to have children pass a beanbag to the next child after they say their number. The child who says "five" sits down. Then the count begins over again with the next child starting with "one." Each child who says "five" sits down. As the count continues, the children who are sitting do not say a number. Continue until all children are sitting.

> **NOTE** You can vary the game and use it as a transition activity by having all children sit in a circle to begin. As they count around, the child who says "five" stands up and moves to the next activity.

Adjusting for Age and Development

During future sessions, repeat the game but vary the sit down number, depending on how high your children are able to count. Some children may enjoy figuring out when they will be sitting, and who will be the last child standing.

▶ Connections

Game Connection Play a simple circle game called *High Five*. One child starts by counting 1–5, opening one finger as he or she says each number. When the counter reaches "five," he or she picks another child and gives that child a high five. The child who received the high five then counts from 1–5 and chooses a different child to high five. Continue until every child has a turn to count or until their interest wanes.

Music Connection Teach children a variety of counting rhymes. *For example:*

> *1, 2, 3, 4, 5, Once I caught a fish alive.*
> *6, 7, 8, 9, 10, Then I let it go again.*
> *Why did you let it go?*
> *Because it bit my finger so!*
> *Which finger did it bite?*
> *The little finger on the right.*

For other counting rhymes and songs, see *Resources for the Pre-Kindergarten Classroom.*

C·8 Cover All Game

Objective To provide practice with counting and one-to-one correspondence through a game.

Key Mathematics Concepts and Skills
• Count dots on a die and counters to match the number of dots. [Number and Numeration Goal 2]
• Use one-to-one correspondence to add counters to spaces on a gameboard. [Number and Numeration Goal 2]

Other Skills Cooperation

Terms to Use cover, fill, all, some

Materials Game Masters (*Math Masters,* pp. 52 and 53); dot dice; counters; spinner or numeral dice (optional)

Planning Tip Choose one or more gameboards from *Math Masters,* pages 52 and 53 that seem appropriate for your class. Make several copies of the gameboards and laminate them for durability, if possible. Most children can start with the 9- or 10-square grid. For younger children, you might use the 6-square grid and create dice labeled with dots 1–3 only.

▶ Main Activity

☐ Whole Group ✔ Small Group ✔ Partners ✔ Center

Give each player a *Cover All* gameboard. Players can share a die. Children take turns rolling the die and saying the number of dots. They take that number of counters and place them on their boards, one counter per space. Children continue taking turns adding counters to their boards until one child covers all of his or her spaces. Before playing, children can decide together whether the grid has to be filled by an exact count to end the game. Once children are familiar with the game, place the materials in a Center for children to play with a partner or small group.

You can customize the gameboards by adding stickers or stamps to reflect a current class theme, or simply to make the boards more interesting. Some children might enjoy

✔ Ongoing Assessment: Kid Watching

You can use this activity to observe whether children can count dots on a dice and/or whether they are beginning to recognize dot patterns without counting. You can also informally assess their abilities to use one-to-one correspondence to count counters and spaces.

using pencils or markers to "X" out the squares instead of using counters. For the latter variation, you'll need to provide an ample supply of grids.

Adjusting for Age and Development

Later in the year, you can incorporate numeral recognition into the game by using spinners or dice with numerals, instead of dot dice, to determine how many counters to add to the board. You can also increase the challenge as the year progresses with questions such as: *How many more counters do you need to fill your grid? Which grid has more (fewer) counters right now?*

▶ Connections

Snack Connection Children can practice one-to-one correspondence while they help you prepare a snack. Line up small cups or cupcake liners in rows and have children put one each of various items (raisins, crackers, pretzels) into each container.

Art Connection Make copies of blank *Cover All* gameboards and invite children to color the squares in a pattern or design.

Game Connection Invite children to invent other games they might play on the *Cover All* gameboards.

Family Connection You might create game bags with materials and directions for *Cover All* that children can check out to play at home with their families.

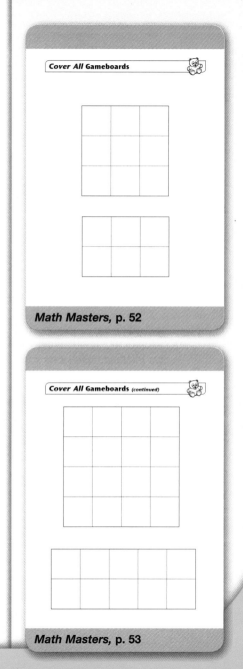

Math Masters, p. 52

Math Masters, p. 53

C·10 Counting Songs to Ten

 **Objective** To provide practice with verbal counting to 10 through counting songs.

Key Mathematics Concepts and Skills

• Verbally count in sequence. [Number and Numeration Goal 1]

• Associate written numerals, quantities, and number names. [Number and Numeration Goal 3]

Other Skills Singing and Rhythmic Movement

Materials large index cards or file folders and a marker (to make number cards 1–10)

> **Planning Tip** Prepare a set of large number cards by writing a large numeral (1–10) on each index card or file folder.

▶ Main Activity   ✔Whole Group ✔Small Group ☐ Partners ☐ Center

Gather children on the rug and show them the number cards. Have children count in unison to 10 as you hold up each card in order. Repeat several times.

Next, sing a counting song together such as "The Ants Go Marching," which is featured on the Sing Everyday! CD. (Choose a song that goes up to 10.) You can use the number cards to help children keep track of which verse comes next. Keep children involved by asking them to hold up fingers for each number. When they are familiar with the song, children will enjoy adding movements or using props to act it out.

> *The ants go marching one by one, hurrah, hurrah,*
> *The ants go marching one by one, hurrah, hurrah,*
> *The ants go marching one by one,*
> *The last one stops to suck her thumb.*

> **NOTE** Over time, introduce a variety of counting songs. You might want to sing counting songs during class walks, too. See *Resources for the Pre-Kindergarten Classroom* for more songs. The Sing Everyday! CD also includes a version of "This Old Man" that children will enjoy singing along with.

And they all go marching,
Down to the ground,
To get out of the rain.
Boom, Boom, Boom…

The ants go marching two by two, … The last one stops to tie his shoe. …
The ants go marching three by three, … The last one stops to climb a tree. …
The ants go marching four by four, … The last one stops to ask for more. …
The ants go marching five by five, … The last one stops to jump and dive. …
The ants go marching six by six, … The last one stops to pick up sticks. …
The ants go marching seven by seven, … The last one stops to write with a pen. …
The ants go marching eight by eight, … The last one stops to roller skate. …
The ants go marching nine by nine, … The last one stops to drink and dine. …
The ants go marching ten by ten, … The last one stops to shout "THE END!"

▶ Connections

Outdoors Connection Children can practice counting as they play Hide and Seek. One child (the "Seeker") hides his or her eyes and slowly counts to 10 (or a higher number) while the other children hide. Then the Seeker opens his or her eyes and searches for the hidden children.

Art Connection Children can dip their hands in paint or ink pads to make handprints on paper. When the prints dry, write a numeral from 1–10 on each finger for counting practice.

Related Books

- *Feast for 10* by Cathryn Falwell (Clarion Books, 1993)
- *The Ants Go Marching* by Jeffrey Scherer (Cartwheel Books, 2005)
- *The Aunts Go Marching* by Maurie J. Manning (Boyds Mills Press, 2003)

Ongoing Assessment: Kid Watching

You can use these Connections activities to assess children's verbal counting skills. Note how high they are comfortable counting.

Building

C·11 Counting in Funny Ways

 Objective To provide playful practice with verbal counting, including starting at numbers other than 1.

Key Mathematics Concepts and Skills

• Verbally count in sequence from 1 and from other numbers. [Number and Numeration Goal 1]

• Verbally count backward from 5. [Number and Numeration Goal 1]

• Match movements and sounds to count words with one-to-one correspondence. [Number and Numeration Goal 2]

Other Skills Gross Motor, Singing and Rhythmic Movement

Materials none

▶ Main Activity

✔ Whole Group   ✔ Small Group   ☐ Partners   ☐ Center

Invite children to count together to 10 or higher. Suggest a funny way to move to the count, or take suggestions from children. You may want to try jumping jacks, clapping, walking backwards, or tapping a beat. To reinforce one-to-one correspondence, encourage children to do one motion per count.

Children also enjoy counting using funny voices or voices of characters. For example, they can count while pinching their noses, count like the Big Bad Wolf, or count like Chicken Little. You may want to suggest counting like a giraffe (counting only in your mind, since a giraffe makes no sound) as a way to settle an exuberant group.

NOTE Children learn the counting sequence through practice and repetition. Use these ideas to keep counting practice fresh and fun. See *Minute Math*® for many other quick, verbal counting activities that you can do during transitions or other spare moments of the day.

When several children in the group seem ready for it, invite children to start counting from a number other than 0 or 1. For example: *Let's count to 10, starting from 3. Let's start at 5 and see how high we can count.* Also incorporate backward counting from 5 (or higher) using movements and funny voices.

▶ Connections

Literacy Connection Teach children nursery rhymes that include counting, such as:

One, two, three, four, Mary's at the cottage door
Five, six, seven, eight, eating cherries off a plate.

One for sorrow, Two for joy, Three for a girl, Four for a boy
Five for silver, Six for gold, Seven for a secret, Ne'er to be told.

Game Connection Children can play Bubble Gum, Bubble Gum. One child stands in the middle of a small circle of children, each with a fist extended. The child in the middle goes around the circle tapping each child's fist as the children chant: *Bubble Gum Bubble Gum in a dish, How many pieces do you wish?* The child who is tapped last says a number between 1 and 10. The child in the middle then goes around the circle and taps one fist for each number as he or she counts to the chosen number. The child who is tapped last moves to the middle and the game repeats. If the group is small, children can extend both fists.

Family Connection You may want to use the Fun with Counting Family Connection (*Math Masters,* page 72) to encourage families to count together at home.

Math Masters, p. 72

Adjusting for Age and Development

If children have difficulty starting to count from a number other than 1, give them a running start. To do this, you can count aloud from 1 and gesture to have children join in at the start number; or have children whisper the numbers from 1 and then count in a regular voice when they get to the start number.

Links to the Future

Counting on from numbers other than 1 and counting backward are often difficult at first, but flexible oral counting skills are useful for problem solving later. Through modeling and practice, children will gradually develop these skills.

Building

C·12 *Kid Race Game*

Objective To provide practice with counting and one-to-one correspondence through a game.

Key Mathematics Concepts and Skills

• Count dots on a die. [Number and Numeration Goal 2]

• Use one-to-one correspondence to move one space for each count. [Number and Numeration Goal 2]

Other Skills Cooperation, Gross Motor, Pretending and Role Play

Materials masking tape, carpet squares, or paper (to make spaces for a gameboard track); large dot die; blank die (optional)

Planning Tip Use tape, carpet squares, or paper to create a gameboard track on a large space on the floor. Two (or more) parallel lanes of 12 spaces is a good size, but it could be longer or shorter. You may want to make an extra-large die by adding dots to a large cube or by using 2 half-pint milk cartons. (See the Art Connection in *Dice Movement Game*, page 46, for instructions.)

▶ Main Activity

☐ Whole Group ✔ Small Group ☐ Partners ☐ Center

Gather the children around the racetrack you created and mark the Start and Finish lines. Invite one child to act as a car for each lane. Children take turns rolling the die and moving the number of spaces shown on the die until they cross the finish line. As each child crosses the finish line, he or she can ring a bell, do a jumping jack, or try some other action appropriate to the theme of the race. This game can be tailored to other themes, such as rabbits hopping to a rabbit hole, bats flying to their cave, or firefighters climbing a ladder. Also see *Racing Cars* Game, page 62, for a similar activity.

NOTE If you are unable to mark a track on the floor, adapt the game by having children take one step for each dot on the die. Establish a standard-size step and have children practice using it.

You can make the game more complex by adding a second die colored red on two sides and green on four sides. Children roll both the colored and the dot dice. If they roll green, they Go the number of dots on the dot die. If they roll red, it means Stop and they skip a turn.

▶ Connections

Music and Movement Connections Children can practice making one movement per action word using a chant such as: *You walk and you walk and you walk and you stop.* (Repeat four times.) Substitute other movements, such as hop, tiptoe, jog, or giant step.

Here is another fun movement chant (to the tune of "Frere Jacques"):

> *Marching, marching,*
> *Marching, marching,*
> *Hop, hop, hop,*
> *Hop, hop, hop,*
> *Running, running, running,*
> *Running, running, running,*
> *Now we stop.*

Outdoors Connection On the playground, children can play games such as Mother, May I? or What Time is It, Mr. Fox? to practice counting steps and moving toward a finish line.

Related Books

- *Harold and the Purple Crayon: Race Car* by Lisa Baker (HarperFestival, 2003)
- *The Big Balloon Race* by Eleanor Coerr (HarperCollins, 1992)

C·13 Racing Cars Game

 Objective To provide practice with counting and one-to-one correspondence through a game.

Key Mathematics Concepts and Skills

• Count dots on a die and spaces on a gameboard with one-to-one correspondence.
[Number and Numeration Goal 2]

Other Skills Cooperation

Materials Game Masters (*Math Masters,* pp. 57 and 58); dot dice; blank die (optional); small cars or other game pieces (You can cut out the race cars from *Math Masters,* p. 57 for game pieces, if desired.)

▶ **Main Activity**   ☐ Whole Group   ✔Small Group   ✔Partners   ✔Center

Show pairs or a small group how to play *Racing Cars.* Each player takes a turn rolling the die and moving a car, or other game piece, the corresponding number of spaces on his or her lane of the gameboard. The game ends when all the cars cross the finish line. Once children are familiar with the game, place it in the Math Center for them to play.

NOTE See *Kid Race* Game, page 60, for a similar game in which children act as game pieces on a life-size gameboard. You might use *Kid Race* as an introduction to the *Racing Cars* game.

Children may enjoy decorating the gameboard. The gameboard can also be tailored for other themes, such as moving frogs to a lily pad, or flying rockets to the moon.

Planning Tip Cut and tape together the tracks from *Math Masters,* pages 57 and 58 to make racetrack gameboards. You can lengthen the track by making additional copies of the middle track sections. The gameboard is designed for 2 players (1 lane per player), but you can tape additional masters next to each other to have more than 2 players use the same gameboard. If possible, laminate or mount the gameboards on cardboard for durability.

Adjusting for Age and Development

You can make the game more complex by adding a second die colored red on 2 sides and green on 4 sides. Children roll both the colored and the dot dice. If they roll green, they Go the number of dots on the dot die. If they roll red, it means Stop, and they skip a turn.

Ongoing Assessment: Kid Watching

You can use this game to informally assess children's abilities to count spaces on a gameboard with one-to-one correspondence. Also note whether children count the dots on the die, or whether they recognize the quantity of any of the dot patterns without counting.

▶ Connections

Blocks and Science Connection Have children use ramp blocks or a slanted board to "race" toy cars down a slope. Suggest that children put a piece of tape down to mark where their cars stop. Children can compare which car goes the farthest. They might try varying the slope and seeing what happens.

Family Connection You may want to use the Playing Games Family Connection (*Math Masters,* page 74) to encourage families to play games together to develop mathematics skills. Consider creating game bags which include the materials and directions for the *Racing Cars* game that children can check out and play at home.

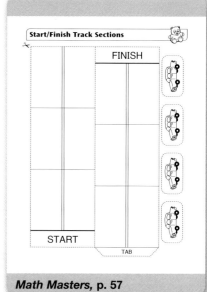

Math Masters, p. 57

One of 2 masters

Playing Games

Many games reinforce children's emerging mathematical skills and concepts. Children have fun playing games while learning at the same time.

Card games such as Go Fish, Memory, and War involve dealing out an equal number of cards at the beginning of the game, recognizing numerals, and counting to determine who has the most cards.

Many board games provide counting practice and help children develop a sense of strategy. Play games with your child frequently. Try to minimize competition, and concentrate instead on playing and learning together.

Math Masters, p. 74

Related Books

• *Wheels on the Race Car* by Alex Zane (Orchard, 2005)
• *My Race Car* by Michael Rex (Henry Holt and Co., 2000)

Building

C·14 *Itsy Bitsy Spider* Game

Objective To provide practice with counting and numeral recognition through a game.

Planning Tip To prepare the gameboard, write *Start* in a corner section of the egg carton or ice tray. Draw an arrow going up from the Start space along the long side of the carton or tray. Draw an arrow going down the other side and label the last space *End*. Make a spinner by labeling the sections 1–4 on the 4-part spinner master (*Math Masters*, page 59). Tape the spinner master to your transparent spinner. Select spider game pieces that players can tell apart.

Key Mathematics Concepts and Skills

- Count spaces on a gameboard with one-to-one correspondence. [Number and Numeration Goal 2]

- Recognize written numerals. [Number and Numeration Goal 3]

Other Skills Cooperation, Fine Motor

Materials Game Master (*Math Masters*, p. 59); transparent spinners; egg cartons without lids or ice cube trays; "spider" game pieces, such as chips, plastic spiders, spider rings, or button spiders (*See* the Art Connection for how children might make button spiders.)

▶ Main Activity

☐ Whole Group ✔ Small Group ✔ Partners ✔ Center

Sing and use finger motions to act out "The Itsy Bitsy Spider" song. Then teach the game to a pair of children or a small group. Place the egg carton or ice-cube tray vertically between two children sitting side-by-side, so the arrows point up and down. Explain that this is the waterspout and that the spiders are going to follow the arrows to go up one side of the spout and down the other side. Point out the Start and End spaces and the arrows.

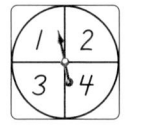

You can also use this gameboard setup to create games for other themes.

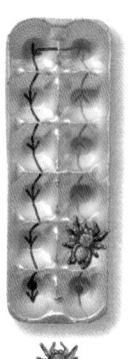

Give each player a spider game piece. Children take turns spinning a number and then moving their spiders that number of spaces, first up and then down the "spout." Children can decide together whether the spiders need to land exactly on the End space. They may want to move their spiders up and down the spout more than once.

When you have taught the game to several children, place it in a Center for children to play alone or with a partner. Gradually teach the game to more children, or have them teach it to each other.

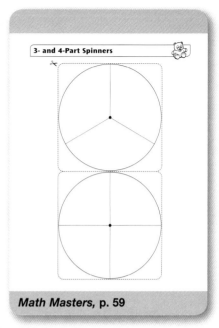

Math Masters, p. 59

Adjusting for Age and Development

Once children are familiar with the game, add challenge by giving each player 2 or 3 spiders and a cup to collect his or her spiders. Be sure children can differentiate their spiders. Children play until they get all of their spiders up and down the spout and into their cups.

▶ Connections

Art Connection Children can make "button spiders." Show pictures of spiders and count the legs together; explain that spiders always have eight legs. Provide a variety of four-hole buttons and chenille stems cut into quarters. Show children how to put a chenille stem piece through a hole to the midpoint, fold it in half, and twist around to make two legs that stay in place. Repeat with the other holes so that there are eight legs. (Children can bend the legs so their spiders can stand up.) Children can decorate their button spiders with markers, dot eyes, felt, and other materials.

Family Connection You may want to create a game bag with an egg carton or ice-cube tray gameboard, a spinner, and spiders. Invite children to borrow the game bag to play *Itsy Bitsy Spider* at home with their families.

Related Books

- *The Itsy Bitsy Spider* by Iza Trapan (Charlesbridge Publishing, 1993)
- *The Itsy Bitsy Spider* by Jeanette Winter (Red Wagon Books, 2000)
- *The Very Busy Spider* by Eric Carle (Philomel, 1985)
- *Spider on The Floor* by Raffi (Knopf Books for Young Readers, 1993)

Building

C·15 Counting Dots

 Objective To incorporate counting in a literacy-based art project.

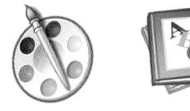

Key Mathematics Concepts and Skills

• Count up to 10 dots. [Number and Numeration Goal 2]

• Represent numbers with the correct number of dots. [Number and Numeration Goal 3]

Other Skills Creative Expression, Fine Motor, Reading and Writing

Materials *Ten Black Dots* by Donald Crews (Greenwillow, 1986), also available in Spanish as *Diez Puntos Negros* (Scholastic, 1986); dot stickers or small paper circles and tape; paper; crayons or markers

---

Planning Tip You can use any color dot stickers (or paper circles) for the activity. If desired, you can make black dots to match the book by using white dot stickers and coloring them with black permanent marker or paint. Many teachers find that it works well to do or review their class number board shortly before or after this activity. (See *Number Board* Game, page 106.)

▶ Main Activity

✔ Whole Group ✔ Small Group ☐ Partners ☐ Center

Read aloud *Ten Black Dots*. As you read, have children count the dots in each illustration. Ask: *What picture are the dots creating?*

After sharing the book, tell children that they will use dots to make pictures. Ask each child how many dots (up to 10) he or she wants to use to make a picture, and give each child that number of dots. Some children will find it easier to draw first and then add their dots, while others might begin by placing some or all of their dots before drawing. Not all children will create representational pictures with the dots, which is fine. When their pictures are complete, children should count how many dots they have used. You might help each child write the numeral at the bottom of his or her page. Children might also like to dictate something about their pictures.

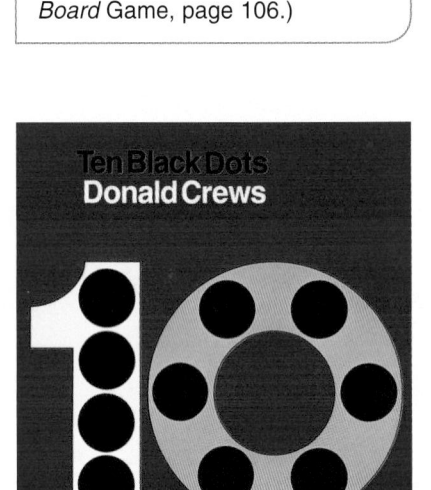

Ten Black Dots
Donald Crews

Redesigned and revised!

Compile the pictures into a class book or use them as the basis for a classroom display. Children could help you group all of the pictures with 1 dot together, all the pictures with 2 dots together, and so on.

▶ Connections

Mathematics Connection Include dominoes and dice in the Math Center for dot-counting practice. Children will find many innovative ways to use these materials. Provide paper and writing tools for children who want to practice drawing dot patterns or writing numerals.

Art Connection Provide washable, non-toxic dot markers in the Art Center. Encourage children to incorporate dots into their artwork and to count them. If you have extra dot stickers, put those out as well.

C·16 Pattern-Block Pictures

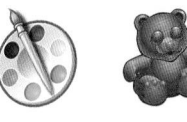

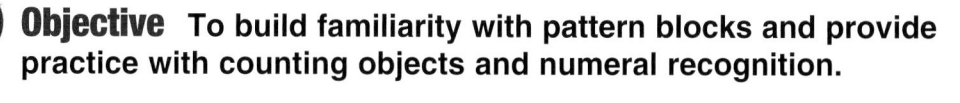

Objective To build familiarity with pattern blocks and provide practice with counting objects and numeral recognition.

Key Mathematics Concepts and Skills

- Count out up to 10 blocks. [Number and Numeration Goal 2]
- Associate number names, quantities, and written numerals. [Number and Numeration Goal 3]
- Use shape names and position words to describe pattern-block pictures. [Geometry Goals 1 and 2]
- Use spatial reasoning to combine shapes to make pattern-block pictures. [Geometry Goal 2]

Other Skills Creative Expression, Fine Motor

Terms to Use pattern-block shape names (hexagon, square, rhombus, triangle, trapezoid), position words (over, under, beside, and so on)

Materials pattern blocks; index cards and marker; paper or tray (optional)

▶ Main Activity

☐ Whole Group ☑ Small Group ☐ Partners ☑ Center

Before doing this activity, be sure children have had an opportunity to freely use and explore pattern blocks. See Exploration of Pattern Blocks, page 308.

To begin the activity, ask children to randomly pick a number card. Have them read the numeral on the card and then make a pattern-block picture or design using the number of blocks indicated on the card. (You might model a picture or show examples from Pattern-Block Puzzles 1–8, *Math Masters,* pages 15–22, to help children get started.)

Planning Tip Create number cards by writing a numeral between 1 and 10 on each index card. You may wish to add the corresponding number of dots to cards for children who need additional help recognizing numerals.

Ongoing Assessment: Kid Watching

You can use this activity to observe children's counting and numeral recognition skills. Also note whether they seem to understand that objects, such as pattern blocks, can be used to represent numbers. Can they think of any other ways to show the numbers on the cards?

Discuss with children how different designs can be made using the same number of blocks. Encourage children to make pictures for more than one number. Leave the materials out in the Math Center for children to work independently.

If a camera is available, you might take photographs of children's pattern-block pictures and compile them into a pattern-block counting book. Write the number of blocks used in each picture on the back of each page so children can count the blocks and then turn the page to check their counting.

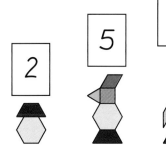

Developing Oral Language ELL

Children enjoy hearing the names of the pattern-block shapes and will gradually learn the names through modeling and informal use. Most children will be able to identify blocks based on their shape names before they independently use the proper names. You can also use this activity to model and provide practice with position words by describing (and inviting children to describe) the arrangements of the blocks in their pictures.

Adjusting for Age and Development

Increase or decrease the numbers on the cards to meet individual or class needs. To provide an extra challenge, encourage children to create a picture, count the blocks, and write the numeral, with assistance as needed, on a blank card.

▶ Connections

Art Connection Children can copy their pattern-block pictures or create new pictures by gluing cutout shapes from the pattern-block shapes found on *Math Masters,* pages 38–43. Invite children to dictate or use a tape recorder to tell a story about their pictures.

Literacy Connection Show children *Changes, Changes* by Pat Hutchins (Aladdin, 1987). Discuss how the same shapes can be put together to make different pictures.

NOTE For additional pattern-block activities, see Pattern-Block Puzzles I and II, pages 278 and 284, and Snake Patterns, page 318.

C·17 Beanbag Counting

Objective To provide practice with rational counting through a gross motor activity.

Key Mathematics Concepts and Skills

- Count beanbag tosses. [Number and Numeration Goal 2]
- Associate numbers of tosses with number names and written numerals. [Number and Numeration Goal 3]

Other Skills Gross Motor

Materials beanbags; set of number cards (optional); balls (optional)

▶ Main Activity

☑ Whole Group ☑ Small Group ☑ Partners ☐ Center

Demonstrate how to toss a beanbag into the air and catch it. Then give each child a beanbag and let him or her practice tossing and catching the beanbag. After practice time, ask questions such as: *Can you toss and catch your beanbag three times? Five times? Eight times?* Allow children ample time to toss, catch, and count with their beanbags. Challenge children to see how many times they can toss their beanbags into the air and catch them.

When children are comfortable catching beanbags, you can extend the activity by showing children a number card and asking them to count out loud as they toss and catch their beanbags that many times.

Repeat this activity over time. As children's motor skills develop, they will be able to get higher counts.

Planning Tip To create your own beanbags, stuff old socks or mittens with unpopped popcorn or dried beans and close them with string or rubber bands. This activity can also be done with playground balls. The activity works best in a gym or outdoor area, where children can spread out and move around. Or, you might do it with a small group in your classroom meeting space.

NOTE Tell children to toss their beanbags so they can catch them easily. Encourage them to begin with low tosses. You may need to remind children periodically that throwing the beanbag high or far is not the purpose of the activity.

Adjusting for Age and Development

Pair children with a partner and have them toss the beanbag back and forth, counting each time the beanbag is caught. Ask the children: *How many times can you toss it back and forth without dropping it? Move farther away from each other and try again.* For younger children, or those not yet adept at catching the beanbag, have them roll a ball back and forth and count the exchanges.

▶ Connections

Movement Connection Continue to develop motor skills by having children perform activities with beanbags to various CDs such as *Bean Bag Activities and Coordination Skills* and *Bean Bag Rock and Roll,* both by Georgiana Stewart (Kimbo, 1998 and 2000), and *Kids in Action* by Greg and Steve (Newsound, 1997).

Mathematics Connection Children can use beanbags to practice position and spatial relationships terminology and concepts. Give them directions such as: *Place the beanbag in front of (or behind) you. Can you balance the beanbag on your head? Can you hold the beanbag under your chin? Put the beanbag in the basket.*

 Family Connection You may want to use the Counting and Movement Family Connection (*Math Masters,* page 77) to encourage families to combine counting and movement at home.

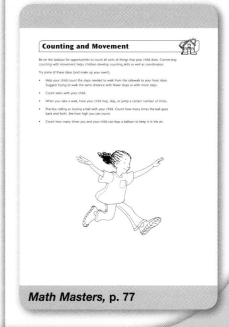

Math Masters, p. 77

Building

C·18 *Building Towers* Game

Objective To incorporate counting and comparing quantities in a block-building game.

Key Mathematics Concepts and Skills

• Count unordered sets of blocks. [Number and Numeration Goal 2]

• Recognize written numerals. [Number and Numeration Goal 3]

• Compare quantities of blocks and describe as *more, fewer, less,* and *same number*. [Number and Numeration Goal 4]

• Make direct comparisons of heights of block towers. [Measurement and Reference Frames Goal 1]

Other Skills Cooperation, Fine Motor

Terms to Use more, fewer, less, same number, same height, taller, shorter

Materials Game Master (*Math Masters*, p. 60); transparent spinners; inch cubes or other small blocks

---

Planning Tip Make a spinner by labeling sections on the 6-part spinner master (*Math Masters*, page 60) with numerals 1–6. If needed, you can add the corresponding number of dots to each section to support numeral recognition, or you can use a spinner with larger or smaller numbers. Tape the spinner master to your transparent spinner. This activity works best in an area away from general block play. Have children sit far enough apart that their blocks won't get mixed up when their towers fall.

▶ Main Activity

☐ Whole Group ✔ Small Group ✔ Partners ✔ Center

Play a building game with a small group of children. Children take turns spinning the spinner, reading the numeral, and taking that number of inch cubes. On each turn, players add the cubes they collect to their own towers. They continue taking turns spinning the spinner and adding blocks until one of the towers falls down. Then they count their blocks and compare the numbers to see which tower used the most blocks.

NOTE See *Making Trains* Game, page 84, for a similar game in which children compare horizontal lengths of connecting cubes, rather than heights of block towers.

As they play, help children develop strategies for counting a random assortment of objects, such as putting the blocks in a line before counting or moving each block away from the fallen pile as it is counted.

Children can also play independently. They will enjoy seeing how high they can build their towers, and how many blocks they can use, before they collapse. After you teach the game to several children, place the materials in a Center for continued play.

NOTE This activity also provides opportunities to explore measurement concepts. Encourage children to use size comparison language *(taller, shorter, same height)* to describe their towers. You can also stimulate children's thinking about non-standard units of measure. (See the Blocks Connection below.)

▶ Connections

Music and Movement Connection You might act out the rhyme "Stretching" with the class.

I am stretching very tall. (stretch up on tip toes and reach high)
And now I'm shrinking very small. (gradually shrink down to a squat position)
Now tall, (reach up again)
Now small, (shrink down again)
Now I'm a tiny ball. (curl up into a ball)

Blocks Connection Put a spinner or die in your block area and invite children to play Building Towers with unit blocks. Some children might be interested in varying the game by using various sizes and shapes of blocks in their towers. You might ask and discuss questions such as: *What if everyone used bigger blocks? What if you used different sizes of blocks in the same tower? Can you make different-size towers using the same number of blocks?*

Family Connection You might want to use the Playing Games Family Connection (*Math Masters,* page 74) to encourage families to explore mathematics by playing games together.

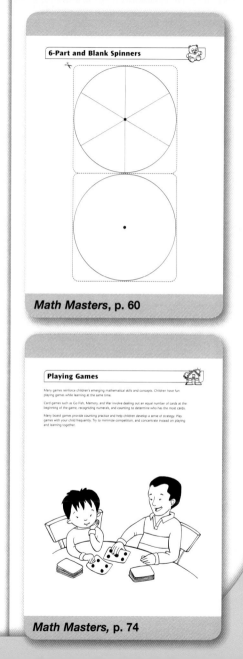

Math Masters, p. 60

Math Masters, p. 74

Building

C·19 Counting Cookie Chips

Objective To provide practice with counting objects and numeral recognition.

Key Mathematics Concepts and Skills
- Count unordered collections of up to 10 objects. [Number and Numeration Goal 2]
- Associate number names, quantities, and written numerals. [Number and Numeration Goal 3]

Other Skills Cooperation, Fine Motor, Pretending and Role Play

Materials heavy paper or cardboard circles; stickers or markers; paper plates, each labeled with a numeral between 0 and 10; small counters; cookie sheet and spatula (optional)

▶ Main Activity

☐ Whole Group   ✔ Small Group   ✔ Partners   ✔ Center

Place the paper cookies chip-side-down on the table or cookie sheet. Children take turns using a spatula or their hands to turn over a cookie. Then they count the chips and put the cookie on the plate that shows that number. Children can work together or independently to move the cookies to the correct plates.

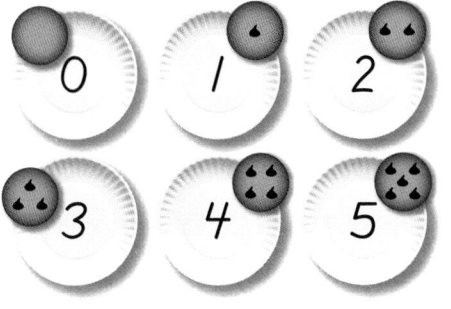

Note that the cookie chips are scattered and cannot be moved, which makes them harder to count than collections that are ordered in a line, or discrete objects that can be counted and moved. As needed, model how to

Planning Tip To make paper cookies, cut 11 same-size large circles from heavy paper or cardboard. Use stickers or markers to add between 0 and 10 chips to one side of each cookie (one cookie with 0 chips; one cookie with 1 chip; one cookie with 2 chips; and so on). Space the chips so that children can place counters on them. Laminate the cookies for durability, if possible. You may want to create more than one set of paper cookies and plates.

NOTE See Finding Cookies, page 114, and *More or Less* Game, page 118, for other activities that use the paper cookies. You may also want to bake cookies with children in connection with this activity. (See Classroom Cooking, page 224.)

use counters or real chips to cover chips as they are counted, which is a useful strategy for keeping track when counting unordered collections.

Place the materials in a Center for children to use independently or with friends. You might encourage children to order the numbered plates before beginning, which makes the task easier and provides practice with sequencing numerals.

Ongoing Assessment: Kid Watching

You can use this activity to informally assess children's abilities to count unordered collections. Do they understand that they shouldn't count any chips twice? Are they able to keep track of chips already counted? If so, what strategies do they use?

▶ Connections

Dramatic Play Connection Invite children to make different kinds of paper cookies for the Dramatic Play Center. Provide containers (cookie jars) for sorting and storing the cookies.

Snack Connection Give children real chocolate chip or oatmeal raisin cookies and let them count how many chips or raisins are inside. Provide toothpicks and napkins. If children enjoy this project, you might chart or graph the results for different cookies.

Adjusting for Age and Development

Children can use cookies with more or fewer chips according to their individual needs. Some children will be able to keep track without using counters as they count the chips.

Related Books

- *The Doorbell Rang* by Pat Hutchins (Greenwillow, 1986)
- *If You Give a Mouse a Cookie* by Laura Joffe Numeroff (Laura Geringer, 1985)
- *Anno's Counting Book* by Mitsumasa Anno (Harper Collins, 1977)

C·20 *Matching Dominoes Game*

 Objective To provide practice with counting and matching sets of dots.

Key Mathematics Concepts and Skills

• Count dots on dominoes. [Number and Numeration Goal 2]

• Match sets with the same number of dots. [Number and Numeration Goal 4]

Other Skills Cooperation

Terms to Use domino

Materials set of double-six dominoes (If you have a set of double-nine dominoes, remove all dominoes with 7, 8, or 9 dots on either end.)

Planning Tip To help children distinguish the two parts of dominoes, you might color in the dots on one end of each domino with a brightly colored permanent marker, or emphasize the dividing line with white correction fluid. You might also have children play with picture dominoes before using dot dominoes, to help them become familiar with the two sides of a domino and with the concept of matching ends.

 **Main Activity**   ☐ Whole Group   ✔ Small Group   ✔ Partners   ✔ Center

Before teaching the game, make sure children are familiar with a domino. Point out that there are two parts on each domino, with a line in between each part. Explain that they will count and match the dots on each part (or end) separately for this game. Have children practice counting the dots on each part of several dominoes before starting to play.

To set up the game, place all the dominoes facedown (dot side down) in a pile between the players. Each player takes five dominoes and places them faceup in front of him or her. Turn over one domino from the center pile to be the "starter" domino. Move the other dominoes to the side, out of play. Play as follows:

The first player looks at his or her collection of dominoes and tries to match one part of any of the dominoes to one part of the "starter" domino. If the player has a match, he or she places it next to the correct end of the "starter" domino to begin a domino "train." If the player has no match, play moves to the next player. Play continues as players add matching dominoes to either "open" end of the growing domino train. (See below for a train after several turns.) The game ends when one player uses all of his or her dominoes, or no more dominoes can be played. At the end of the game, players can count how many dominoes are in the train they created.

A domino train

▶ Connections

Manipulatives Connection Children can use the dominoes for building or sorting.

Game Connection Invite children to make up and share their own games using the dominoes.

Snack Connection Children can make graham cracker "dominoes" using two-part graham crackers for the base; raisins or chocolate chips for the dots; and peanut butter, honey butter, or other sticky spread to attach the dots to the graham crackers. Encourage children to count the number of dots on each part of their dominoes, as well as the total number of dots on their dominoes.

Adjusting for Age and Development

Dominoes with the same number of dots on both sides can be placed crosswise in traditional domino style, which creates more ends for possible matches. In this version, children create a domino maze, instead of a train.

C·21 Making Caterpillars

Objective To incorporate counting and comparing in a literature-based art activity.

Key Mathematics Concepts and Skills

• Count paper circles. [Number and Numeration Goal 2]

• Associate number names, quantities, and written numerals. [Number and Numeration Goal 3]

Other Skills Creative Expression, Fine Motor, Reading and Writing

Materials paper circles (different colors, if possible), pompons, or cotton balls; long sheets of white paper; glue; crayons or markers; *The Very Hungry Caterpillar* by Eric Carle (Philomel, 1981)

Planning Tip Cut out paper circles of the same size, at least 10 per child. Alternatively, you can use pompons or cotton balls.

▶ Main Activity
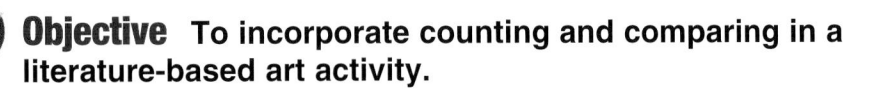 ☐ Whole Group ✔ Small Group ☐ Partners ✔ Center

Begin by reading *The Very Hungry Caterpillar*. Ask children what they notice about the caterpillar. Ask: *What happens when the caterpillar eats?*

Put out materials to make caterpillars. Have children glue circles (or pompons or cotton balls) on paper to create caterpillars of different lengths. Encourage children to count the number of circles they use. They can tell you the total number to write on their papers (or children can write it). Children can use crayons or markers to add details, such as eyes, antennae, or legs. They might also want to draw food for their caterpillars.

As children work, they may explore a range of mathematical ideas, including making repeating color patterns, comparing numbers of circles, or comparing lengths of

Note See the Mathematics with Eric Carle Theme in *Resources for the Pre-Kindergarten Classroom* for other literature-based mathematics activities.

caterpillars. Some children may want to make two caterpillars—a shorter one that hasn't eaten all of the food, and a longer one that has.

Consider displaying the caterpillars in the classroom, in order by number of circles. (Children may be interested in helping with this.)

Adjusting for Age and Development

You might ask children to create a caterpillar that is a specified number of circles long. For example, you might say: *Can you make a caterpillar that is 8 circles long?* or *Can you make a caterpillar that has 1 more circle than mine?*

▶ Connections

Science Connection Children might enjoy learning more about caterpillars. If possible, bring a real caterpillar into the classroom (in a clear container with air holes) for children to observe and perhaps draw. Talk with them about the differences between real caterpillars and their paper caterpillars. You might also read about and discuss the life cycle of a butterfly.

Art Connection Children can experience symmetry in an informal, experiential way by painting butterflies. Cut a large, butterfly-shaped paper for each child and fold it in half to make a crease in the middle. Have children open the butterfly and paint one wing. Help them re-fold the paper and press down. Then open the paper to reveal a symmetrical butterfly.

C·22 Counting Beyond Ten

◎ **Objective** To provide playful practice with counting beyond ten.

Key Mathematics Concepts and Skills

- Verbally count in sequence to numbers beyond ten. [Number and Numeration Goal 1]
- Count movements with one-to-one correspondence. [Number and Numeration Goal 2]
- Associate number names with written numerals for numbers beyond 10. [Number and Numeration Goal 3]

Other Skills Gross Motor

Materials index cards; container to hold cards

Planning Tip Write one numeral on each index card, using numbers that are appropriate for your class. Start with 10–20 and add higher numbers if your class is ready.

▶ **Main Activity**   ✔Whole Group   ✔Small Group   ☐ Partners   ☐ Center

Invite a child to close his or her eyes, pick a number card from the container, and show the number to the class. Help the class read the number, then lead them in counting together to the number on the card. The child who chose the card can decide how the group will count: for example, count and clap, count and touch their heads, count in a funny voice, or sing the numbers. Repeat by counting in a different way and/or by choosing another number card.

Do this counting activity during your group time on a regular basis. You can also work with small groups who are ready for higher numbers, or to give extra practice with the teens.

NOTE Look for other fun ways to practice choral counting. *Minute Math®* is a good source of quick counting activities that can be extended beyond 10.

Ongoing Assessment: Kid Watching

You can use this activity to informally assess children's counting and numeral recognition skills.

▶ Connections

Movement Connection Incorporate counting into exercise activities by saying one count for each movement. For example, count and do 12 jumping jacks or 14 squats.

Literacy Connection Read aloud counting books that go beyond 10. Encourage children to count along as the books are read. See the Related Books and *Resources for the Pre-Kindergarten Classroom* for book suggestions.

 Related Books

- *One Moose, Twenty Mice* by Clare Beaton (Barefoot Books, 1999)

- *Chicka Chicka 1, 2, 3* by Bill Martin, Jr. (Simon & Schuster Children's Publishing, 2004)

- *Teeth, Tails, & Tentacles: An Animal Counting Book* by Christopher Wormell (Running Press Book Publishers, 2004)

- *I Spy Two Eyes: Numbers in Art* by Lucy Micklethwait (Greenwillow, 1993)

C·23 Count Down Game

◎ Objective To provide practice with counting backward through a movement game.

Key Mathematics Concepts and Skills

- Count backward. [Number and Numeration Goal 1]

- Say one count for each child when counting around the circle. [Number and Numeration Goal 2]

Other Skills Cooperation, Gross Motor

Materials none

Planning Tip Plan to do this activity where children have adequate space to run, such as in a gym or outdoors.

▶ Main Activity

☑ Whole Group ☑ Small Group ☐ Partners ☐ Center

Gather children in a circle to play a counting version of Duck, Duck, Goose. Demonstrate how to play the game by walking around the circle, tapping each child's head. As you tap, count down from 5 (or another number) until you get down to 1. Announce "Blast off!" as you tap the next child's head. That child gets up and chases you around the circle, trying to catch you before you sit in the empty spot. Now, the child takes a turn counting down to blast off. Repeat the activity until all children have had a turn to blast off, or until interest wanes.

NOTE Make counting backward a part of daily classroom life. For example, count down to cleanup time or ask children to count down while they wait for a turn at the sink. See *Minute Math*® for other quick, backward counting activities that you can do during transitions or other spare moments of the day.

▶ Connections

Literacy Connection Share counting books that count backward. See Related Books and *Resources for the Pre-Kindergarten Classroom* for suggestions.

Art Connection Invite children to build a rocket using recycled materials (boxes, cardboard tubes, plastic cups, and so on), glue, paint, and other art supplies. Children can count down to make their rockets blast off.

Movement Connection As a group, slowly count backward in unison from 5 (or another number) to blast off. With each count, children move down a bit lower into a squat. On *blast off,* everyone jumps up.

Related Books

- *Ten in the Bed* by Penny Dale (Black Pursuit, 1988)
- *Ten Little Fish* by Audrey and Bruce Wood (Blue Sky Press, 2004)
- *Ten, Nine, Eight* by Molly Bang (Greenwillow, 1983)
- *Ten Seeds* by Ruth Brown (Knopf Books for Young Readers, 2001)

Expanding

C·24 *Making Trains* Game

Objective To provide practice with counting and making comparisons through a game.

Key Mathematics Concepts and Skills

• Count dots on a die and cubes. [Number and Numeration Goal 2]

• Compare numbers of cubes in "trains" and describe as *more, fewer, less,* and *same number.* [Number and Numeration Goal 4]

• Compare lengths of trains and describe as *longer, shorter,* and *same length.* [Measurement and Reference Frames Goal 1]

Other Skills Cooperation, Fine Motor

Terms to Use more, fewer, less, same number, longer, shorter, same length

Materials dot die; connecting cubes

Planning Tip Separate the connecting cubes before beginning the game.

▶ Main Activity

☐ Whole Group ✔ Small Group ✔ Partners ✔ Center

Teach *Making Trains* to a small group of children. Put a pile of connecting cubes between the players. Have children take turns rolling a die and taking that number of cubes from the pile. Children should connect their cubes to make a "train." On each turn, children roll the die and add cubes to their trains. Every few rounds, children should count the number of cubes on their trains and compare the lengths of their trains. Remind children to line up the ends of their trains when comparing lengths. Encourage children to use comparison words such as *more, fewer, less, same number, longer, shorter* and *same length* to describe the trains.

NOTE See *Building Towers* Game, page 72, for another comparison activity. In *Building Towers,* children make height comparisons, while in *Making Trains* children compare horizontal lengths.

Some children may want to start with new trains when they can no longer count how many cubes they have. Others may want to create very long trains, beyond the numbers they can count. In this case, provide help with counting or have them help each other. If the trains get so long that counting is impractical, simply have children compare the train lengths.

Children line up the ends of their trains to compare lengths. Some children may make patterned trains.

Children can play a one-person variation of *Making Trains* by making a new train with each roll of the die. They can save their trains, and then compare and describe the trains from different rolls. After children have several trains, encourage them to try to put their trains in order from fewest to most cubes, or shortest to longest.

Put the cubes and die in the Math Center for continued play. Children may invent new variations and games with the materials.

▶ Connections

Game Connection Play *Show Me More* (or *Show Me Less*). Show a number of fingers on one hand and ask children to show you more fingers. Explain that there is more than one correct response. Repeat with different numbers of fingers, each time asking children to show more (or less). When children are familiar with the game, use the fingers on both hands. This is a good game to play during transition times.

Ongoing Assessment: Kid Watching

You can use this activity to informally assess children's abilities to compare and describe quantities and lengths.

Related Book

- *Ten Apples Up on Top!* by Theo LeSieg (Dr. Seuss), (Random House, 1998)

Number Concepts

Overview

Number Concepts Goals

In Pre-K, children should have experiences that help them:

• Develop an awareness of numbers and their uses. [Number and Numeration Goal 3]

• Associate number names, quantities, and written numerals. [Number and Numeration Goal 3]

• Recognize and use different ways to represent numbers (for example, groups of objects or dots). [Number and Numeration Goal 3]

• Compare and order groups of objects using words such as *more, fewer, less, same.* [Number and Numeration Goal 4]

Children come to school with many intuitive understandings about numbers and their uses. For example, *My brother's older than me; he's 7 and I'm 4,* or *My apartment is on the third floor.* Number sense develops gradually as a result of exploring and using numbers and numerals, visualizing them, and relating them in a variety of contexts.

Even before young children count, they are able to visualize and label small groups of 2 or 3 objects without counting. Later, children are able to automatically identify finger patterns and number patterns such as those on dice and dominoes.

Given meaningful contexts, children learn that numbers can be represented in multiple ways (objects, movements, sounds, words, pictures or other informal symbols, and numerals). Just as in literacy, children benefit from a number-rich environment. As children learn to recognize numerals, and explore writing them, the focus should remain on the meaning of the numerals.

Young children visually compare two groups of objects to determine whether the groups are the same or which group has more. When their counting skills have developed, children use counting or matching (one-to-one correspondence) to compare groups. With experience, they become more accurate despite any distracting appearances, such as when one group has larger objects than the other or when the objects are spread out. Eventually, children come to understand that the later a number comes in the counting sequence, the larger the quantity represented.

 ## Professional Development

See Chapter 8 of the *Teacher's Reference Manual* for more information about number concepts and other aspects of the Number and Numeration strand.

Choosing Activities

Beginning

Beginning activities increase children's awareness of numbers and build on children's intuitive sense of small numbers. In these activities, children

- notice numerals in their environment;
- think about uses of numbers;
- recognize and match small quantities without counting;
- compare two groups of objects visually.

Building

Building activities deepen children's number sense. In these activities, children

- make associations between number names, quantities, and written numerals;
- represent numbers in various ways;
- identify and use numerals in context;
- compare two groups of objects using one-to-one matching and/ or counting.

Expanding

Expanding activities focus on number symbols and other uses of numbers. In these activities, children

- explore ordinal numbers;
- explore numeral shapes and formation.

Activities in Perspective

Activity	Objective	Core	Usage	Page
N•12	*Matching Sets* Game II To deepen children's number sense with a matching game involving the same numbers of objects in different arrangements.	**Core**		116
N•13	**More or Less** Game To provide practice with comparing sets and determining more or less through a game.			118
N•14	**Number Scavenger Hunt** To increase children's awareness of numbers in the environment and provide practice with numeral recognition.			120
N•15	*High/Low* Game To provide practice with comparing numbers through a card game.	**Core**		122
N•16	**Animals on Parade** To introduce concepts and language for ordinal numbers.			124
N•17	*Child Bingo* Game To reinforce numeral recognition through a game.			126
N•18	**Number Books** To reinforce numeral recognition and provide opportunities to represent numbers with pictures.			128
N•19	**Number Shapes** To provide opportunities to explore the shapes of numerals using sensory materials.			130

Building

Expanding

KEY

 Art   Dramatic Play   Manipulatives and Games   Rug Time   Sensory   **Core** Core Activity

 Books   Excursion   Music and Movement   Science   Snack

Teaching Resources

Home-School Connection

Family Connections suggest home activities that link to activities children have done at school. The following Number Concepts activities contain Family Connections: N◆1, Classroom Addresses; N◆2, Number Walk; N◆5, *Matching Sets* Game I; N◆9, *Match Up* Game; N◆13, *More or Less* Game; N◆14, Number Scavenger Hunt; N◆15, *High/Low* Game. Note that the same Family Connections are suggested in multiple activities, so keep track of which ones you have already sent home.

Mathematics at Home **Books 1–3** provide additional ideas for enjoyable mathematics activities that families can do together, as well as lists of children's books related to the topics in the teacher's guide. Families can do activities from *Mathematics at Home* Books 1–3 throughout the year.

◄*Home Connection Handbook* provides more ideas to communicate effectively with parents .

◄*Resources for the Pre-Kindergarten Classroom* provides additional teaching ideas, including suggestions for bringing mathematics into thematic instruction, as well as using games, literature, technology, songs, and rhymes to support mathematics learning.

Minute Math provides brief activities ► for transition times and spare moments throughout the day.

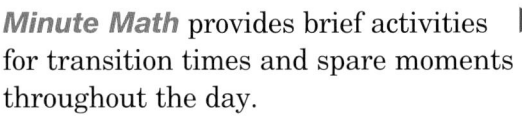

Ongoing Assessment

 Kid Watching

The following activities in the *Teacher's Guide to Activities* include Ongoing Assessment notes related to number concepts. See the *Assessment Handbook* for an expanded table.

Activity	Content Assessed
C◆9, N◆1, N◆2, N◆3, C◆16, N◆8, N◆9, N◆10, N◆14, C◆22, N◆17, N◆18	Recognize and name numerals. [Number and Numeration Goal 3]
N◆3, C◆16, N◆8, N◆10, N◆12, O◆7, N◆18	Represent numbers. [Number and Numeration Goal 3]
N◆4	Identify 1–5 objects without counting. [Number and Numeration Goal 3]
N◆5, N◆12	Match similar and dissimilar sets by number. [Number and Numeration Goal 3]
N◆16	Know ordinal numbers. [Number and Numeration Goal 3]
N◆6, G◆3, N◆13, N◆15, C◆24	Compare groups of objects or compare numbers. [Number and Numeration Goal 4]

Assessment Handbook

- ◆ Pre-Kindergarten goals, p. 6–11
- ◆ Number Concepts Assessment Overview, p. 28–29
- ◆ Baseline Periodic Assessment Tasks 3 and 4, p. 19
- ◆ End-of-Year Periodic Assessment Tasks 3 and 4, p. 22

Differentiated Instruction

Adjusting for Age and Development

Pre-Kindergarten Everyday Mathematics is designed to be flexible enough to adapt to a wide range of preschool classrooms, including classrooms with mixed age groupings and classrooms with a wide range of developmental levels. Many activities include suggestions to help teachers modify the activity to make it accessible and interesting to children with varying needs, learning styles, or levels of proficiency or understanding.

N◆6	Comparing in Trays	**N◆15**	*High / Low* Game
N◆8	Number Pockets	**N◆16**	Animals on Parade
N◆9	*Match Up* Game	**N◆17**	*Child Bingo* Game
N◆11	Finding Cookies	**N◆18**	Number Books
N◆13	*More or Less* Game	**N◆19**	Number Shapes
N◆14	Number Scavenger Hunt		

Language Support

Everyday Mathematics provides activity-specific suggestions to help all children, including non-native English speakers, develop the language necessary to acquire, process, and express mathematical ideas.

Developing Oral Language

N◆6 Develop comparative language *(more, fewer, less, same)*.

N◆15 Develop context for *high* and *low*.

N◆16 Develop ordinal number language.

Language & Vocabulary

Informally use these terms that are related to number concepts.

number names	higher	least
order	highest	fewer
first	low	fewest
second	lower	same
third	lowest	same number
fourth	more	same amount
last	most	tie
high	less	match

Activity Connections

The Connections for each activity link the Main Activity to different curricular and classroom areas. They are useful for meeting individual needs and integrating mathematics throughout the day. The following connections are in the Number Concepts section.

Art

N✦12 *Matching Sets* Game II
N✦14 Number Scavenger Hunt
N✦18 Number Books
N✦19 Number Shapes

Dramatic Play

N✦1 Classroom Addresses
N✦14 Number Scavenger Hunt

Family Connections

See Home-School Connection on page 90.

Games

N✦4 Intuitive Numbers
N✦5 *Matching Sets* Game I
N✦7 *Number Board* Game
N✦9 *Match Up* Game
N✦12 *Matching Sets* Game II
N✦13 *More or Less* Game
N✦15 *High/Low* Game
N✦17 *Child Bingo* Game

Literacy

N✦2 Number Walk
N✦8 Number Pockets
N✦13 *More or Less* Game
N✦16 Animals on Parade
N✦18 Number Books

Mathematics

N✦5 *Matching Sets* Game I
N✦6 Comparing in Trays
N✦7 *Number Board* Game
N✦8 Number Pockets
N✦11 Finding Cookies
N✦19 Number Shapes

Music and Movement

N✦1 Classroom Addresses
N✦3 Number Stations I
N✦10 Number Stations II
N✦11 Finding Cookies
N✦17 *Child Bingo* Game
N✦18 Number Books

Outdoors

N✦2 Number Walk

Snack

N✦3 Number Stations
N✦6 Comparing in Trays
N✦10 Number Stations II

Writing

N✦1 Classroom Addresses

N·1 Classroom Addresses

 Objective To explore the use of numbers in addresses and provide practice with numeral recognition.

Key Mathematics Concepts and Skills

• Develop an awareness of numbers and their uses. [Number and Numeration Goal 3]

• Associate number names and written numerals. [Number and Numeration Goal 3]

Other Skills Reading and Writing

Terms to Use address

Materials large index cards or paper; markers or crayons; stickers; tape; clear contact paper (optional)

Planning Tip If your classroom does not have a room number, choose a number and post it where children can easily see it. Also assign a number to each child according to the order of his or her cubby or storage bin. Write the numbers in large print on index cards or paper. Create a large border around the numbers for children to decorate.

▶ Main Activity

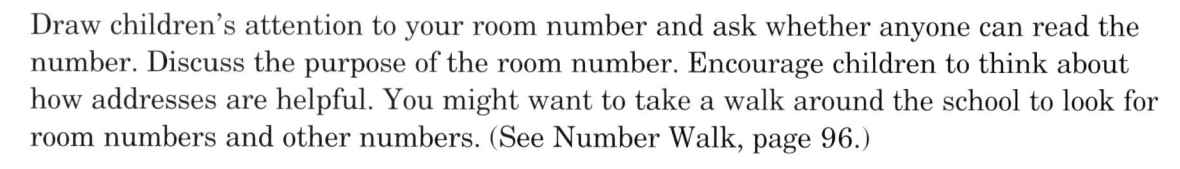
✔Whole Group   ✔Small Group   ☐ Partners   ☐ Center

Draw children's attention to your room number and ask whether anyone can read the number. Discuss the purpose of the room number. Encourage children to think about how addresses are helpful. You might want to take a walk around the school to look for room numbers and other numbers. (See Number Walk, page 96.)

Explain that children will each get an address number for a cubby, locker, or storage bin. Give each child his or her assigned number on an index card. Invite children to decorate the border any way they like using markers, crayons, and stickers. Explain that they shouldn't color over the numeral on their card. You may also want to create an address card for your desk or workspace.

Attach the address cards to children's cubbies or storage bins in a visible place. Laminate or cover the cards with clear contact paper if possible.

You can refer to the children's address numbers throughout the year. If you label the materials with the proper address number, children can deliver and sort materials—such as artwork, notes home, or notes to each other—into the proper cubbies. (See the Writing Connection below.)

NOTE On birthdays or holidays, such as Valentine's Day, encourage children to use cubby addresses and "mail" cards to each other.

 Ongoing Assessment: Kid Watching

You can use this activity to informally observe children's numeral recognition skills.

▶ Connections

Music Connection The class can sing "My Address" to the tune of "Jingle Bells."

My address, my address,
Classroom _____ (say your classroom address),
Oh, what fun it is to have an address of my own. HEY!

Writing Connection You or the children can make a classroom address book or list to use at the Writing or Drawing Center. Encourage children to create and deliver pictures and notes to each other using their cubby addresses.

Dramatic Play Connection Consider setting up a post office in your Dramatic Play Center. You can include old envelopes and stamps, rubber stamps and inkpads, a mailbox fashioned from a box that children decorate, and a postal carrier bag. Children can sort and deliver mail labeled with cubby addresses.

 Family Connection You might want to use the Numbers All Around Family Connection (*Math Masters*, page 75) to help children become familiar with their home addresses.

 Related Book

• *My Global Address* by Tamara Nunn (Creative Teaching Press, 1996)

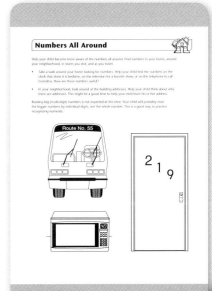

Math Masters, p. 75

N·2 Number Walk

 Objective To increase children's awareness of numbers in the environment and provide practice with numeral recognition.

Key Mathematics Concepts and Skills
- Develop an awareness of numbers and their uses. [Number and Numeration Goal 3]
- Associate written numerals and number names. [Number and Numeration Goal 3]

Other Skills Listening and Speaking

Materials none

Planning Tip Taking number walks in small groups provides more opportunity for interaction and discussion.

▶ **Main Activity**   ✔Whole Group   ✔Small Group   ☐ Partners   ☐ Center

Encourage children to look around the classroom and to point out and name any numerals they see. Talk about the various uses of the numerals they notice, such as on the clock to tell time, on the classroom door as an address, on a game box to tell how many players, and so on. Next, take children for a "number walk" around the school. Encourage them to look for numerals on signs, displays, clocks, calendars, doors, and so on. Talk with children about the numerals they see and their uses, and help children notice patterns that might exist. For example, they might notice that all the numbers on the first floor start with 1, or that the classroom numbers are in order. Encourage children to share and discuss their observations.

NOTE Children may read two- or three-digit numbers digit by digit. They might say "2" "8" for 28, for example. You can model how to say the number correctly, but don't expect children to be able to read these larger numbers. It is good practice for them to simply read the digits one at a time.

Ongoing Assessment: Kid Watching

You can use this activity to informally assess children's numeral recognition skills. Also note whether the children make a distinction between letters and numerals.

▶ Connections

Literacy Connection Share *Count Down to Clean Up!* by Nancy Elizabeth Wallace (Houghton Mifflin, 2001). Encourage children to look for the numerals on the pages and to try to keep track of the number of bunnies and other objects on each page.

Outdoors Connection Take children on a neighborhood walk to see what numbers they can find outside of school.

 Family Connection You might want to use the Numbers All Around Family Connection (*Math Masters,* page 75) to encourage families to help children think about and notice numbers in their environment.

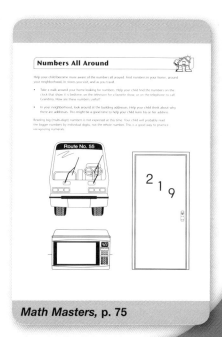

Math Masters, p. 75

N·3 Number Stations I

Objective To provide opportunities for children to develop number sense.

Key Mathematics Concepts and Skills

• Count out a given number of objects (between 3 and 5). [Number and Numeration Goal 2]

• Associate number names, quantities, and written numerals. [Number and Numeration Goal 3]

• Represent numbers 3 through 5 with groups of objects and recognize that numbers can be represented in different ways. [Number and Numeration Goal 3]

Other Skills Fine Motor

Materials various manipulatives, such as craft sticks, pattern blocks, connecting cubes, beads, and inch cubes; index cards

---

Planning Tip This activity can last several weeks, with the focus on each number lasting several days. Decide how many different stations to set up each day and when to introduce new stations. Introduce the stations to small groups first, and then open up the stations during Center time for free exploration.

▶ Main Activity

☐ Whole Group ✔ Small Group ☐ Partners ✔ Center

Set up several stations where children will count and arrange manipulatives to represent a given number. Each station should include one type of manipulative. Label each station by writing the featured number on an index card. The goal of the activity is for children to use a variety of manipulatives to explore numbers, beginning with 3, progressing to 4, and then 5.

NOTE By making numbers in a variety of ways using many different materials, children discover and gradually internalize the unique patterns and combinations each number forms naturally. They also begin to recognize that numbers can be represented in different ways.

Links to the Future

Later in the year, you will extend this activity to include larger numbers. (See Number Stations II, page 112.)

Possible stations:

▷ **Craft Sticks:** Children make different arrangements with the featured number of craft sticks.

▷ **Pattern Blocks:** Children make different arrangements with the featured number of pattern blocks.

▷ **Inch Cubes:** Children make different arrangements with the featured number of inch cubes.

▷ **Connecting Cubes:** Children use different-color cubes to make stacks with the featured number of connecting cubes.

▷ **Beads:** Children count out the featured number of different-color beads and put them in small cups or cupcake liners.

Encourage children to move among the stations. At each station, encourage them to describe their designs and combinations. For arrangements that don't include the correct quantity, help children count, then add or subtract objects, as needed. If children are mostly making piles, encourage more variety with questions such as: *How else can you arrange the materials? Can you make a shape or a line or a letter?* Leave the arrangements on display for comparison and discussion. All children should have the opportunity to go to each station over several days before you change to the next featured number.

▶ Connections

Music and Movement Connection Sing counting songs or play counting games, such as Can You Do What I Do? on page 44 and *Dice Movement* Game on page 46, and focus on the number that children are currently exploring at number stations.

Snack Connection Have children count out the featured number of snack items. For example, children take 3 carrot sticks, 3 celery sticks, and 3 crackers for a snack.

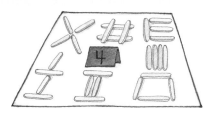

A craft-stick station for the number four

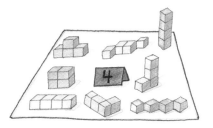

An inch-cube station for the number four

Ongoing Assessment: Kid Watching

You can use this activity to observe children's abilities to count out a given number of objects and to associate a numeral and its quantity. Also note whether they can represent a number in different ways.

N·4 Intuitive Numbers

 **Objective** To develop children's understanding of quantities through 5.

Key Mathematics Concepts and Skills

• Identify small numbers of objects (1–5) without counting. [Number and Numeration Goal 3]

Other Skills Cooperation

Materials Game Masters (*Math Masters,* pp. 54–55)

Planning Tip Copy and cut apart several sets each of butterfly cards and beetle cards (horizontal arrangements) from *Math Masters,* pages 54 and 55. If possible, laminate them for durability. (See *Matching Sets* Game I, page 102, and *Matching Sets* Game II, page 116, for other activities that use these picture cards.)

NOTE The immediate perception of small groups of objects, without counting, is called subitizing. See *Minute Math®* for subitizing activities that use fingers.

▶ **Main Activity**   ✔Whole Group ✔Small Group ✔Partners ☐ Center

Numbers less than 5 are sometimes called intuitive numbers because most children, even at a very young age, can recognize these small quantities without counting. The ability to immediately perceive small quantities develops naturally as children gain experience with collections of objects in their everyday world. Gradually, they begin to recognize the unique patters and combinations each number naturally forms. The following activity asks children to identify small quantities without counting. It is a quick and fun way for children (and you) to see what they can do.

Show a picture card quickly and then hide it. Children watch closely and then say how many butterflies or beetles were shown. Children may need encouragement to try to say the number without counting. You may then show the same card again so that children can check by counting. Begin with cards 0–3. Add cards with 4 and 5 objects as children are ready. Encourage children to try this activity with partners.

Ongoing Assessment: Kid Watching

If you work with small groups, you can use this activity to informally assess children's understanding of quantities up to five. Can children identify the picture cards by number? Do they count the pictures, or quickly "see" the number?

▶ Connections

Game Connection Partners or small groups take turns rolling a dot die and taking that number of beads from a common pile. The pair or group plays until all the beads have been taken. Watch to see whether children count the dots on the die or if they immediately perceive the number without counting. Similarly, do children count out the beads one by one, or take the total all at once?

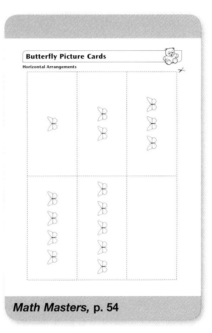

Math Masters, p. 54

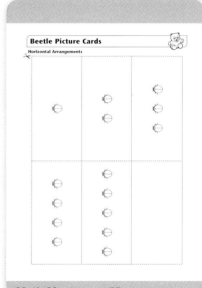

Math Masters, p. 55

N·5 *Matching Sets Game I*

Objective To introduce matching sets by number.

Key Mathematics Concepts and Skills

• Count (or recognize without counting) up to 5 pictures on a card. [Number and Numeration Goal 2]

• Match sets of 1 to 5 objects. [Number and Numeration Goal 3]

Other Skills Cooperation

Terms to Use match, same number, more, less, fewer

Materials Game Masters (*Math Masters,* pp. 54 and 55)

Planning Tip Copy and cut apart several sets each of the butterfly cards and beetle cards (horizontal arrangements) from *Math Masters,* pages 54 and 55. If possible, laminate them for durability. (See Intuitive Numbers, page 100, and *Matching Sets Game II,* page 116, for other activities that use these picture cards.)

▶ **Main Activity**   ☐ Whole Group ✔Small Group ✔Partners ✔Center

Shuffle together two sets of identical picture cards (all butterflies or all beetles) and place the 10 cards in 2 rows faceup. Partners take turns matching cards by the number of objects on each card. When they find a match, they say the number and remove the pair of cards from play. Children continue until all cards have been matched. Later, children may want to play with the cards facedown, like the game Memory.

Once children are proficient with matching identical picture cards, add challenge by shuffling together one set of butterfly and one set of beetle cards and having children match the butterfly cards to the beetle cards that have the same number of insects.

NOTE It is easier for children to match sets that are visually similar. When they begin to use dissimilar picture cards, they will initially have the most success matching small sets (1–3 objects) that they can recognize without counting.

Ongoing Assessment: Kid Watching

You can use this activity to informally assess children's abilities to identify and match picture cards by number. Can children match similar sets, such as butterfly to butterfly, by number? Can they match different sets, such as butterfly to beetle, by number?

▶ Connections

Mathematics Connection Include dot dice and dominoes in the Math Center; both have patterned sets of dots that children can match. Have partners each take a die. At the same time, both players roll until the two dice match. Or, have partners work together to find all the dominoes with matching sides, called the "doubles."

Game Connection Remove the 2 through 5 cards of one suit from a deck of playing cards and glue them on posterboard, numeral side up. Give children the remaining 2 through 5 cards from the deck and invite them to find number matches for the cards on the posterboard. Add cards for higher numbers as children are ready.

 Family Connection Create game bags with materials and directions for *Matching Sets* Game I that children can check out to play at home with their families.

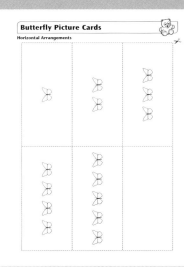

Math Masters, p. 54

Math Masters, p. 55

N·6 Comparing in Trays

Objective To provide concrete experiences with comparing quantities.

Key Mathematics Concepts and Skills

• Count dots on a die. [Number and Numeration Goal 2]

• Visually compare two sets of objects. [Number and Numeration Goal 4]

• Use terms such as *more, less, fewer,* and *same* to describe comparisons. [Number and Numeration Goal 4]

Other Skills Cooperation, Pretending and Role Play

Terms to Use more, less, fewer, same amount

Materials ice-cube trays or egg cartons; masking tape or marker; counters; dot dice; small and large toy animals and paper plates (optional)

Planning Tip If you do not have ice-cube trays or egg cartons, you can use masking tape to divide a cookie sheet or cafeteria tray into 12 sections.

The ice-cube tray (or egg carton) helps children line up or match objects one-to-one, which is a useful comparison strategy. Some children will not need the tray, or may only need to use this strategy when comparing larger numbers.

▶ Main Activity

Whole Group ✔Small Group ✔Partners ✔Center

Have partners sit side-by-side with an ice-cube tray or egg carton between them. Place the tray vertically between the children, so that each child has his or her own column of cups. Mark the start at the bottom edge of the tray with masking tape or a marker.

Children take turns rolling a die. They say the number, count out that number of counters, and put one counter in each cup on their side of the tray. (Be sure children start filling cups from the bottom of the tray.) After each partner has had a turn, they compare the number of counters on each side of the tray. Encourage children to use comparison words such as *more, less, fewer,* and *same.* Children clear the tray before they roll and compare again.

To add interest, you may want to allow children to "feed" the counters to stuffed animals after each round. Provide two toy animals (one larger than the other) and two paper plates. After each round, the child with more counters feeds them to the larger animal, and the child with fewer counters feeds them to the smaller animal. Children make a food pile for each animal and add counters with each turn.

Children may want to "feed" the larger set to the larger bear and the smaller set to the smaller bear.

Adjusting for Age and Development

For some children, you may want to begin with dice having 1–3 dots, then expand to numbers 4–6.

Ongoing Assessment: Kid Watching

You can use this activity to informally assess children's ability to visually compare sets of objects and describe the comparisons using words such as *more, fewer, less,* and *same.*

▶ **Connections**

Snack Connection Give each child a small handful (6 or less of each) of two different types of small snacks (pretzels and raisins, for example). Have them line up each type of snack side by side so they can compare which type they have more of. You may need to help children arrange the items side by side. Provide trays or egg cartons for children who need them.

Mathematics Connection Have a small group of 3–4 children each roll a dot die. Children line up the dice in order from the least to the most dots. Dice with the same number of dots can be stacked.

Developing Oral Language   ELL

This activity will help children develop their understanding of the words *more, less, fewer,* and *same amount.* You can enhance children's learning by modeling the use of comparative language. For example: *You have* more *because all of your cups are full and she has an empty cup. Yours both go up this high, so you have the* same *amount.*)

N·7 Number Board Game

Objective To develop number sense and provide experiences with counting and numeral recognition.

Key Mathematics Concepts and Skills

• Count dots on a die and objects to match the number of dots. [Number and Numeration Goal 2]

• Associate number names, quantities and written numerals. [Number and Numeration Goal 3]

• Discover the "one more" pattern of sequential numbers. [Number and Numeration Goal 3]

Other Skills Cooperation

Materials Game Master (*Math Masters*, p. 56); posterboard or flannel board; large paper circles and markers, or large felt circles and felt numerals; dot dice; counters

Planning Tip Have the materials ready in advance, but create the large number board with the class. You will need 21 paper or felt circles.

▶ Main Activity

✔Whole Group ✔Small Group ✔Partners ✔Center

With children's assistance, construct a large number board with numbers from one to six. (See *Math Masters*, page 56, for a model.) Begin with 1, and ask a child to place one circle above the numeral. As each numeral and corresponding dots are added, discuss what children notice. You may want to ask: *What happens when you count one more? What shape do the dots make? What do you think it would look like if we added more numbers?*

When the large number board is complete, use it to play the *Number Board* game. Place the number board on the floor or table where children can see it. Have a child roll a die, count the dots on the die, and find the corresponding number on the number board. Then he or she uses counters to cover the circles above that number on the board. Call on different children to take turns rolling the die and covering circles until all the numbers have been rolled and covered. If a child rolls a number that is already covered, he or she doesn't add counters to the board.

Place copies of the *Number Board* Gameboard (*Math Masters,* page 56), counters, and dice in the Math Center. Explain that children can use the small boards to play *Number Board.* Children can work alone or together to fill up one board. You might also place the large number board at the Center and invite children to use it for the game. When not in use, hang the large number board up as a reference.

NOTE Although the focus of the *Number Board* game is on numeration skills, such as counting, numeral recognition, and number patterns, children may also explore probability concepts as they realize that the goal is to roll numbers they haven't already covered on the board.

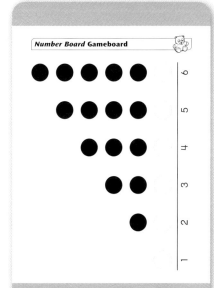

Math Masters, p. 56

▶ Connections

Mathematics Connection If you have an abacus or counting frame, make it available for children to explore in the Math Center. Encourage children to order the beads in groups from one to six and beyond, and to notice the stair-step pattern. Children can also build a model of the number board by making and ordering towers of connecting cubes. Observe whether they extend the pattern to higher numbers.

Game Connection Children can play a variation of the *Number Board* game, called *Number Board Race,* with a partner or small group. Each player gets a board. They "race" to fill their own boards by taking turns rolling the die and covering dots on their boards.

Related Books

- *Ten Black Dots* by Donald Crews, (Greenwillow, 1986) (See Counting Dots, page 66 for an activity that uses this book.)

- *Rooster's Off to See the World* by Eric Carle (Simon & Schuster Children's Publishing, 1991)

N·8 Number Pockets

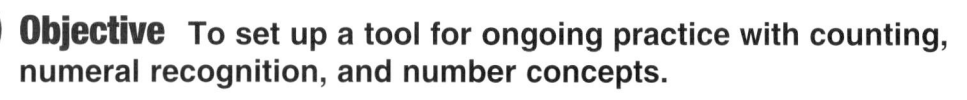 **Objective** To set up a tool for ongoing practice with counting, numeral recognition, and number concepts.

Key Mathematics Concepts and Skills

- Count out a specified number of objects. [Number and Numeration Goal 2]
- Represent numbers with different groups of objects. [Number and Numeration Goal 3]
- Associate number names, quantities, and written numerals. [Number and Numeration Goal 3]
- Compare and order numbers and groups of objects. [Number and Numeration Goal 4]

Terms to Use more, fewer, less, most, fewest, least, order

Materials hanging pockets (such as clear plastic shoe holders); index cards and masking tape or other removable labels; dots or stickers; assorted manipulatives or other small countable objects

▶ Main Activity

⬚ Whole Group ✔ Small Group ✔ Partners ✔ Center

Show children the labeled hanging pockets. Invite children to work alone or in pairs to put the correct number of manipulatives, such as plastic dinosaurs, bear counters, buttons, coins, beads, or connecting cubes, in each pocket. As children work, talk with them about what they are doing and ask questions that develop number sense, such as: *Which of these two pockets has more (or fewer) items? Which pocket has the most (or least) items?*

Over time, vary children's work with the pockets. Try one or more of the following:

▷ Remove the labels and have children add them to the pockets, in order, before counting out the items.
▷ Switch the order of the labels on two (or more) pockets and see whether children can find the problem and fix the order.
▷ Place different numbers of objects in the pockets, not necessarily in order from smallest to largest, and have children add the correct label to each pocket.
▷ Attach the labels in order from 10 to 0 to provide practice with backward counting.
▷ Change the labels so that only the numeral is depicted.
▷ Invite children to think of their own ways to work and play with the pockets.

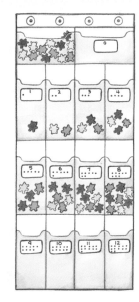

Place the removable labels so that children can see the contents of the pockets.

 Adjusting for Age and Development

Some children may benefit from taking the index cards or labels off the hanging pockets and laying them flat so they can match objects to the dots or stickers using one-to-one correspondence. This self-correcting feature can help build children's independence. You can also create an identical set of cards to use for this purpose.

▶ Connections

Mathematics Connection Children can also use the pockets to sort objects. For example, you might label the pockets with different shapes or colors and have children find classroom items that match the shapes or colors.

Literacy Connection You can label the pockets with letters and invite children to find things, or pictures of things, that begin with each letter to place in the appropriate pockets.

✔ Ongoing Assessment: Kid Watching

You can use hanging pockets to informally assess children's counting and numeral-recognition skills. Note whether they correctly associate written numerals and quantities and whether they can represent numbers with different types of objects.

N·9 *Match Up* Game

 **Objective** To provide practice with matching written numerals and quantities.

Key Mathematics Concepts and Skills

• Count dots on cards. [Number and Numeration Goal 2]

• Associate number names, quantities, and written numerals. [Number and Numeration Goal 3]

Other Skills Cooperation

Materials Game Masters (*Math Masters,* pp. 61–63); number line or chart (optional)

Planning Tip Copy the numeral cards and the dot cards onto different-color paper or cardstock (numeral cards on one color; dot cards on a different color). Laminate them for durability, if possible.

▶ Main Activity

☐ Whole Group ✔ Small Group ✔ Partners ✔ Center

Introduce *Match Up* to a small group of children. Show children the numeral cards and the dot cards, then set up the game by separately shuffling one set of numeral cards and one set of dot cards. Place the numeral cards facedown in one row and the dot cards facedown in another row.

The first player turns over one numeral card and one dot card and says the number name for each card. If the number of dots matches the numeral, the child keeps the cards. If the cards do not match, they are turned facedown again. Players take turns until all the matching pairs are found. Place the cards in the Math Center for ongoing play. If children know the counting sequence but have difficulty remembering what some numerals look like, they may be able to count on a number line for reference.

A matched pair

Adjusting for Age and Development

You can introduce the game in stages by having children play with all cards faceup at first, and then with one set (dots or numerals) faceup and the other set facedown. Some children may also benefit from matching numeral cards to numeral cards and/or dot cards to dot cards before matching numeral cards to dot cards. (For this variation, you need two sets of the numeral and/or dot cards.) You can also vary the difficulty of the game by using higher or lower numbers.

Ongoing Assessment: Kid Watching

You can use this game to informally assess children's abilities to associate number names, quantities, and written numerals for numbers through 9. You might note whether children count the dots or whether they know the quantity of any of the dot patterns without counting.

▶ Connections

Game Connection Provide a variety of memory or concentration card games. Use store-bought versions or make your own cards to match a current classroom theme.

Family Connection You might create game bags with materials and directions for *Match Up* that children can check out to play at home with their families. Or make a set of numeral and dot cards for each child to keep at home.

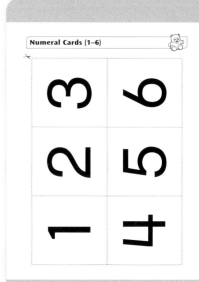

Math Masters, p. 61

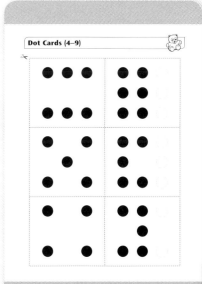

Math Masters, p. 63

N·10 Number Stations II

Objective To provide opportunities for children to deepen their number sense by extending previous work with number stations.

Key Mathematics Concepts and Skills

• Count out a given number of objects (between 6 and 10). [Number and Numeration Goal 2]

• Associate number names, quantities, and written numerals. [Number and Numeration Goal 3]

• Represent numbers 6 through 10 with groups of objects and recognize that numbers can be represented in different ways. [Number and Numeration Goal 3]

Other Skills Fine Motor

Materials various manipulatives, such as craft sticks, pattern blocks, connecting cubes, beads, and inch cubes; index cards

▶ Main Activity

☐ Whole Group ✔Small Group ☐ Partners ✔Center

The goal of this activity is for children to use a variety of manipulatives to explore numbers 6–10. (If children need more experiences with smaller numbers, see Number Stations I, page 98, which focuses on numbers 3–5.)

Set up several stations where children will count out and arrange manipulatives to represent the featured number. Each station should include one type of manipulative. Use the same manipulatives as you had in Number Stations I, or introduce new ones. Children might enjoy a penny or coin station. Label each station by writing the featured number on an index card.

Planning Tip This activity is a continuation of Number Stations I, page 98. Like the earlier activity, this activity is designed to last several weeks, with the focus on each number lasting several days.

NOTE By making numbers in a variety of ways using many different materials, children discover and gradually internalize the unique patterns and combinations each number forms naturally. They also experience that numbers can be represented in different ways.

Encourage children to move among the stations. At each station, ask them to describe their designs and combinations. For arrangements that don't include the correct quantity, help children count, then add or subtract objects as needed. If children are mostly making piles, encourage more variety with questions such as: *How else can you arrange the materials? Can you make a shape or a line or a letter?* Leave the various arrangements on display for comparison and discussion. All children should have the opportunity to go to each station over several days before you change to the next featured number.

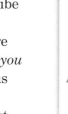

A pattern-block station for the number six

 Ongoing Assessment: Kid Watching

You can use this activity to observe children's abilities to count out a given number of objects between 6 and 10, and to associate numerals and quantities for these numbers. Also note whether they can represent numbers in different ways.

▶ Connections

Music and Movement Connection Sing counting songs or play counting games, such as Can You Do What I Do? on page 44 and *Dice Movement* Game on page 46. Focus on the number that children are currently exploring at number stations.

Snack Connection Have children count out the featured number of snack items. For example, invite children to take 8 pretzels and 8 grapes for snack.

 Related Book

- *6 Sticks* by Molly Coxe (Random House Books for Young Readers, 1999)

N·11 Finding Cookies

 Objective To provide practice with reading numerals and counting.

Key Mathematics Concepts and Skills

• Count unordered collections of up to 10 objects. [Number and Numeration Goal 2]

• Associate number names, quantities, and written numerals. [Number and Numeration Goal 3]

Other Skills Pretending and Role Play

Materials small paper plates, numbered 0–10 and paper cookies (Both materials are from Counting Cookie Chips, p. 74.)

Planning Tip You may want to do this activity in conjunction with Counting Cookie Chips, page 74, which also uses the paper cookies, or with Classroom Cooking, page 224, if you plan to bake cookies with children. Also see *More or Less* Game, page 118, for another activity that uses the paper cookies.

 ▶ **Main Activity**   ✔Whole Group ✔Small Group ☐ Partners ☐ Center

Hide the paper cookies around the room. (Don't hide them too well.) Give each child or pair of children a numbered plate and have them read the numeral. Tell children they will look for the cookies that have that number of chips and bring them to you as they find them. Explain that if they find a cookie that doesn't match their numeral, they should leave the cookie in its hiding place for others to find.

Invite children to begin searching. When children bring you a cookie, have them count the chips out loud. After all of the cookies have been found, mix them up and enlist children's help in hiding them again. Give children plates with different numbers, or begin with a new group of children.

Alternatively, you can reverse the order of the game: Children begin by finding a cookie, and then choose the numbered plate that matches the number of chips on their cookie.

Tailor the difficulty of the activity by giving the larger number plates to children with more advanced counting skills. Because of the random arrangement of the chips, children may need to find a strategy for keeping track of chips as they count. See Counting Cookie Chips, page 74, for suggestions.

▶ Connections

Music and Movement Connection Play "Who Took the Cookie from the Cookie Jar?" You might act out the song using one of your paper cookies. There are also several book versions of this song.

Mathematics Connection Put the paper cookies and numbered plates at a Center. Invite children to work alone or with a partner to order the cookies from the fewest chips to the most chips. To help them get started, have them find the lowest number of chips and go up one-by-one from there. They might find it useful to order the plates first.

N·12 Matching Sets Game II

 Objective To deepen children's number sense with a matching game involving the same numbers of objects in different arrangements.

Key Mathematics Concepts and Skills

- Count (or recognize without counting) up to 5 pictures on a card. [Number and Numeration Goal 2]
- Recognize different representations of numbers 1 through 5. [Number and Numeration Goal 3]
- Match sets of 1 to 5 objects in different arrangements. [Number and Numeration Goal 4]

Other Skills Cooperation

Materials Game Masters (*Math Masters,* pp. 54, 55, 64, and 65)

Planning Tip Copy several sets of the beetle and butterfly cards (dice-dot arrangements) from *Math Masters,* pages 64 and 65. Also copy or collect the butterfly and beetle cards (horizontal arrangements) from *Math Masters,* pages 54 and 55. You will mix these sets in different combinations for different versions of the matching game. Laminate the cards for durability, if possible.

▶ **Main Activity**   ☐ Whole Group ✔Small Group ✔Partners ✔Center

Choose either beetles or butterflies to use for the initial game. Shuffle together one set of cards with the chosen pictures arranged horizontally and one set of cards with the same pictures arranged in dice-dot patterns. Place the 10 cards faceup in 2 rows. Partners take turns finding a match by number. When they do, they say the number and remove the pair of cards from play. Children continue until all cards have been matched. Later, children may want to play with the cards facedown, like the game Memory.

As children are ready, introduce a more challenging version in which children make matches between cards with different pictures and different arrangements. For this version, shuffle together one set of beetle cards (horizontal arrangements) and one set of butterfly cards (dice-dot arrangements), or vice versa. As in the other game, have children find numerical matches. Place decks with different combinations of cards in the Math Center for ongoing play.

NOTE This game builds on *Matching Sets* Game I, page 102. In the earlier game, children match picture cards with the same number of pictures in the same arrangements. In this game, children match cards with the same number of pictures in different arrangements. When children first work with cards with different arrangements and/or different pictures, they may have difficulty focusing on the *number* of objects. Working toward this skill builds their understanding that numbers can be represented in different ways.

 Ongoing Assessment: Kid Watching

You can use this activity to informally assess children's understanding of numerical equivalence and the concept that numbers can be represented in different ways. Can children match sets by number when pictures are arranged differently? Can they match sets by number when the pictures *and* arrangements are different?

▶ Connections

Game Connection Shuffle all the sets of picture cards together and use them to play a version of Slap Jack. Partners or small groups evenly divide the deck of cards and make facedown piles. In unison, each child turns over his or her top card and compares it to the other players' cards. If any two cards have the same number of pictures, the first player to say the number and "slap" the cards gets to keep the cards. Play continues until one or more children runs out of cards.

Art Connection Supply index cards and dot markers or stickers for children to create their own decks of cards. Children can take their cards home to play *Matching Sets* or other games.

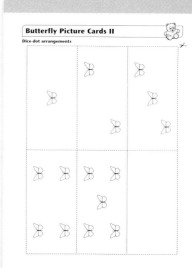

Math Masters, p. 64

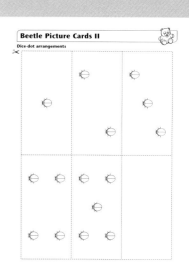

Math Masters, p. 65

N·13 *More or Less Game*

 Objective To provide practice with comparing sets and determining *more* or *less* through a game.

Key Mathematics Concepts and Skills

- Count chips on cookies. [Number and Numeration Goal 2]

- Compare numbers of chips on cookies and describe as *more, less, fewer,* and *same number.* [Number and Numeration Goal 4]

Other Skills Cooperation

Terms to Use more, less, fewer, same number

Materials Game Master (*Math Masters,* p. 66); transparent spinner; paper cookies from Counting Cookie Chips, p. 74; cookie jar or other opaque container; counters; extra paper cookie with 5 chips that can be covered by counters (optional); dice (optional); number cards from *Math Masters,* pp. 61–62 or pp. 67–70 (optional)

▶ Main Activity

☐ Whole Group ☐ Small Group ✔ Partners ✔ Center

Show children the *More or Less* spinners and discuss how they can use the pictures to tell which side is more and which is less, or fewer. Explain that children will use the spinners to play a partner game in which they compare the number of chips on cookies.

To start, one player spins the spinner and announces whether it is pointing to More or Less. Each player then closes his or her eyes and takes a cookie from the cookie jar. If the spinner is pointing to More, the player with more chips on his or her cookie wins the round and takes a counter. If the spinner is pointing to Less, the player with fewer chips on his or her cookie wins the round and takes a counter. Players spin the

Planning Tip If you haven't already done so for a previous activity, create a set of 11 paper cookies according to the directions in the Planning Tip on page 74. You may want to do Counting Cookie Chips, page 74 and/or Finding Cookies, page 114 before doing this activity.

NOTE Children can also compare dots on dice instead of chips on cookies. The dice version of the game can last longer because it is not limited by the number of paper cookies you have. You might want to set an ending point, such as when the first player gets five counters.

More/Less spinner again before each round. Play continues until there are not enough cookies left in the cookie jar for each player to take one. Players then count and compare their counters. They might spin the spinner one last time to see whether the "winner" is the person with more or fewer counters at the end of the game.

For a non-competitive variation, create an extra cookie with 5 chips. After each round, the winner of the round covers one of the chips on the extra cookie with a counter. Play ends when all of the chips on the extra cookie are covered.

NOTE Technically, *fewer* and *less* have slightly different meanings and usages. However, in casual speech the two words are often used interchangeably, so it is a good idea to expose children to both terms.

 Adjusting for Age and Development

To add numeral recognition to the game, have children play with number cards instead of cookies. For numerals only, use the numeral cards on *Math Masters,* pages 61 and 62. For cards with numerals and pictures, use the number cards on *Math Masters,* pages 67–70.

▶ Connections

Literacy Connection *More, Fewer, Less* by Tana Hoban (Greenwillow, 1998) invites children to compare familiar objects. Use comparison words when discussing the photographs.

Game Connection In a Center, place a large bowl with 15–20 counters. Partners both reach into the bowl and take one handful of counters. Then they count and compare the number of counters to determine who has more and who has fewer.

 Family Connection You can create a game bag with materials and directions for the dice variation of *More or Less.* Or, children can create paper cookies to play the cookie version at home.

✔ **Ongoing Assessment: Kid Watching**

You can use this activity to informally observe whether children can compare groups of objects and determine which has *more* and which has *less,* or *fewer.*

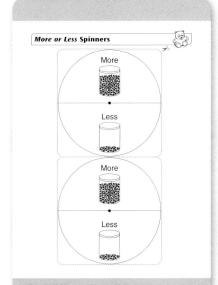

More or Less Spinners

More

Less

More

Less

Math Masters, p. 66

N·14 Number Scavenger Hunt

◎ **Objective** To increase children's awareness of numbers in the environment and provide practice with numeral recognition.

Key Mathematics Concepts and Skills

• Recognize numerals in the environment and explore their uses. [Number and Numeration Goal 3]

• Associate number names with written numerals. [Number and Numeration Goal 3]

Other Skills Fine Motor, Reading and Writing

Materials paper strips; writing tools; clipboards or heavy cardboard and clips (optional)

▶ **Main Activity**   ✔Whole Group   ✔Small Group   ✔Partners   ☐ Center

While sitting in a group, ask children to look around the room to see whether they can find any written numbers. Invite several children to share the numbers they see. Show the class one of the numeral strips and explain that they will go on a scavenger hunt to find all the numbers from 0 to 9. Demonstrate how children can mark off numerals as they find them, so they can keep track of which ones they are still looking for. Provide each child with a numeral strip and a writing tool. Then invite the group to start "hunting." Encourage children to check in periodically and show you the numbers they have found.

Children cross off numbers as they find them.

Planning Tip Prepare a strip of paper for each child with the numerals 0–9 written in order. Some teachers laminate the strips to make them reusable. You might want to provide clipboards or pieces of heavy cardboard and binder clips. Make sure there are numerals in your classroom that are easily visible to children.

NOTE Technically, *numerals* refers to the symbols that are used to represent a number, but you do not need to make this distinction with children. In casual speech, we often use the terms *number* and *numeral* interchangeably.

You may want to begin the number scavenger hunt in the classroom, and at another time take children on a walk outside of the classroom to search for numerals. Discuss the various uses of numbers children find.

Ongoing Assessment: Kid Watching

You can use this activity to informally assess children's numeral recognition skills.

▶ Connections

Dramatic Play Connection Add telephones and phone numbers to the Dramatic Play Center. Put phone numbers in a notebook or on index cards in a file box for easy reference. Encourage children to make pretend phone calls as a part of their play. Also encourage children to draw or cut out numerals to make signs and props for their dramatic play (grocery store signs, restaurant menus, addresses, and so on).

Art Connection Provide old newspapers, magazines, or grocery flyers for cutting. Children can make number collages by cutting out numbers and gluing them on paper. They might want to make designs or patterns with the numbers or write their own numbers on their collages. (Provide pre-cut numbers for children who can't yet use scissors proficiently.)

Family Connection You might want to use the Numbers All Around Family Connection (*Math Masters,* page 75) to encourage families to look together for numerals in their environment.

Adjusting for Age and Development

For additional support, invite children to work with partners. A child less familiar with numerals might be paired with a child who recognizes more numerals. Other children might enjoy the challenge of keeping track of how many times they find each numeral. You can show them how to make a tally under each numeral and then count the marks. Children may also come up with their own recording systems.

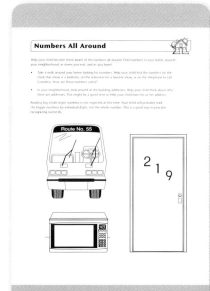

Math Masters, p. 75

N·15 *High/Low Game*

 Objective To provide practice with comparing numbers through a card game.

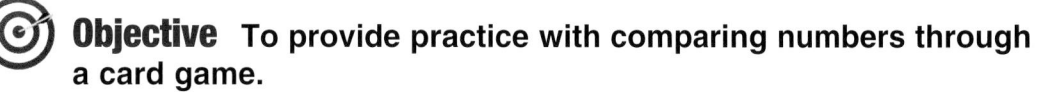

Key Mathematics Concepts and Skills

- Count pictures on a card. [Number and Numeration Goal 2]
- Associate number names, quantities, and written numerals. [Number and Numeration Goal 3]
- Compare numbers to determine high and low cards. [Number and Numeration Goal 4]

Other Skills Cooperation

Terms to Use high, higher, highest, low, lower, lowest, same, tie

Materials Game Masters (*Math Masters,* pp. 67–70); Game Masters (*Math Masters,* pp. 61 and 62; optional)

Planning Tip Use number cards (*Math Masters,* pages 67–70) in the range that is appropriate for your class. You can reduce the number of cards in play by using less than 4 suits. Laminate or mount the number cards on heavy paper for durability.

▶ **Main Activity**   ☐ Whole Group ✔ Small Group ✔ Partners ☐ Center

Show partners how to play *High/Low* with a set of number cards. Children divide the cards evenly and place their cards facedown in a pile in front of them. This game is played in rounds. On each round, children turn over their top card and read the number. Partners compare numbers to determine which card has the higher number. The child having the higher card calls out "high," and the child having the lower card calls out "low." Then both children place their cards in a discard pile. If there is a tie, children discard the cards and turn over two more. Play ends when all the cards have been played.

 **Developing Oral Language** ELL

Children may not be familiar with the mathematical meanings of the words *high* and *low*. Ask children to share how they use these words; then explain the meanings of the words in the context of the game. Help children connect *high* and *low* to other words they may know, such as *big* and *small* or *more* and *less.*

You can adapt the game for a small group by having 3 or 4 children turn over cards and find the highest and lowest cards.

NOTE Children enjoy calling out whether they have the high or low number and do not need for the game to have a winner. While this game is similar to War, it is meant to be noncompetitive, so cards are placed in a discard pile rather than back in players' piles. This also makes it easier for children to keep track of their cards.

> ### Adjusting for Age and Development
> For a more difficult game, have children use a set of cards with numerals only. You can use *Math Masters,* pages 61 and 62 for this variation.

▶ Connections

Games Connections Play *Find the Bear.* Turn 6 small cups upside down. Label each with a numeral from 1–6. Hide a bear under one of the cups. Ask a child to guess the number the bear is under. Give number clues to help find the bear: *It is under a cup with a higher number. It is under a cup with a lower number.* Add more cups when children are ready.

Play *Missing Number.* Place number cards 0–6 in a row in order. Ask children to close their eyes. Remove a card and close up the empty space. Children open their eyes and determine what number is missing. If needed, give clues such as: *The missing number is higher than 3.* Add more number cards as children are ready. You and the children can also invent other games to play with the number cards.

 Family Connection Consider creating game bags with the materials and directions for the *High/Low* Game, or for one of the games described in the Games Connections. Children can check the bags out to play at home.

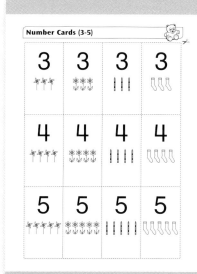

Number Cards (3–5)

Math Masters, p. 68

One of 4 masters

N·16 Animals on Parade

 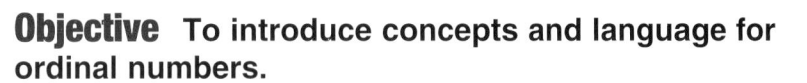

◎ Objective To introduce concepts and language for ordinal numbers.

Key Mathematics Concepts and Skills

• Become aware of ordinal numbers and their uses. [Number and Numeration Goal 3]

• Use ordinal numbers to describe the order of objects. [Number and Numeration Goal 3]

Other Skills Listening and Speaking, Pretending and Role Play

Terms to Use first, second, third, fourth, fifth, last

Materials small toy animals (3 to 5 per child)

▶ Main Activity

☐ Whole Group ✔ Small Group ☐ Partners ☐ Center

Gather a small group of children and tell them that you are going to make a parade of animals. Order a collection of 3–5 small toy animals while you tell a simple story, such as:

> *In the parade, the lion went first. Second was the bear.*
> *The elephant was third. The monkey came fourth; it was last.*

Together with children, use ordinal numbers to describe the position of each animal relative to the front of the line. Ask questions such as: *What animal is third in the parade? In what place is the bear?*

Give each child a collection of 3–5 animals. If all children have the same animals, you may want to begin by asking them to order their animals according to a simple "ordinal

 **Developing** **ELL**
Oral Language

This language-based activity may be difficult if ordinal number language is new for children. Repeat and vary the activity to provide additional practice. Some children will be able to follow your language but not yet be able to say ordinal numbers themselves.

number story" that you tell. Then you and the children can alter the story, and children can rearrange their animals accordingly.

If children have different animals in their collections, invite them to make their own animal parades. Ask each child to share his or her parade with the group by telling the order of the animals. Encourage children to compare how they ordered their animals. For example, "I put a bear first, but you put a rabbit first." Children can act out animal parades using puppets, stuffed animals, or animal masks. They will also enjoy participating in kid parades and describing their positions with ordinal numbers.

Adjusting for Age and Development

If children are interested, you may choose to extend the parade to 10 animals. Children will enjoy hearing the higher ordinal numbers, and may even notice their relation to the counting numbers, but do not expect them to know or remember all the ordinal numbers at this time.

NOTE Ordinal numbers are probably already part of your daily routines and conversations with children. For example, you probably use the language of *first, second, third,* and so on when you give multi-step directions or help children take turns. You can also include ordinal numbers in your Linear Calendar Routine. See *Minute Math®* for other quick activities to reinforce ordinal numbers that you can do during transitions or other spare moments of the day.

▶ Connections

Literacy Connection Read *Good Night Gorilla* by Peggy Rathmann (Putnam Juvenile, 1994) or *1, 2, 3, To The Zoo* by Eric Carle (Philomel, 1982). Have children use ordinal numbers to describe the order of the animals.

Related Books

- *Henry the Fourth* by Stuart J. Murphy (HarperCollins, 1999)
- *Make Way for Ducklings* by Robert McCloskey (Viking Juvenile, 1941)
- *10 Little Rubber Ducks* by Eric Carle (HarperCollins, 2005)

N·17 *Child Bingo Game*

Objective To reinforce numeral recognition through a game.

Key Mathematics Concepts and Skills

• Associate number names with written numerals. [Number and Numeration Goal 3]

• Use spatial reasoning to navigate a life-size Bingo grid and identify filled rows. [Geometry Goal 2]

Other Skills Cooperation

Materials 2 sets of numeral cards 1–9 made from Game Masters (*Math Masters,* pp. 61 and 62) or made from index cards and markers; chairs; tape; basket or other container; 2 sets of numeral cards 10–16 (optional)

▶ **Main Activity** ✔Whole Group ✔Small Group ☐ Partners ☐ Center

Teach children how to play a life-size version of Bingo. Call children up one at a time to pick a number from the basket without looking. Each child reads his or her number aloud, matches it to a number on a chair, and then sits on that chair. Continue playing until children get Bingo by filling 3 chairs in a row—across, up and down, or diagonally. Repeat the game by returning the cards to the basket and having children select again.

NOTE If children stand while they wait for their turn, they can more easily see and call Bingo when a row is filled. It may be difficult for children who are on the chairs in the grid to see Bingo.

Planning Tip At least 9 children are needed to play the game. Set up 9 chairs in a 3 x 3 grid. Use one set of numeral cards to label chairs randomly 1–9. Tape the cards where children can easily see them. Put the second set of numeral cards in a basket or other opaque container.

NOTE This game will be easier for children if they have played picture Bingo on cards before doing the activity, so they understand the concept of filling a row to get Bingo. If you do not have a Bingo game that is appropriate for young children, playing Tic-Tac-Toe can help children become aware of what constitutes 3 in a row.

Adjusting for Age and Development

Add 7 more chairs to make a 4 x 4 grid and use numeral cards up to 16.

▶ Connections

Game Connection At a Center, provide Bingo boards for small groups of children to play. Many school-supply stores sell Bingo games with pictures or with numbers appropriate for young children, or you can make your own by drawing or using stickers on tagboard or posterboard.

Music Connection Sing "Bingo" and discuss with children any patterns they notice in the song:

> *There was a farmer had a dog,*
> *And BINGO was her name-o.*
> *B-I-N-G-O, B-I-N-G-O, B-I-N-G-O,*
> *And BINGO was her name-o.*

(Repeat the song 5 times, replacing a successive letter of B-I-N-G-O with a clap at each verse.)

 Ongoing Assessment: Kid Watching

You can use this activity to informally assess children's abilities to recognize numerals 1–9 (or 1–16 in the more difficult variation).

Expanding

N·18 Number Books

(◎) **Objective** To reinforce numeral recognition and provide opportunities to represent numbers with pictures.

Key Mathematics Concepts and Skills

• Count pictures. [Number and Numeration Goal 2]

• Represent numbers with the correct number of pictures. [Number and Numeration Goal 3]

• Associate number names, quantities, and written numerals. [Number and Numeration Goal 3]

Other Skills Creative Expression, Fine Motor, Reading and Writing

Materials Teaching Masters (*Math Masters,* pp. 23–25); markers or crayons; stapler; construction paper (optional); stickers or stamps and stamp pads (optional)

Planning Tip Copy and cut *Math Masters,* pages 23–25 so each child will have one set of number pages 1–5. Use the blank page or construction paper for covers. Plan to work with small groups of children over a period of several days to create individual number books.

▶ Main Activity

☐ Whole Group ✔ Small Group ☐ Partners ☐ Center

For each of the number pages 1–5, help children read the numeral, and then ask them to draw that number of things on the page. Children might find it useful to have a chart to use as a reference, such as the Numbers 1–10 Poster or the Number Board (*Math Masters,* page 56). Encourage children to draw whatever they would like on their pages. Children might draw one type of item on each page, such as all flowers on the "2" page. Or, they might draw an assortment of objects on each page: one child, one cat, and one dog on the "3" page, for example. Some children may want to use the same object for all their pages. You can provide stickers or stamps and stamp pads for children to use.

Children may dictate captions and decorate covers for their books. Staple the books together. Display the number books in your classroom library or in the Math Center.

Ongoing Assessment: Kid Watching

You can use this activity to assess whether children represent numerals with the correct number of objects. If children do not put the correct number of objects on their pages, note whether they are having difficulty reading the numerals or counting out the objects.

▶ Connections

Art Connection Make a large chart divided into sections labeled 1–5. Have children draw groups of objects, such as 3 turtles, 5 fish, or 1 house. Then they can add the pictures to the appropriate section on the chart.

Literacy Connection Add new counting books to your classroom library.

Music and Movement Connection Children may enjoy saying the following rhyme and thinking of different ways to show the numbers with their bodies:

> *I love the number one; it's so much fun.*
> *I love the number one. Show me one.*

> (Children might show one finger or point to one nose or mouth.)

> *I love the number two; yes I do.*
> *I love the number two. Show me two.*

> (Children might show two fingers or two hands.)

> *I love the number three; it's for me...* (three fingers, or two arms and one leg)
> *I love the number four; it's one more...* (two legs and two arms)
> *I love the number five; it's so alive...* (two arms, two legs, and one head)

Adjusting for Age and Development

Tailor the number of pages to the individual needs of your children. Making a book of 3 may be challenging enough for some children. For children who are ready to go beyond 5, use the blank page on *Math Masters,* page 25 to make additional pages.

ACTIVITY N-18 | **Number Book Pages**

Use with Number Books.

1

2

Math Masters, p. 23

One of 3 masters

N·19 Number Shapes

Objective To provide opportunities to explore the shapes of numerals using sensory materials.

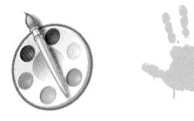

Key Mathematics Concepts and Skills

- Associate number names and written numerals. [Number and Numeration Goal 3]
- Explore numeral shapes using sensory materials. [Number and Numeration Goal 3]

Other Skills Fine Motor

Terms to Use straight line, curve, circle, number names

Materials sensory materials such as finger paint, shaving cream, rice, sand, and flour; trays or box lids; large numerals (0–9) for reference; resealable plastic bags (optional); sandpaper numerals 0–9 (optional)

> **Planning Tip** Make this activity available with a variety of sensory materials over an extended period of time. You can put the finger paint in resealable plastic bags to create a reusable and "messless" medium for exploration.

▶ Main Activity

☐ Whole Group ✔ Small Group ☐ Partners ✔ Center

Allow time for free exploration with the chosen media before beginning any guided activity. When children seem ready, encourage them to practice making straight lines, curves, and circles in the sensory material.

Next, show children the large numerals and help them notice the different parts that make up the number shapes. For example, point out that there is a circle and a straight line in a 9, and that a curve and straight line make a 2. Invite children to try to form different numerals in the sensory material and to think about the shapes in the numerals as they work.

Adjusting for Age and Development

You might provide numerals that children can trace with their fingers. Use sandpaper numbers to increase the sensory experience. (See the Mathematics Connection below.)

Links to the Future

The focus of this activity is for children to think about numerals and their formation without being overwhelmed by potential difficulties and mistakes when using paper and pencil. The sensory materials also provide an important tactile experience. Children will focus on proper numeral formation in Kindergarten and First Grade.

▶ Connections

Art Connection Encourage children to make play dough snakes and then form them into numbers.

Mathematics Connection Cut a set of numbers 0–9 out of sandpaper. Put the sandpaper numbers in a container. Invite children to reach in without looking, select a number, and hold the number under a table—without looking—to identify it by feel. Place a 0–9 number strip or the Numbers 1–10 Poster where children can readily see it for comparison. Children can also make crayon rubbings of the sandpaper numbers.

 Related Books

- *Arlene Alda's 123: What Do You See?* by Arlene Alda (Tricycle Press, 1998)
- *Grandpa Gazillion's Number Yard* by Laurie Keller (Henry Holt and Co., 2005)

Operations

Overview

> **Operations Goals**
>
> In Pre-K, children should have experiences that help them:
> - Solve and create number stories using concrete modeling. [Operations and Computation Goal 1]
> - Explore part-whole relationships (for example, 5 is made of 2 and 3). [Operations and Computation Goal 1]

Early on, children gain the understanding that a group of objects can be made larger by adding more, or smaller by taking some away. Whether they are adding blocks to a tower or eating pretzels at snack time, children intuitively recognize a change in quantity. Teachers can use real-life experiences like these to pose simple problems for children to solve. *Paul stacked 3 blocks. He put 1 more block on top. How many blocks did Paul have in his tower?*

Children are able to solve and create number stories by acting out the problem situation, either physically or concretely with manipulatives. Typically, children count to create an initial group, count to add or subtract a specified number of objects, and then count the resulting group. Later, as children develop their counting skills and problem-solving strategies, they are able to solve problems by counting on or counting back from the initial number.

Children need experiences that help them recognize part-whole relationships. For example, the number 5 can be represented as a 4 and a 1, or as a 3 and a 2. Knowing that any number is made of smaller parts, and that the parts can be combined to make a number, is an important precursor to understanding addition and subtraction and the relationship between them.

A wealth of informal experiences should precede children's introduction in Kindergarten to the more formal meanings of addition and subtraction. Introducing symbols and paper-and-pencil problems is not necessary in Pre-Kindergarten, and focusing on them too soon can limit children's understanding of the underlying concepts.

Professional Development

See Chapter 9 of the *Teacher's Reference Manual* for more information about the Operations and Computation strand.

Choosing Activities

Beginning	Building	Expanding
Beginning activities build a foundation for addition and subtraction. In these activities, children	**Building** activities focus on exploring addition and subtraction informally, without symbols. In these activities, children	**Expanding** activities expose children to problems of different types or structures. In these activities, children
◆ sing songs that add or subtract one item with each verse.	◆ act out number stories with their bodies, felt board figures, and/or puppets; ◆ develop and use concrete strategies to model and solve problems; ◆ explore part-whole relationships in numbers with manipulatives.	◆ figure out how many more are needed to reach a target number; ◆ find different ways to "take apart" a number using manipulatives; ◆ divide a collection of objects into two equal groups.

Activities in Perspective

KEY Art Dramatic Play Manipulatives and Games 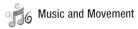 Rug Time Sensory **Core** Core Activity

 Books Excursion Music and Movement Science Snack

Teaching Resources

Home-School Connection

Family Connections suggest home activities that link to activities children have done at school. The following Operations activities contain Family Connections: O♦5, Bear Stories: Taking Away; O♦6, Animal Number Stories; O♦8, Number Stories Everywhere; O♦12, Fair Shares. Note that the same Family Connections are suggested with multiple activities, so keep track of which ones you have already sent home.

Mathematics at Home Books 1–3 provide additional ideas for enjoyable mathematics activities that families can do together, as well as lists of children's books related to the topics in the teacher's guide. Families can do activities from *Mathematics at Home* Books 1–3 throughout the year.

◄*Home Connection Handbook* provides more ideas to communicate effectively with parents.

◄*Resources for the Pre-Kindergarten Classroom* provides additional teaching ideas, including suggestions for bringing mathematics into thematic instruction, as well as using games, literature, technology, songs, and rhymes to support mathematics learning.

Minute Math provides brief activities ► for transition times and spare moments throughout the day.

Assessment

Ongoing Assessment

Kid Watching

The following activities in the *Teacher's Guide to Activities* include Ongoing Assessment notes related to operations. See the *Assessment Handbook* for an expanded table.

Activity	Content Assessed
O♦3, O♦4, O♦5, O♦10	Model and solve joining and taking-away situations and number stories with manipulatives. [Operations and Computation Goal 1]
O♦7	Combine parts to make numbers. [Operations and Computation Goal 1]
O♦10	Develop and use problem-solving strategies. [Operations and Computation Goal 1]

Assessment Handbook

◆ Pre-Kindergarten goals, pp. 6–11

◆ Operations Assessment Overview, p. 30

◆ End-of-Year Periodic Assessment Task 5, p. 23

Differentiated Instruction

Adjusting for Age and Development

Pre-Kindergarten Everyday Mathematics is designed to be flexible enough to adapt to a wide range of preschool classrooms, including classrooms with mixed age groupings and classrooms with a wide range of developmental levels. Many activities include suggestions to help teachers modify the activity to make it accessible and interesting to children with varying needs, learning styles, or levels of proficiency or understanding.

O♦1   One More Elephant

O♦9   *"How Many More?"* Game

O♦11   Taking Apart Numbers

O♦12   Fair Shares

Language Support

Everyday Mathematics provides activity-specific suggestions to help all children, including non-native English speakers, develop the language necessary to acquire, process, and express mathematical ideas.

Developing Oral Language

O♦4   Distinguish between number stories and other stories.

Language & Vocabulary

Informally use these terms that are related to operations.

all	more	half
all together	one more	group
in all	fewer	number story
how many	less	fair
join	one less	zero
take away	same	
left	some	
equal	part	

Activity Connections

The Connections for each activity link the Main Activity to different curricular and classroom areas. They are useful for meeting individual needs and integrating mathematics throughout the day. The following connections are in the Operations section.

Art

O♦1 One More Elephant
O♦2 "Take-Away" Songs
O♦4 Bear Stories: Joining
O♦6 Animal Number Stories
O♦8 Number Stories Everywhere

Dramatic Play

O♦5 Bear Stories: Taking Away
O♦12 Fair Shares

Family Connections

See Home-School Connection on Page 136.

Games

O♦2 "Take-Away" Songs

Literacy

O♦1 One More Elephant
O♦2 "Take-Away" Songs
O♦3 *Mystery Change* Game
O♦4 Bear Stories: Joining
O♦5 Bear Stories: Taking Away
O♦6 Animal Number Stories
O♦8 Number Stories Everywhere
O♦9 *"How Many More?"* Game
O♦10 Hiding Bears
O♦11 Taking Apart Numbers

Mathematics

O♦5 Bear Stories: Taking Away
O♦7 Building Numbers
O♦9 *"How Many More?"* Game

Music

O♦1 One More Elephant
O♦11 Taking Apart Numbers

Outdoors

O♦10 Hiding Bears

Snack

O♦7 Building Numbers
O♦9 *"How Many More?"* Game
O♦12 Fair Shares

0·1 One More Elephant

 Objective To provide concrete experiences with counting up and adding one through a counting song.

Core Activity

Key Mathematics Concepts and Skills

- Verbally count to at least 5. [Number and Numeration Goal 1]
- Count up to 5 objects (elephants). [Number and Numeration Goal 2]
- Add one more. [Operations and Computation Goal 1]

Other Skills Gross Motor, Pretending and Role Play, Singing and Rhythmic Movement

Terms to Use one more

Materials yarn (optional); Numeral Cards 1–5 (*Math Masters*, p. 61; optional)

Planning Tip You may want to set out some tangled yarn in your class meeting area to use as a spider web.

▶ Main Activity

☑ Whole Group ☐ Small Group ☐ Partners ☐ Center

Invite one child to stand in front of the group (on a tangled yarn "spider web," if you made one) to be the first elephant. Encourage the child to imitate an elephant, with hands clasped and arms swinging like a trunk, as the class sings the following song, which is featured on the Sing Everyday! CD:

> *One elephant went out to play,*
> *Upon a spider's web one day.*
> *She had such ENORMOUS fun,*
> *That she called for another elephant to come.*

 **Adjusting for Age and Development**

To provide experience with numeral recognition, give each elephant a numeral card as they join the line. You can use the cards on *Math Masters*, page 61. When children are comfortable with the activity, you can vary the song by calling two, three, or more elephants to come at once, then counting the total.

All children can cup their mouths with their hands and call out "Elephant!" Have the first elephant pick a classmate to join him or her at the front. The children then count the number of elephants and sing the second verse:

> *Two elephants went out to play...*

Continue adding one child after each verse until there are five elephants. Have the elephants stand in a line to make it easier for children to visualize the addition of one more and count the elephants. Sing the final verse together while the elephants act it out:

> *Five elephants went out to play,*
> *Upon a spider's web one day.*
> *They had such ENORMOUS fun,*
> *They jumped and played all day in the sun!*

▶ Connections

Art and Literacy Connections Read *Elmer* by David McKee (HarperCollins, 1989), or any of the other books in the *Elmer* series. Provide children with an outline of an elephant (or have them draw one) and a variety of colored paper squares. Have them glue the squares onto the elephant to resemble Elmer. You may want to ask children to make patterns with the colored squares.

Music Connection Teach the class the Spanish song "Elefantes." See *Resources for the Pre-Kindergarten Classroom* for the lyrics and listen to the Sing Everyday! CD for the tune. Change the lyrics to count up to any number in Spanish or English.

Links to the Future

As children sing and act out the song, they practice counting forward by 1s and gain concrete experiences with addition, although it is not necessary to use this terminology with children yet. Other familiar counting songs develop the concepts of "one less" and subtraction. (See "Take-Away" Songs, page 142.) Children will explore addition and subtraction through informal number stories and concrete modeling in later activities.

Related Book

- *The Right Number of Elephants* by Jeff Sheppard (Harper Collins, 1990)

Beginning

O·2 "Take-Away" Songs

 Objective To provide concrete experiences with counting back and "one less" through familiar counting songs.

Key Mathematics Concepts and Skills

• Verbally count backward from 5. [Number and Numeration Goal 1]

• Take away one. [Operations and Computation Goal 1]

Other Skills Singing and Rhythmic Movement

Terms to Use one less, zero

Materials animal crackers or animal counters; napkins or sheets of paper

Planning Tip If you use animal crackers, you can conduct this activity with small groups or the whole class during snack time. If you don't want to use food, you can use animal counters or another manipulative.

▶ **Main Activity**   ✔ Whole Group ✔ Small Group ☐ Partners ☐ Center

Sing "Five Little Monkeys Jumping on the Bed." Give each child five animal crackers or counters and have children spread their crackers in a line on a napkin or sheet of paper, the "bed." Sing the song again and have children move one animal off the bed as they sing each verse of the song. Repeat until there are no more (zero) monkeys jumping on the bed. You might discuss with children what zero means.

NOTE As children sing the song, they practice counting backward. As they take away one monkey at a time, they gain concrete experiences with subtraction, although it is not necessary to use this terminology with children at this time.

Repeat at other times using familiar counting songs such as "Five Little Ducks" or "Five Green and Speckled Frogs." (See *Resources for the Pre-Kindergarten Classroom* for lyrics and other suggestions.)

Children take away one cracker as they sing each verse.

▶ Connections

Game Connection Play animal charades. Invite one child to act like an animal, and the other children to guess the animal. Children can also provide mathematical clues, such as the number of legs the animal has or whether it is large or small.

Literacy and Art Connection Share one or more of the books listed in Related Books (or a similar book). If you find two book versions of the same song, invite children to compare them and discuss similarities and differences. Children may enjoy collaborating on illustrating a class book version of one of the songs.

Related Books

- *Five Little Ducks* by Mary Gruetzke (Orchard Books, 2006)
- *Five Little Ducks* by Raffi (Crown Books for Young Readers, 1992)
- *Five Little Monkeys Jumping on the Bed* by Eileen Christelow (Clarion Books, 1989)
- *Five Little Monkeys Sitting in a Tree* by Eileen Christelow (Clarion Books, 1991)
- *Five Little Monkeys with Nothing to Do* by Eileen Christelow (Clarion Books, 1996)

0·3 *Mystery Change* Game

 Objective To provide concrete, nonverbal experiences with addition and subtraction through a game.

Key Mathematics Concepts and Skills

• Count objects to solve simple problems. [Number and Numeration Goal 2]

• Compare sets of objects to determine whether they have the same number. [Number and Numeration Goal 4]

• Use concrete objects to model joining and taking-away situations. [Operations and Computation Goal 1]

Other Skills Cooperation

Materials chip counters or pennies; file folder or large index card (5" x 8")

Planning Tip You may want to introduce this game to a small group of 1–3 children.

▶ **Main Activity** ☐ Whole Group ✔ Small Group ✔ Partners ✔ Center

Introduce the *Mystery Change* game by giving each child a set of 5 counters and telling them that they will use the counters to solve a "mystery." Explain that they'll need to pay close attention to what you do, so they can be good detectives.

Play the game as follows:

1. Place a number of counters (3 or fewer) on the table for children to see. Say: *I have this many.* Give children ample time to see or count how many counters you have.

2. Hide your counters using a large index card or manila file folder as a screen.

NOTE Some children will have more success with a nonverbal operations activity than with more traditional verbal number stories. For this activity, avoid presenting the "mysteries" as verbal number stories. The idea is to see whether children can model and solve joining and taking-away problems without the possible distraction of too much language or unfamiliar vocabulary.

3. Prompt children to carefully watch what you are doing. Then, one by one, add to or take away from your collection of counters behind the screen. (Only add or take away 1 or 2 counters at first.) Make sure children are paying attention and can easily see you adding or removing the counters, but keep the total hidden behind the screen.

4. Say: *Use your counters to show how many I have behind the screen now.*

5. When children are ready, remove the screen so they can check to see whether their number of counters is the same as yours. If children are not sure the numbers match, they can count each group of counters or match them one-to-one.

When children are familiar with *Mystery Change* game, they will enjoy holding the screen and modeling an operation for you. Partners can also play this game at the Math Center.

▶ Connections

Literacy Connection Read aloud a variety of lift-the-flap books that involve surprises or a mystery. Ask children to guess what's under the flap.

Building

0·4 Bear Stories: Joining

Objective To introduce the concept of joining (addition) number stories.

Key Mathematics Concepts and Skills

- Count objects to solve simple problems. [Number and Numeration Goal 2]
- Solve joining (addition) number stories using concrete objects and modeling. [Operations and Computation Goal 1]
- Recognize that a collection of objects can be made larger by adding objects to it. [Operations and Computation Goal 1]

Other Skills Listening and Speaking, Pretending and Role Play

Terms to Use number story, all together, in all, how many

Materials bear counters; small blocks

Planning Tip This activity is best done in an area away from the Block Center to minimize distractions from general block play.

▶ Main Activity

☐ Whole Group ✔ Small Group ☐ Partners ✔ Center

Build, or have children build, a simple enclosure with blocks. Leave it open on top so children can easily see inside. Put two bear counters in the enclosure and tell children it is the bears' house. Using additional bear counters, tell and act out a simple joining (addition) number story, such as: *Two bears were playing in their house. They invited a friend to come inside and play. How many bears are in the house now?* After children have had a chance to answer, continue modeling and telling the story: *The three bears called for another friend to come over, so one more bear comes in the house. How many are in the house now?*

Invite children to make simple constructions with the blocks. Use their structures as the basis for additional joining number stories. For example, if a child makes a car, put one bear in the car, have another bear join the first bear, then ask: *How many bears are in the car now?* Or if a child builds a rocket, say, *Three bears are about to blast off in the rocket. Two more bears get in the rocket. How many are blasting off now?*

If any children seem ready, invite them to tell stories for others to solve using the bears. Initially, they can become involved by helping you tell number stories. It may take time and quite a bit of modeling for children to independently create their own number stories. Use small numbers (0–3) at first, and encourage children to do the same. Gradually, numbers can be increased. Put the bears and blocks in a Center and encourage children to use them to tell and act out number stories with friends.

Ongoing Assessment: Kid Watching

Over time, you can use this activity to observe whether children can use manipulatives to model and solve number stories. Do they understand that adding objects to a collection results in a change in the number of objects? Do they understand that the number of objects increases?

▶ Connections

Literacy Connection Read *The Relatives Came* by Cynthia Rylant (Atheneum/Richard Jackson Books, 2001) and discuss children's experiences planning for visitors. You might use the book and illustrations as the basis for some number stories.

Art Connection Invite children to draw a room in their house and include people in their pictures. Ask them to use numbers to describe what is happening in their pictures. For example: *In my kitchen, two people are eating and one is cooking.* You might write children's words as captions for their pictures.

Developing Oral Language ELL

It is helpful for children to distinguish between number stories and other stories. Explain that *number stories* always have numbers and a problem to solve.

NOTE Bear Stories: Taking Away, page 148, focuses on taking-away (subtraction) number stories. Animal Number Stories, page 150, includes both joining and taking-away stories.

0·5 Bear Stories: Taking Away

◎ **Objective** To introduce the concept of taking-away (subtraction) stories.

Key Mathematics Concepts and Skills

- Count objects to solve simple problems. [Number and Numeration Goal 2]
- Solve taking-away (subtraction) number stories using concrete objects and modeling. [Operations and Computation Goal 1]
- Recognize that a collection of objects can be made smaller by taking away objects from it. [Operations and Computation Goal 1]

Other Skills Listening and Speaking, Pretending and Role Play

Terms to Use number story, take away, how many

Materials bear counters; small blocks

▶ **Main Activity**   ☐ Whole Group ✔Small Group ☐ Partners ✔Center

Use blocks to build, or have children build, an enclosed space to represent a playground. Add features such as a sandbox, climber, bench, or other equipment children suggest. Place two bears in the sandbox and tell and act out a simple taking-away number story, such as: *Two bears were digging in the sandbox and one bear left to play on the climber. How many bears were left in the sandbox?* After children have had a chance to answer, place three bears on the bench and tell another story, such as: *Three bears were on the bench eating a snack. One finished eating and went to play on the swings. How many bears are still on the bench? Another bear finished snack and left to play on the swings. How many are now on the bench?* Continue with more number stories, keeping the stories short and playful.

Planning Tip This activity is best done in an area away from the block center to minimize distractions from general block play.

NOTE Bear Stories: Joining, page 146, focuses on joining (addition) number stories. Animal Number Stories, page 150, includes both joining and taking-away stories.

As they seem ready, invite children to help you tell number stories for others to solve using the bears. Children may tell joining or taking-away stories, which is fine. Use small numbers (0–3) at first, and encourage children to do the same. Gradually, numbers can be increased.

Put the bears and blocks in a Center and encourage children to use them to tell and act out number stories with friends. Over time, provide other materials that interest your class. You might use cars in a garage, dolls in a dollhouse, and toy animals in a play farm or zoo as subjects for number stories.

▶ Connections

Literacy Connection Read *Blueberries for Sal* by Robert McCloskey (Viking Juvenile, 1948). Discuss how the number of blueberries in Sal's pail changes during the story.

Mathematics Connection Tell number stories in which children are the subjects. Children will enjoy acting out the stories as they solve them.

Dramatic Play Connection Set up a grocery store in your Dramatic Play Center and help children incorporate number stories in their play.

 Family Connection You may want to use the Solving Problems at Home Family Connection (*Math Masters*, page 78) to encourage families to explore natural problem-solving opportunities.

Math Masters, p. 78

NOTE In addition to acting out number stories with manipulatives, encourage children to use their fingers to help them solve number stories.

 Ongoing Assessment: Kid Watching

Over time, you can use this activity to observe whether children can use manipulatives to model and solve number stories. Do they understand that taking away objects from a collection results in a change in the number of objects? Do they understand that the number of objects decreases?

Related Book

- *Ten Red Apples* by Pat Hutchins (Greenwillow, 2000)

0·6 Animal Number Stories

◎ Objective To explore problem solving through literature-based number stories.

Key Mathematics Concepts and Skills

• Count objects to solve simple problems. [Number and Numeration Goal 2]

• Solve number stories using concrete modeling. [Operations and Computation Goal 1]

• Create number stories using concrete modeling. [Operations and Computation Goal 1]

Other Skills Listening and Speaking, Pretending and Role Play, Reading and Writing

Terms to Use all together, in all, take away, how many, number story

Materials *The Mitten* by Jan Brett (Putnam Juvenile, 1989) or another version of the Ukrainian folktale (*See* Related Books.); large blanket or sheet; stuffed animals, puppets, or flannel board cutouts (optional); small blanket or large mitten (optional)

Planning Tip Plan to do this activity after Bear Stories: Joining, page 146, and Bear Stories: Taking Away, page 148, which provide an introduction to number stories.

▶ Main Activity

☑ Whole Group ☑ Small Group ☐ Partners ☐ Center

Read aloud *The Mitten*. Have children use the illustrations to predict what will happen next. You may want to read the book several times to familiarize children with the story.

Invite children to act out the story by pretending to be animals and crawling under a large blanket or sheet. You might help the class keep track of the total number of animals under the blanket as you read.

Continue by using the animals in the story as the basis for simple number stories, which children can act out using the blanket or sheet. Be sure to tell joining and taking-away stories.

The Mitten

ADAPTED AND ILLUSTRATED BY **JAN BRETT**

For example:

- *Two animals are in the mitten. The hedgehog and the owl join in. How many animals are in the mitten now?*
- *There are six animals in the mitten. The fox leaves and goes home. How many animals are left?*
- *How many more animals do you think can fit in the mitten?*

Encourage children to make up their own number stories based on the book. You may want to provide stuffed animals, puppets, or flannel board cutouts for children to use to act out their number stories. Provide a small blanket or a large mitten for hiding the animals.

▶ Connections

Literacy Connection Gather a collection of books by Jan Brett for the classroom library. Use the characters in the books as the basis for number stories. (See www.janbrett.com for related materials, including animal cutouts and suggested activities.)

Art Connection Show children how to trace their hands to draw a mitten shape, or provide a mitten pattern to trace. Help children cut out a pair of paper mittens. Provide paint, glitter, and collage materials for children to decorate their mittens. If you want children to explore symmetry, have them paint one mitten and press it to the other to make a symmetrical pair of mittens.

 Family Connection You may want to use the Solving Problems at Home Family Connection (*Math Masters,* page 78) to encourage families to explore natural problem-solving opportunities.

 Related Book
- *The Mitten* by Alvin R. Tresselt (William Morrow & Co., 1970)

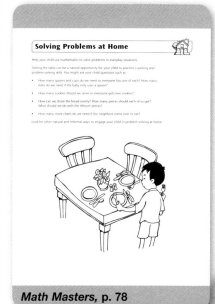

Math Masters, p. 78

Building

0·7 Building Numbers

 Objective To provide concrete experiences with part-whole relationships.

Key Mathematics Concepts and Skills

- Count out a given number of objects. [Number and Numeration Goal 2]
- Recognize different ways to represent the same number. [Number and Numeration Goal 3]
- Combine groups of objects to total a given number. [Operations and Computation Goal 1]

Materials connecting cubes in 2 or 3 different colors

▶ Main Activity

☐ Whole Group   ✔ Small Group   ☐ Partners   ✔ Center

With a small group of children, make a stack with 5 connecting cubes of the same color. Ask children to count and verify that your stack makes 5. Then, invite children to make more stacks of 5 using different-color cubes. Place your stack where children can use it to compare to their stacks.

Observe as children build their stacks. Do they use all one color? Do they use two or three colors? Do they make a pattern? Do they count the cubes or match the stacks visually? Do they make more than one stack using different combinations? Ask children to describe the different ways they made 5: for example, *My 5 stack has 2 reds and 3 blues.* Encourage children to compare their stacks. Line up all the stacks together so children can see that they all make 5. Ask: *How many different ways did we make 5?*

NOTE This activity involves "composing" numbers, or the idea that parts can be combined to form the whole. Although it lays a foundation for addition, do not expect children to extend this experience to equations (for example, 2 + 3 = 5) at this stage. See Taking Apart Numbers, page 160, for a similar activity that involves decomposing numbers.

Examples of ways to make 5

Leave the cubes and stacks out at the Math Center for children to continue the activity. At another time, you can vary the target number and have children make stacks of 6, 7, or 8. Children may do this spontaneously at the Math Center.

 Ongoing Assessment: Kid Watching

You can use this activity to informally assess whether children can count out a given number of objects. Also note whether they can make 5 in more than one way.

▶ Connections

Mathematics Connection Ask children to show 5 fingers, using some fingers on both hands. Encourage them to repeat this using different combinations of fingers. This activity reinforces the idea that there is often more than one right answer.

Snack Connection At snack time, put out a choice of 2 or 3 different foods. Allow children to take 5 pieces of snack in any combination (for example, 4 pretzels and 1 apple slice). Listen as children discuss and compare their selections.

0·8 Number Stories Everywhere

 Objective To provide varied opportunities for children to create, act out, and solve number stories.

Key Mathematics Concepts and Skills

- Count out objects to model number stories. [Number and Numeration Goal 2]
- Solve and create number stories using concrete modeling. [Operations and Computation Goal 1]

Other Skills Listening and Speaking, Pretending and Role Play, Reading and Writing

Terms to Use more, less, fewer, same, join, take away, left, all together, how many

Materials one or more of the following: manipulatives, books, flannel board and cutout figures, paper and crayons or markers

---

▶ Main Activity

☑Whole Group ☑Small Group ☐ Partners ☐ Center

Provide children with many opportunities to tell, act out, and solve number stories. Encourage children to use fingers or manipulatives, pictures on a flannel board, drawings, and their own actions to help model the problems and keep track of the numbers.

Include activities such as the following to incorporate number stories into the classroom:

▷ Look for number stories in the illustrations or text of favorite books. (See Related Books for a few suggestions.) Children can use the pictures and words to respond to questions such as: *Now how many people are looking for the king? How many animals are there when the cat leaves?*

NOTE Keep numbers small and stories simple, and remember that you do not need to use mathematical symbols or write the stories down. The purpose is to begin to develop children's understanding of mathematical language and operations through natural language and familiar contexts. It can be counterproductive to introduce symbols too soon.

▷ Invite children to use a flannel board to tell and show number stories to each other. Provide cutout figures and props to stimulate story telling. Model how to ask questions, such as: *How many now? Are there more (or fewer) now? If there is one more coming for soup, how many more bowls do we need?*

▷ Share brief number stories during group or transition times. *Minute Math®* is a good source for number stories. Include children's names and familiar situations in the stories. For example: *Natasha was playing in the sand and Jorges and Susan joined her. How many are in the sandbox now? Nicole, Ellen and Eliza all want a cookie. How many cookies should we get? Peter, Nick, May and Eugene are riding home on the bus, then Nick and May get off. How many are still riding the bus?* Encourage children to make up stories for others to figure out.

▶ Connections

Art and Literacy Connections Children might enjoy drawing number stories and sharing them with the class. Children might dictate a story for their pictures.

Children can also collaborate on a large mural of a story such as "The Gingerbread Man." Ask each child to illustrate a part of the story. Use the picture as a source for many number stories. For example: *If the old woman and the old man went home, how many would be chasing the gingerbread man? What if another cow joined the chase?* Engage children in helping you tell or write a number story to answer the question: *How many were chasing the gingerbread man?* (The gingerbread man was chased by 1 old woman and 1 old man and 2 farmers, and so on.)

 Family Connection You may want to use the Solving Problems at the Grocery Family Connection (*Math Masters,* page 79) to help families recognize problem-solving opportunities in everyday situations.

 Related Books

- *I Went Walking* by Sue Williams (Gulliver Books, 1990)
- *One Guinea Pig Is Not Enough* by Kate Duke (Dutton Juvenile, 1998)
- *Splash!* by Ann Jonas (Greenwillow, 1995)
- *The Doorbell Rang* by Pat Hutchins (Greenwillow, 1986)
- Familiar stories such as "Chicken Licken" or "The Gingerbread Man"

Solving Problems at the Grocery

Math Masters, p. 79

0·9 "How Many More?" Game

Objective To explore the concept of "How many more?" through a game.

> **Key Mathematics Concepts and Skills**
> • Count out objects to match the number on a die. [Number and Numeration Goal 2]
> • Determine how many more are needed to make 10. [Operations and Computation Goal 1]
> • Explore part-whole relationships. [Operations and Computation Goal 1]
>
> **Other Skills** Cooperation
>
> **Materials** inch cubes or small blocks; bear counters; inch cube or blank die marked 1, 2, 3, 1, 2, 3

Planning Tip Use a permanent marker to label one or more inch cubes or blank dice with 1, 2, and 3 on two faces of each die.

▶ Main Activity

☐ Whole Group ✔ Small Group ✔ Partners ✔ Center

Teach *"How Many More?"* to a small group of children. Give each player 10 small blocks or cubes. Have each child make a row with his or her blocks and then count them. Next, give the group a die numbered 1–3. Demonstrate how to roll the die, take that number of bears, and put each bear on a block. Children should take turns rolling the die and adding bears to their own rows. After each roll, children should figure out and announce how many more bears they need to fill their rows. To finish, a player must roll the exact number needed to fill his or her row. You or the children can decide whether the game ends when the first player's row of blocks is filled, or when all children have filled their rows.

Adjusting for Age and Development

Use more or fewer blocks and bears according to children's interests and needs.

Leave the materials in the Math Center for continued play. Children can also play independently by rolling and filling their own row of blocks.

▶ Connections

Literacy Connection Read *Hippos Go Berserk* by Sandra Boynton (Aladdin, 1996) and count the hippos as they arrive in groups of increasing size.

Snack Connection Pose "How many more?" situations at snack time. For example, you might tell all children that they will get 10 raisins. Then give children fewer than 10 raisins and ask them to tell you how many more they need.

Mathematics Connection The need to find out "How many more?" arises naturally in many situations. Look for opportunities during your calendar routine *(How many more days until Alejandra's birthday?),* when passing out materials *(How many more cups do we need?),* and when counting children *(How many more children need to wash their hands?).* You can modify familiar games by adding a rule that children need an exact roll to cross the finish line or fill all the spaces. This encourages children to figure out how many more they need to finish or win.

Expanding

0·10 Hiding Bears

Objective To explore part-whole relationships through a partner activity.

Key Mathematics Concepts and Skills

- Count objects to solve a number story. [Number and Numeration Goal 2]
- Explore part-whole relationships. [Operations and Computation Goal 1]

Other Skills Cooperation, Pretending and Role Play

Terms to Use some, all

Materials plastic cup or small box; bear counters

▶ Main Activity

☐ Whole Group ✔ Small Group ✔ Partners ✔ Center

Tell children that they will act out a story in which a group of bears decides to play hide-and-seek. Have children work in pairs. Give each pair a collection of bear counters and a cup or box for hiding the bears. Start with 5 bears. You can add more bears after children have experience with the activity.

To begin, have partners count their bears. Then, while one child covers his or her eyes, the other child takes a few of the bears and hides them under the cup or box, leaving the remaining bears in plain sight. The first child then opens his or her eyes, looks at the remaining bears, and tries to figure out how many bears are hiding. After guessing, the child looks under the cup or box and counts to check the answer. Repeat, with children taking turns hiding the bears.

 Links to the Future

This can be a challenging task for preschoolers, who tend to focus on the bears they see rather than the hidden ones. Understanding part-whole relationships, or the idea that numbers are made up of other numbers, provides a basis for understanding addition and subtraction.

If children are having difficulty figuring out the number of hidden bears, encourage them to try using their fingers to help them keep track. You might also provide an extra set of 5 bears for children to work with. Invite children to share successful strategies with one another, and reinforce the idea that there is more than one way to solve problems.

 Ongoing Assessment: Kid Watching

You can use this activity to observe children's problem-solving strategies. Do children understand the problem situation? Have they developed a workable strategy—such as using fingers or a second set of bears, or counting on from the number of bears remaining—to figure out how many bears are missing? Can they use one of these strategies if you model it for them?

▶ Connections

Literacy Connection Share and discuss the book *Quack and Count* by Keith Baker (Harcourt Children's Books, 1999), which introduces all the different combinations for the number 7. Seven ducks group together on opposite sides of each 2-page spread to illustrate ways to make the sum of 7.

Outdoor Connection Children can play hide-and-seek during outdoors time. This familiar game provides good practice for rote counting (*...8, 9, 10. Ready or not, here I come!*) and reinforces position and spatial relationships as children hunt *under* the slide, *between* the bushes, and *on top* of the monkey bars. You might play a version similar to the Hiding Bears activity by having 5 children hide and the "Seeker" (or Seekers) keep track of how many more children they still need to find.

Expanding

0·11 Taking Apart Numbers

Objective To explore part-whole relationships using concrete objects.

Key Mathematics Concepts and Skills

• Count out a given number of objects up to 10. [Number and Numeration Goal 2]

• Recognize different ways to represent the same number. [Number and Numeration Goal 3]

• Group a quantity of objects into smaller parts. [Operations and Computation Goal 1]

Terms to Use part, group

Materials connecting cubes; paper and crayons (optional)

▶ Main Activity

☐ Whole Group   ✔ Small Group   ☐ Partners   ✔ Center

With a small group of children, count out 6 connecting cubes of the same color and make a stack. Ask children to count and verify that you have 6. Then, separate the stack into two smaller parts, such as 4 and 2. Ask children whether there are still 6 cubes in all. They may count or restack the cubes to help explain their answers.

Invite each child to count out 6 cubes of the same color and make a stack. Then, ask them to take apart the cubes to make smaller parts of 6. Have children describe to the group how they made the number 6. Ask children how they know that they still have 6 cubes. Prompt them to find more ways to make 6. Leave out the different groupings of 6 cubes. After children have had a chance to explore, they may want to count the total number of different ways they found to make 6.

> **NOTE** This activity involves "decomposing" numbers, or the idea that a number can be broken into parts. Try Building Numbers, page 152, for a similar activity that focuses on composing numbers.

Examples of groupings of 6 cubes

Links to the Future

Although this concrete activity lays a foundation for addition and subtraction, do not expect children to extend this experience to equations or number models, such as 3 + 1 + 2 = 6. Children will represent part-whole relationships with number models in Kindergarten and First Grade.

Leave the cubes in the Math Center for children to continue exploring. At another time, you can vary the starting number and have children take apart 7, 8, 9, or 10 cubes. Children may do this spontaneously.

Adjusting for Age and Development

Children may want to record different groupings of a given number of cubes. They can draw the cubes in groups and label each part with a numeral. Do not expect children to use the +, −, or = symbols.

▶ Connections

Literacy Connection Read *Seven Blind Mice* by Ed Young (Philomel, 1992). Discuss how the parts that the mice describe combine to make the whole elephant. There are many other "guess who" books that ask children to name an animal, person, or object from a partial picture.

Music Connection When listening to or playing music together, discuss how each instrument in a band or orchestra has a part to play that contributes to the whole musical sound. Children can play a familiar rhythm such as "Twinkle, Twinkle, Little Star" and experiment with adding or subtracting instruments to achieve different sounds.

Expanding

0·12 Fair Shares

◎ **Objective** To introduce concrete equal-partitioning (fair sharing) experiences.

Key Mathematics Concepts and Skills

- Count objects. [Number and Numeration Goal 2]
- Compare quantities in two groups of objects. [Number and Numeration Goal 4]
- Explore part-whole relationships to divide a quantity into equal groups. [Operations and Computation Goal 1]

Other Skills Cooperation, Pretending and Role Play

Terms to Use fair, equal, half, same

Materials pairs of teddy bears or other toy animals; plastic cups; miniature plastic food or other small manipulatives; small paper plates (optional); paper food pieces (optional)

> **Planning Tip** Put an even number of manipulatives (between 2 and 10) into several plastic cups. Each cup should have a different number of objects. You need at least one cup for each child or pair of children.

▶ Main Activity

☐ Whole Group ✔ Small Group ✔ Partners ✔ Center

Give each child or pair of children two teddy bears. Tell the children that their bears are hungry. You may want to give children a plate for each bear. Hand out the cups containing an even number of manipulatives. Explain that inside the cups are pieces of pretend food for the bears. To be fair, each bear should get the same number of pieces.

Observe as children distribute the food to their bears. Do they divide the pile visually and then count how many are in each pile? Do they divide the objects by distributing them one at a time (one for this bear, one for that bear, and so on)? Do they use trial and error? Regardless of their strategies, are they able to divide the set of objects equally? Once children have distributed the food, have them count to see whether both

> **NOTE** Children may find feeding the bears very appealing. Allow them time to play with the bears and food before asking them to make fair shares.

bears have the same number of pieces. Ask: *Is it fair? Do both bears have the same amount of food?* Allow children to collect the food, switch cups with each other, and feed their bears with a different number of pieces.

Once children are familiar with the activity, you can leave the bears and cups of food out in the Math Center for children to use. Remind children to count their shares to make sure they are fair, or they can ask a friend to check.

 Adjusting for Age and Development

Give children cups with an odd number of pieces to introduce the idea of sharing with some left over. You may want to use paper food pieces, so you can cut the remainder in half. Observe what children do with the extra piece of food. Children may offer many solutions, including setting it aside or giving it to one bear who is "hungrier." If nobody suggests it, ask whether it would be fair to cut the extra piece in half. Cut the remaining piece in half and ask children to share the halves fairly. They can check by counting the number of whole pieces and then the number of half pieces for each bear. For another challenge, children can try sharing pieces among more than two bears.

▶ Connections

Snack Connection There are many opportunities for equal partitioning at snack and meal times. Ask children to help you figure out how much food each child should get and how to share equally. Listen for children's use of words such as *fair, same, equal,* and *half* and note whether they seem to understand their mathematical meanings.

Dramatic Play Connection Place the toys and food in the Dramatic Play Center. Encourage children to continue sharing the food as part of their dramatic play.

Family Connection You may want to use the Sharing at Home Family Connection (*Math Masters,* page 90) to encourage families to find opportunities to divide groups of items into fair shares.

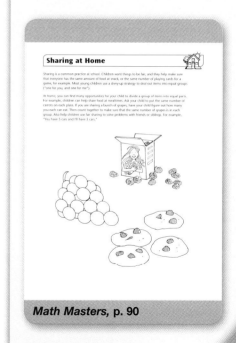

Math Masters, p. 90

Expanding

Graphing

Overview

Graphing Goals

In Pre-K, children should have experiences that help them:

• Collect and represent data in a variety of ways, focusing on concrete and pictorial representations.
[Data and Chance Goal 1]

• Use graphs to answer simple questions. [Data and Chance Goal 2]

Graphing integrates and applies many of children's emerging mathematics skills. As children collect, display, and analyze data, they also **sort** data into categories, **count** data from each category, and **make comparisons,** such as which category has more or fewer, or which "bar" is tallest or shortest. Graphing also involves **problem solving** as children figure out how to collect or display data and how to answer questions based on a graph.

An abundance of interesting and meaningful graphing topics emerge from classroom life and from children's own questions. At first, children may need help formulating questions in ways that make data manageable. For example, "Do you prefer chocolate or vanilla ice cream?" is an easier question for data collection and graphing than "What is your favorite ice cream flavor?" Over time, children will become adept at graphing more open-ended questions, but it is most useful to begin with questions that have a limited number of possible answers.

To build their understanding that graphs represent a collection of information, children's earliest graphs should be concrete and children should be actively involved in constructing them. The most concrete graphs involve real objects: fruit lined up by type, for example. Using connecting cubes, pictures, or paper squares to represent data is slightly more abstract, but still generally accessible to children—through experience and discussion about what each item stands for on the graph.

Talking with children about their graphs *(Which flavor was most popular? Does this graph tell us if anyone likes strawberry?)* helps them learn that graphs have meaning and figure out how to extract that meaning.

 ## Professional Development

See Chapter 10 of the *Teacher's Reference Manual* for more information about the Data and Chance strand.

Choosing Activities

Beginning

Beginning activities establish graphing techniques that can be used repeatedly throughout the year, with any topic that interests your class. In these activities, children

◆ use real objects to create graphs;

◆ use personal graphing markers to reflect data about themselves on graphs;

◆ graph topics of particular interest at the start of the year;

◆ use graphing to record the results of class votes;

◆ analyze and discuss completed graphs.

Building

Building activities suggest additional topics and techniques, although it is important to keep in mind that all of the graphing techniques in this program can be used for virtually any topic. The most meaningful graphing activities emerge from real-life questions and situations. In these activities, children

◆ graph favorite school activities;

◆ use connecting cubes and paper squares to create graphs;

◆ analyze and discuss graphs.

Expanding

Expanding activities encourage children to be more independent with data collection and graphing. In these activities, children

◆ conduct surveys, and graph and analyze the results;

◆ collect, graph, and analyze data about the weather over a period of at least a month.

Activities in Perspective

Expanding

KEY

 Art

 Books

 Dramatic Play

 Excursion

 Manipulatives and Games

 Music and Movement

 Rug Time

 Science

 Sensory

 Snack

 Core Core Activity

Teaching Resources

Home-School Connection

Family Connections suggest home activities that link to activities children have done at school. The following Graphing activities contain Family Connections: G♦2, Age Graph; G♦9, Taking Surveys. Note that the same Family Connections are suggested with multiple activities, so keep track of which ones you have already sent home.

Mathematics at Home Books 1–3 provide additional ideas for enjoyable mathematics activities that families can do together, as well as lists of children's books related to the topics in the teacher's guide. Families can do activities from *Mathematics at Home* Books 1–3 throughout the year.

◀ *Home Connection Handbook* provides more ideas to communicate effectively with parents.

▼ *Resources for the Pre-Kindergarten Classroom* provides additional teaching ideas, including suggestions for bringing mathematics into thematic instruction, as well as using games, literature, technology, songs, and rhymes to support mathematics learning.

Minute Math provides brief activities ▶ for transition times and spare moments throughout the day.

Assessment

Ongoing Assessment

Kid Watching

The following activities in the *Teacher's Guide to Activities* include Ongoing Assessment notes related to graphing. See the *Assessment Handbook* for an expanded table.

Activity	Content Assessed
G♦2, G♦6, G♦8, G♦10	Represent data on a graph. [Data and Chance Goal 1]
G♦2, G♦5, G♦6, G♦8, G♦10	Interpret data on a graph. [Data and Chance Goal 2]

Assessment Handbook

- Pre-Kindergarten goals, pp. 6–11
- Graphing Assessment Overview, p. 31
- End-of-Year Periodic Assessment Task 6, p. 23

Differentiated Instruction

Adjusting for Age and Development

Pre-Kindergarten Everyday Mathematics is designed to be flexible enough to adapt to a wide range of preschool classrooms, including classrooms with mixed age groupings and classrooms with a wide range of developmental levels. Many activities include suggestions to help teachers modify the activity to make it accessible and interesting to children with varying needs, learning styles, or levels of proficiency or understanding.

G◆9   Taking Surveys

Language Support

Everyday Mathematics provides activity-specific suggestions to help all children, including non-native English speakers, develop the language necessary to acquire, process, and express mathematical ideas.

Developing Oral Language

G◆1   Develop language to describe feelings.

G◆9   Develop listening and speaking skills.

Language & Vocabulary

Informally use these terms that are related to graphing.

graph	most	zero
survey	some	equal
vote	more	tie
groups	less	same
sort	least	same number
all	fewer	
none	fewest	

Activity Connections

The Connections for each activity link the Main Activity to different curricular and classroom areas. They are useful for meeting individual needs and integrating mathematics throughout the day. The following connections are in the Graphing section.

Art

G♦1   Feelings Graph

G♦3   Shoe Graph

G♦4   Getting-to-Know-You Graphs

G♦10 Graphing Weather

Family Connections

See Home-School Connection on Page 168.

Literacy

G♦3   Shoe Graph

G♦6   Graphing Favorite Activities

G♦7   Graphing with Connecting Cubes

G♦8   Planning a Snack

Mathematics

G♦2   Age Graph

G♦4   Getting-to-Know-You Graphs

G♦7   Graphing with Connecting Cubes

G♦9   Taking Surveys

G♦10 Graphing Weather

Sensory Table

G♦2   Age Graph

Music and Movement

G♦1   Feelings Graph

G♦5   Classroom Voting

Science

G♦8   Planning a Snack

G♦10 Graphing Weather

G·1 Feelings Graph

Objective To help children create a class graph to show their feelings about school, using stickers to represent information.

Key Mathematics Concepts and Skills

- Count data (stickers) on a graph. [Number and Numeration Goal 2]
- Compare data on a graph. [Number and Numeration Goal 4]
- Represent data on a graph. [Data and Chance Goal 1]
- Use a graph to get information and answer questions. [Data and Chance Goal 2]

Other Skills Listening and Speaking

Terms to Use graph, most, least, more, fewer, less, same number, none, zero, some, all

Materials narrow strips of paper (Adding machine tape works well.); posterboard or construction paper; marker; stickers; book about starting school or feelings (optional; *See* Related Books for suggestions.)

▶ Main Activity

✔Whole Group ☐ Small Group ☐ Partners ☐ Center

Begin a discussion about the various ways children feel about coming to school. Consider reading a book to begin the discussion.

Next, show the posterboard or paper you prepared. Explain that children will use it to show the different ways they felt about coming to school today. Label the columns with words and faces to reflect the feelings children mentioned in the discussion. Be sure to include a range of emotions, such as happy, sad, scared, or worried. Give each child a sticker, which they should place on the strip under the word that describes how

Planning Tip Before starting the activity, write a title for the graph on the posterboard or construction paper. Wait to add faces and to attach the paper strips until children have shared their feelings, so you know which feelings to include on the graph. Also choose a book to begin the activity, if desired.

Developing Oral Language ELL

You might ask children to make faces to show how they feel. Share and model language to describe different feelings and help children begin to use and understand feelings words. There are also many good "feelings" books for young children.

they felt about coming to school. (Children may need reminders to place their stickers according to their own feelings, rather than those of their friends.)

After the graph is complete, help children count and record the number of stickers on each strip. Ask questions such as: *Which feeling has the most stickers? Which has the least? Were more children happy or sad about coming to school?*

See Getting-to-Know-You Graphs on page 178 for more suggestions of early-in-the-year graphing activities.

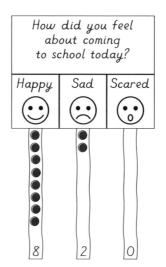

► Connections

Music and Movement Connection Sing and act out "If You're Happy And You Know It."

> *If you're happy and you know it, clap your hands.*
> *If you're happy and you know it, clap your hands.*
> *If you're happy and you know it then your face will surely show it.*
> *If you're happy and you know it, clap your hands.*

Invite children to suggest other feelings and movements, such as:

> *If you're mad and you know it, stomp your feet.*
> *If you're sleepy and you know it, nod your head.*

Art Connection Place mirrors in the Art Center. Provide paper and drawing materials for children to draw pictures of their faces that show how they feel. You might create a display of children's drawings or of photos of faces showing different emotions.

NOTE Some teachers have found that creating a new Feelings Graph on different days, especially at the beginning of the school year, helps children talk about their feelings as they get used to coming to school and helps establish a sense of community in the classroom. Graphing the same topic on different days also gives children a chance to notice changes in data.

 Related Books

- *Will I Have a Friend?* by Miriam Cohen (Aladdin, 1989)
- *The Kissing Hand* by Audrey Penn (Tanglewood Press, 2006)
- *My First Day at Nursery School* by Becky Edwards (Bloomsbury USA Children's Books, 2002)
- *Mouse's First Day of School* by Lauren Thompson (Simon & Schuster Children's Publishing, 2003)
- *I Love You All Day Long* by Francesca Rusackas (HarperCollins, 2002)
- *The Way I Feel* by Janan Cain (Parenting Press, 2000)

G·2 Age Graph

Objective To use age information to create and interpret a class graph that can be updated and used throughout the year.

Key Mathematics Concepts and Skills

• Count data (name cards) on a graph. [Number and Numeration Goal 2]

• Compare data on a graph. [Number and Numeration Goal 4]

• Represent data on a graph. [Data and Chance Goal 1]

• Use a graph to get information and answer questions. [Data and Chance Goal 2]

Other Skills Reading and Writing

Terms to Use graph, more, fewer, less, most, least, same number, none, zero, some, all

Materials paper strips; posterboard or blank wall space; removable adhesive; writing tools

---

Planning Tip Prepare a graph by labeling columns for children's ages. Include a column for the oldest age that children will be at the end of the year. Cut paper strips for children to write their names on. Use removable adhesive so that children can move their names to the next column on their birthdays.

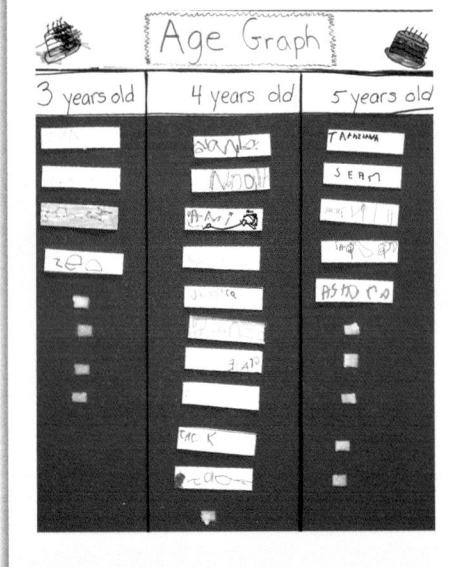

▶

| ✔ Whole Group | ☐ Small Group | ☐ Partners | ☐ Center |

Give each child a paper strip and ask him or her to write his or her name on it. You might have children write their names ahead of time so you can provide the support they need. (Alternatively, you can write children's names and they can decorate the strips.)

Gather children in a circle with their name strips and say: *How old are you? Hold up your fingers to show how many years old you are.* Ask all the 3-year-olds (or whatever age your youngest children are) to stand up. Count the number of children standing, then ask: *How can we remember who is 3 (or 4, or 5) after you sit down?* After discussion, suggest that they use their name strips to show how old they are. Help the standing children attach their names to the proper column on the graph you prepared.

To reinforce the meaning of the graph, count the number of names in that column and compare it to the number of children standing. You might ask: *Why is the number the same? How could we show the other children's ages?*

Repeat this process with children of different ages. When the graph is complete, ask questions such as: *How many 4-year-olds are in our class? Are more children 4 or 5 years old?* Display the graph in a place that children can reach. On children's birthdays, help them move their names to the next column. Plan to revisit the Age Graph many times throughout the year as it changes.

 Ongoing Assessment: Kid Watching

You can use this activity to informally assess children's abilities to use a graph to represent and interpret data. As children move their names over the course of the year, you will have many opportunities to revisit the Age Graph and see how children's understanding of the graph grows over time.

▶ Connections

Mathematics Connection You can create a Birthday Graph by having each child decorate a paper cake, or other graph marker, with his or her name. Help children attach their graph markers next to, or above, their birthday months on the graph. Use the graph when marking birthdays on the calendar for your calendar routine.

Sensory Table Connection Put birthday candles, toothpicks, or sticks in the sand table. Encourage children to make sand cakes and count candles for their cakes.

 Family Connection You may want to use the Birthday Counting Family Connection (*Math Masters,* page 73) to suggest ways to include mathematics in family birthday celebrations.

NOTE You can do this activity in conjunction with Age Collage, page 42. See Feelings Graph, page 172, and Getting-to-Know-You Graphs, page 178, for other early-in-the-year graphs.

 Related Books

- *Little Gorilla* by Ruth Lercher Bornstein (Clarion Books, 1979)
- *Happy Birthday, Moon* by Frank Asch (Aladdin, 2000)

Birthday Counting

Birthdays provide an excellent opportunity to count and learn about numbers. As you prepare for family celebrations, you can find many pleasurable counting experiences to share with your child:

- Count the number of people coming to the party.
- Set the table with the right number of napkins, cups, and utensils.
- Count candles for the cake.
- Make a card or birthday banner. (Grandma is 60! or Happy 1st Birthday!)

As you celebrate birthdays together, talk about the ages of people in your family. Ask questions like "How old will you be on your next birthday?" or "Which cousin is older?" Informal conversations like this help children use numbers in ways that have meaning for them.

Math Masters, p. 73

G·3 Shoe Graph

 Objective To help children sort and classify shoes and use the categories to create a "real graph."

Key Mathematics Concepts and Skills

- Count and compare data (shoes) on a graph. [Number and Numeration Goals 2 and 4]
- Represent data using real objects. [Data and Chance Goal 1]
- Use a graph to get information and answer questions. [Data and Chance Goal 2]
- Create and apply rules to sort objects. [Patterns, Functions, and Algebra Goal 1]

Other Skills Listening and Speaking

Terms to Use sort, groups, graph, more, fewer, less, most, least, same number, none, zero, some, all

Materials plain white window shade or shower curtain; masking tape or permanent marker; stick-on notes; children's shoes

---

Planning Tip Use masking tape or permanent marker to mark a reusable grid (about 4 columns by 12 rows) on the shower curtain or window shade. The grid spaces should be about the same size as each other and should be at least big enough for a child's shoe. Commercial floor graphs are also available, or you can tape a grid directly on the floor or rug.

▶ Main Activity

✔Whole Group ☐ Small Group ☐ Partners ☐ Center

Tell children to look at their shoes and those of the child next to them. Ask: *What do you notice? What is the same? What is different?* Next, have children look around at everyone's shoes. Ask them to think of ways to group, or sort, the class's shoes. Discuss children's suggestions (you might want to list them) and as a class choose one way to group the shoes. For example, the class might decide to group shoes by how they fasten, such as laces, straps, slip-ons, and so on.

Show children the grid that you created on the shower curtain or window shade. Use stick-on notes to label the columns according to each category of shoe the class created. You may need an "other" category. Have each child place one of his or her shoes in the appropriate column on the grid. Explain that they have used their shoes to create a graph!

Have children answer questions based on the graph, such as: *How many children have shoes with laces? Are there more shoes with laces or more with straps?* If children seem interested, you might ask whether they can think of other ways to group and graph their shoes.

Use your grid throughout the year for other graphing activities using real objects. Children might enjoy sorting and graphing mittens, hats, stuffed animals, lunch boxes, or other collections that you or they suggest.

▶ Connections

Literacy Connection Read one of the Related Books and have children guess and discuss who wears the different kinds of shoes in the book.

Art Connection Invite children to trace their shoes, decorate the tracings, and cut them out. The cut-out shoes could be used to make a permanent graph or sorted to make a display.

✔ Ongoing Assessment: Kid Watching

You can use this activity to informally assess children's abilities to count and compare numbers and to identify and sort by attributes.

Related Books

- *Shoes, Shoes, Shoes* by Ann Morris (Harper Collins, 1995)
- *Shoes* by Elizabeth Winthrop (HarperTrophy, 1988)
- *Whose Shoes?* by Anna Grossnickle Hines (Harcourt Children's Books, 2001)
- *Whose Shoe?* by Margaret Miller (Greenwillow, 1991)

G·4 Getting-to-Know-You Graphs

 Objective To introduce and use individual graphing markers for collecting and displaying data.

Key Mathematics Concepts and Skills

- Count data on a graph. [Number and Numeration Goal 2]
- Compare data on a graph. [Number and Numeration Goal 4]
- Represent data on a graph. [Data and Chance Goal 1]
- Use a graph to get information and answer questions. [Data and Chance Goal 2]

Other Skills Listening and Speaking, Reading and Writing

Terms to Use graph, more, fewer, less, most, least, same number, equal, some, none, zero, all

Materials chart paper and writing tools; individual graphing markers (*See* the Planning Tip.); books that explore differences and similarities among children (optional; *See* Related Books for suggestions.)

Planning Tip Prepare a graph marker for each child. These can be saved and reused for graphing activities throughout the year. Suggestions for easy-to-make and easy-to-use individual graphing markers include small photos of children or laminated handprint cutouts with children's names. Also choose a book to begin the activity, if desired.

▶ Main Activity

✔Whole Group ☐ Small Group ☐ Partners ☐ Center

Prior to the activity, decide on a topic to graph and prepare chart paper to make a graph that fits your topic and choice of individual graphing markers. Some good early-in-the-year topics for graphing include:

▷ Hair or eye color
▷ Number of people, or siblings, in family
▷ Number of pets or types of pets
▷ Favorite food, color, or season

Discuss with children ways that they are the same as others and ways that they are different. You might want to read a book to introduce the topic.

Next, give each child his or her individual graphing marker, such as a photo or handprint. Explain that they will use these to create a graph. Help children understand that their graphing markers will represent them, or information about them, on the graph. You might joke with the class about the difficulties of actually placing children themselves on a graph.

Explain the topic that you selected and show the chart paper you prepared. Call on children one by one and help them place their graph markers in the correct spots on the graph. Look at the completed graph together and pose questions that help children draw conclusions about themselves and their classmates. To reinforce the meaning of the graphing markers and the completed graph, ask children to find where their own information is represented. You might also ask them to locate information about other children on the graph.

Later, remove the markers and save them to reuse for other graphs and for classroom voting. (See Classroom Voting, page 180.)

▶ Connections

Mathematics Connection Children can also collect and count data using craft sticks labeled with their names and containers labeled with different responses. For example, you might label two containers with pictures and words: one for "house" and the other for "apartment." Give each child his or her own craft stick to put in the proper container. Then have children count and compare the number of sticks in each. The sticks can be saved for other data collections, and the containers can be saved and relabeled.

Art Connection Children can make All About Me books or posters to share with the class.

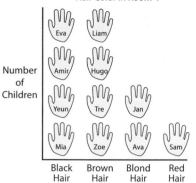

A sample hair color graph

Related Books

- *We Are All Alike, We Are All Different* by Cheltenham Elementary School Kindergartners (Scholastic, 1991)
- *The Colors of Us* by Karen Katz (Henry Holt and Co., 1999)
- *Whoever You Are* by Mem Fox (Harcourt Children's Books, 1997)
- *Farfallina & Marcel* by Holly Keller (Greenwillow, 2002)

G·5 Classroom Voting

 Objective To incorporate data collection and analysis into classroom decision making.

Key Mathematics Concepts and Skills

- Count data (votes) on a graph. [Number and Numeration Goal 2]
- Compare data on a graph. [Number and Numeration Goal 4]
- Represent data on a graph. [Data and Chance Goal 1]
- Use a graph to get information and answer questions. [Data and Chance Goal 2]

Terms to Use vote, graph, more, fewer, less, most, least, same number, tie, none, zero, some, all

Materials For a paper graph: chart paper or posterboard; writing tools; individual graphing markers (*See* the Planning Tip.) For a clothespin graph: strips of thick cardboard or wide ribbon; clothespins; stick-on notes

Planning Tip If you haven't already done so, prepare individual graphing markers that are easy to reuse, such as small photos or laminated handprint cutouts. (See Getting-to-Know-You Graphs, page 178.) You can also use clothespins labeled with each child's name.

▶ Main Activity

✔ Whole Group ☐ Small Group ☐ Partners ☐ Center

Voting is a way to connect graphing to children's everyday lives. Look for opportunities for children to participate in classroom decision making. For example, they can vote to help decide which book to read, what snack to have, or whether to have recess indoors or outdoors. Limit children to two or three choices, and make sure that all choices are equally acceptable to you, since you will need to honor the outcome of the vote.

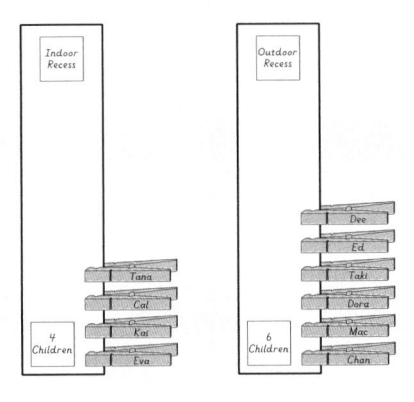

Voting for indoor or outdoor recess

There are many ways to graph children's votes. You might choose one of the following:

▷ To create a paper graph, label chart paper or posterboard with the choices and columns that fit your choice of individual graphing markers.

▷ To create a graph with clothespins, cut long strips of thick cardboard or wide ribbon. These strips can be propped up or taped on an easel or wall and can be reused. Use stick-on notes to label each strip with one of the choices. Each child clips his or her clothespin to the appropriate strip to record his or her vote. After counting the clothespins, use stick-on notes to label the number of votes for each choice.

Children can use the voting graph to come to a decision. Help children analyze the data by asking questions such as: *Which choice has the most votes? Is there a tie?* Use classroom votes often throughout the year.

▶ Connections

Music and Movement Connection Sing "What Shall We Do When We All Go Out?" (sung to tune of "Here We Go 'Round the Mulberry Bush"). Ask children for suggestions and motions for what they might do:

> *What shall we do when we all go out, all go out, all go out?*
> *What shall we do when we all go out, when we all go out to play?*
> *When we go out, we'll climb on the bars, climb on the bars, climb on the bars.*
> *When we go out, we'll climb on the bars, climb on the bars all day.*

Substitute with children's suggestions, such as crawl in the grass, swing on the swings, slide on the slide, and so on. Have children raise their hands for a quick vote of who might do each suggested activity.

NOTE The concept of one child, one vote can be difficult for children to understand. Using concrete objects to vote helps reinforce the idea that each child can make only one choice.

Ongoing Assessment: Kid Watching

You can use this activity to informally assess children's abilities to analyze data on a graph. You might also note whether children are able to accept the outcome of the vote.

Related Book

• *Wibbly Pig Likes Bananas* by Mick Inkpen (Viking Juvenile, 2000)

G·6 Graphing Favorite Activities

Objective To help children collect and interpret data about favorite classroom activities.

Key Mathematics Concepts and Skills

- Count data on a graph. [Number and Numeration Goal 2]
- Compare data on a graph. [Number and Numeration Goal 4]
- Represent data on a graph. [Data and Chance Goal 1]
- Use a graph to get information and answer questions. [Data and Chance Goal 2]

Other Skills Listening and Speaking

Terms to Use graph, more, fewer, less, most, fewest, least, same number, equal, some, none, zero, all

Materials chart paper or posterboard; writing tools; individual graphing markers (*See* Getting-to-Know-You Graphs, p. 178.); pictures of children engaged in different classroom activities (optional)

▶ Main Activity

✔ **Whole Group**   ☐ **Small Group**   ☐ **Partners**   ☐ **Center**

Begin a discussion about different activities during the school day. Tell children that they will decide which of three activities they like best. Explain that this information will help you plan activities that children like to do. Show the chart paper or posterboard you prepared. Call on children one by one to place their graph markers on the graph. Provide assistance as needed.

When the graph is complete, children can help decide on a title for the graph. Ask questions to prompt discussion about the graph, such as: *Which of these activities did the*

Planning Tip Prepare chart paper or posterboard to make a graph that fits your choice of individual graphing markers. Label 3 columns with 3 different classroom activities such as story time, snack time, and outside time. Add drawings or photographs to illustrate the activities.

NOTE Ordering the Day, page 214, is another mathematics activity based on classroom activities.

most children like best? Which did the least, or fewest, children like best? What does this tell us about our class? You might also gather children's ideas about other activities they wish you had included. Create another graph with different activities, if desired.

Post the graph where children can easily see it. Children will enjoy referring to it and seeing themselves represented on the graph. Try to plan an activity based on the results of the graph so children can see a real-life application of their efforts.

You can also use the individual graphing markers to graph other favorites, such as favorite animal, favorite book, favorite song, and so on.

 Ongoing Assessment: Kid Watching

You can use this activity to informally assess whether children understand how to use their graphing markers to create a graph. Also note whether they can answer questions based on the graph.

▶ Connections

Literacy Connection Take photographs or have children draw different activities from the school day. Label the pictures with children's dictation and make them into a class book. Read the book aloud and make it available for children in the book corner.

G·7 Graphing with Connecting Cubes

Objective To introduce the use of connecting cubes to gather and represent data.

Key Mathematics Concepts and Skills

- Count and compare data represented physically by children and by connecting cubes. [Number and Numeration Goals 2 and 4]

- Represent data with connecting cubes. [Data and Chance Goal 1]

- Use a cube graph to get information and answer questions. [Data and Chance Goal 2]

Other Skills Listening and Speaking, Reading and Writing

Terms to Use graph, more, fewer, less, most, fewest, least, same number, equal, some, none, zero, all

Materials familiar children's books; red, blue, and yellow connecting cubes; small containers; index cards or stick-on notes

---

> **Planning Tip** You may want to do this graphing activity using three books by the same author or with a similar theme, such as fairy tales or winter books.

▶ Main Activity

✔ Whole Group ▢ Small Group ▢ Partners ▢ Center

Show the group three familiar books. Tell children that they will have a chance to pick which of these books they like the best. Set out a container of connecting cubes next to each book, one color for each book. Tell children that they will take a cube to show their choices. Give children a few moments to think, and then invite each child to take one cube of the color that corresponds to his or her chosen book.

Ask children how they might figure out which book was chosen by most children. If no one suggests it, have the group of children who chose each book line up together. Count and record how many children are in each line, and compare the lengths of the lines.

> **NOTE** You can use connecting cubes to graph many different topics. Once children are familiar with the method, you can make it part of your classroom voting routine. (See Classroom Voting, page 180.)

Some children may suggest that each group puts its cubes together. If this doesn't come up, propose the idea. Explain that if they show the information with the cubes, they will be able to see it even after they sit down again. Have each group put its cubes together in a stack and count them. Ask: *Did you count the same number of cubes as people in the line? Why?* Put the cube stacks next to each other and compare them. Ask children questions about the results, such as: *Which book is most popular? Which book did the fewest children choose?* Place the cube stacks where children can see them. Label the stacks with index cards or stick-on notes.

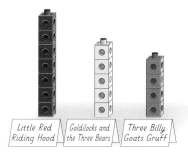

Little Red Riding Hood | Goldilocks and the Three Bears | Three Billy Goats Gruff

▶ Connections

Literacy Connection Read and compare several versions of a familiar fairy tale. (If your class graphed fairy tales in the main activity, you might use the class favorite.) You may want to act out the story and/or create your own version of the story as a class.

Mathematics Connection Have children pick up a handful of connecting cubes in each hand, attach the cubes from each hand into a line, and compare the lengths. Ask questions such as: *Did one hand hold more than the other? Were there a lot more cubes or just a few more?*

NOTE Be sure children understand that the cubes they add to the graph represent *their* own choices, just as their personal graphing markers represented their own choices in previous graphs. (See Getting-to-Know-You Graphs, page 178, and Graphing Favorite Activities, page 182.) You may also need to help children understand that each color cube represents a different book.

G·8 Planning a Snack

 Objective To extend children's graphing abilities by translating a connecting cube graph to a paper graph.

Key Mathematics Concepts and Skills

- Count data on a graph. [Number and Numeration Goal 2]
- Compare data on a graph. [Number and Numeration Goal 4]
- Represent data with connecting cubes and on a paper graph. [Data and Chance Goal 1]
- Use graphs to get information and answer questions. [Data and Chance Goal 2]

Other Skills Listening and Speaking

Terms to Use graph, more, fewer, less, most, fewest, least, same number, equal, some, none, zero, all

Materials large paper; markers; connecting cubes in two colors; pictures of two snack options; small squares of paper or small stick-on notes in two colors (Match the connecting cubes colors, if possible.)

Planning Tip Choose 2 possible snack foods. Prepare a large sheet of paper with 2 columns. Label each column with one of the snack foods you have chosen. Add a picture if you wish. Also label each column with the color of the connecting cube that will represent that snack. It is best to do this graph after your class has made several graphs using connecting cubes. See Graphing with Connecting Cubes, page 184.

▶ Main Activity

✔Whole Group ☐ Small Group ☐ Partners ☐ Center

Show the class the pictures of two snack choices and tell them that tomorrow they can each have one of these items for snack. Explain that today they will make a graph that shows each child's food choice, and tomorrow you will use the graph to prepare the snack.

Put a pile of connecting cubes next to each snack picture. One picture should have cubes of one color; the other picture should have cubes of a different color. Invite children to show which snack they want by taking a connecting cube from the correct pile. Put the

NOTE This activity is intended to help children transition from making a concrete graph using objects or personal graphing markers to making a more abstract paper graph.

same-color connecting cubes together into columns, then count and compare the number of cubes in each column.

Next, show the large paper you prepared for the graph. Have children come up to the graph, one at a time, and attach a small square of paper or stick-on note to the column that shows the snack they want. (To reinforce the connection between the connecting cube graph and the paper graph, children should use paper squares that match the colors of the connecting cubes.) After children have added their paper squares to the graph, prompt them to compare the paper graph to the connecting cube graph. Help children recognize that the numbers for each snack choice are the same on each graph. You might ask for volunteers to explain why this is the case. Point out that, since they have the paper graph to help them prepare tomorrow's snack, they can take apart the connecting cubes graph so the cubes can be used for other things.

Serve the snack on individual napkins so children can see that the number of servings of each snack matches the graph results. Display the graph near the snack area.

▶ Connections

Science Connection Provide a choice of seeds for children to plant. Graph their choices and help children use the graph to get ready for planting.

Literacy Connection Read aloud a book such as *You Choose* by Mary Murphy (Houghton Mifflin, 2000) or *Would You Rather...* by John Burningham (Chronicle Books, 2003). Have a discussion about making choices. The books may inspire new class graphs.

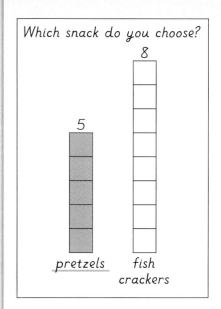

Which snack do you choose?

pretzels — 5
fish crackers — 8

Ongoing Assessment: Kid Watching

Note whether children understand the relationship between the cube and paper graphs. Do they understand that their choice is represented by one of the squares of paper? Can they answer questions based on the paper graph?

Building

G·9 Taking Surveys

Objective To provide practice with collecting, recording, and comparing data by conducting surveys.

Key Mathematics Concepts and Skills

- Count and compare survey data. [Number and Numeration Goals 2 and 4]
- Collect and represent data on a graph. [Data and Chance Goal 1]
- Use a graph to answer simple questions. [Data and Chance Goal 2]

Other Skills Cooperation, Listening and Speaking, Reading and Writing

Terms to Use survey, more, most, fewer, fewest, same, equal, none, zero, all

Materials paper; pencil or marker; clipboard; class list of children's names (optional); individual graphing markers or small paper squares (optional); connecting cubes (optional)

Planning Tip Prepare paper for children's surveys, such as a class list or two-column chart, and make copies. If you do not have clipboards, you can make some using sturdy cardboard and binder clips. Once the activity is introduced, children can conduct surveys on their own during choice time or center time.

▶ Main Activity

☐ Whole Group ☐ Small Group ✔ Partners ✔ Center

Show a few individual children or partners how to conduct class surveys. Gradually, more children will learn how to conduct surveys by watching and helping each other. Encourage the "Survey Taker" to think of a question, such as: *Do you like apple juice?* or *Which do you like better, sharks or whales?* (Help children phrase their questions so there are only two possible responses.) There are several ways that children can record their survey data. You might choose one of the following:

▷ Make a list with every child's name in its own row. Add two columns for children to make an *X* or other mark next to their names. Leave space at the top of the columns to write words or draw pictures to represent two choices.

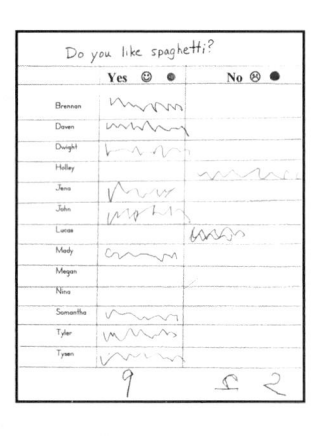

▷ Make a chart with two columns for children to make marks or write their names. Label the columns.

Have the Survey Taker collect classmates' responses. Children can help the Survey Taker find or write their names on the chart, as needed. The Survey Taker then counts the number of each response and reports the findings. Have children compare the numbers.

Leave clipboards and paper in the Writing or Math Center for children to use to conduct surveys independently. Over time, children may want to collect and display data about their survey questions in a variety of ways, such as using individual graphing markers or small paper squares to make a graph. Also be on the lookout for natural opportunities to collect and display data that arise in the classroom. Encourage children to figure out how to organize and display the data, and always prompt children to analyze the results of the graphs.

Developing Oral Language   ELL

Conducting and sharing surveys provides rich opportunities for developing listening, speaking, and other language skills. Some children may benefit from a partner's language model.

▶ Connections

Mathematics Connection Toward the end of the year, some teachers add a Question of the Day to their daily routines. Make a T-chart with room for children to write or clip their names in two columns. Each day, label the chart with a question and two possible responses. Have the class count and compare results.

Family Connection Use the Taking Surveys Family Connection (*Math Masters* page 91) to encourage families to help children collect data at home.

Adjusting for Age and Development

Children can use 2 colors of connecting cubes (one color for each response) to record survey data more concretely. Children keep track of their classmates' responses by making a stack of cubes for each choice and then counting and comparing the number of cubes in each stack.

Math Masters, p. 91

Expanding

G·10 Graphing Weather

 Objective To provide an opportunity to collect and display data over an extended period of time.

Key Mathematics Concepts and Skills

• Count and compare data on a graph. [Number and Numeration Goals 2 and 4]

• Represent data on a graph over an extended period of time. [Data and Chance Goal 1]

• Use a graph to get information and answer questions. [Data and Chance Goal 2]

Other Skills Listening and Speaking

Terms to Use graph, more, fewer, less, most, least, same number, equal, some, none, zero, all

Materials Teaching Master (*Math Masters*, p. 26); large construction paper or posterboard; markers, crayons, or tape

---

Planning Tip Photocopy and cut apart the weather symbols from *Math Masters*, page 26. Attach each picture to the bottom of a piece of large construction paper or posterboard. Create a grid for graphing each type of weather. Consider making multiple copies of each symbol to use for the graph. Reduce the size as needed to fit your graph.

▶ Main Activity

✔ Whole Group ☐ Small Group ☐ Partners ☐ Center

Show children the weather symbols on the graphing grid that you prepared, and talk about the different types of weather that occur in your area. Explain to the class that they are going to observe the weather each day and make a graph that shows how many days have each type of weather. You might ask children to make predictions about what they will discover.

Call on a child to look out the window and report on today's weather. Prompt with questions as needed, such as: *What do you see in the sky (rain, clouds, or sun)? Did you need an umbrella (or boots or mittens) when you came to school today?* Help the child mark the day's weather on the graph that you prepared by putting an *X* in the space

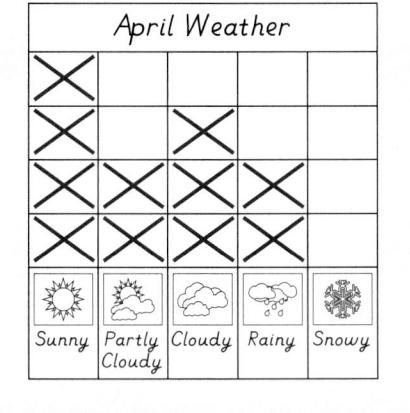

above the appropriate symbol(s), or by taping a copy of the symbol(s) in the appropriate column(s) on the graph. Repeat the procedure each day with a new "Weather Reporter." Compile data for a month or more, or at least until every child has a turn to report on the weather. Periodically ask questions about the Weather Graph, such as: *How many days has it rained since we began the graph? Have there been more sunny days than rainy days? Can you figure out how many more sunny days? Based on the graph, what do you think the weather will be tomorrow?*

You might graph daily weather information for the rest of the school year. Begin a new graph each month and have children compare information from each graph.

Ongoing Assessment: Kid Watching

Note whether children seem to understand the concept of collecting and charting data over time. Also note the types of questions they are able to answer about the graph. Can they correctly identify more and less when comparing 2 columns? Can they figure out "How many more?"

▶ Connections

Art Connection Children can use colored chalk on construction paper to create weather pictures. Watercolor paints also work well for weather scenes.

Science and Mathematics Connections Children will enjoy a variety of weather-related science and math activities, such as tracing and measuring shadows on a sunny day, collecting rain in a large measuring cup on a rainy day, or looking at the shapes of snowflakes under a magnifying lens on a snowy day.

NOTE See the Weather and Seasons Theme in *Resources for the Pre-Kindergarten Classroom* for other activity suggestions related to the weather.

NOTE You might incorporate the weather reporting and charting into your calendar routine. Consider adding the job of "Weather Reporter" to your Job Chart or classroom helper routine.

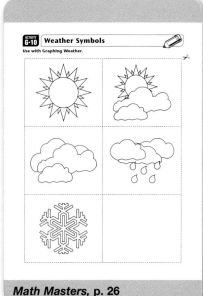

Math Masters, p. 26

Related Book

- *Cloudy With a Chance of Meatballs* by Judi Barrett (Atheneum, 1978)

Expanding

Measurement

Overview

Measurement Goals

In Pre-K, children should have experiences that help them:

• Distinguish and describe size attributes, including length, weight, and capacity or volume. [Measurement and Reference Frames Goal 1]

• Compare objects according to various size attributes. [Measurement and Reference Frames Goal 1]

• Become familiar with standard measuring tools and their uses. [Measurement and Reference Frames Goal 2]

• *Begin to understand the concept of measurement units and the idea that measurement can be quantified.* [Measurement and Reference Frames Goal 2]

• Sequence familiar events in time. [Measurement and Reference Frames Goal 3]

Goals in italics are more advanced and may be appropriate only for some children.

Children's earliest experiences with measure involve describing and comparing the sizes of objects according to how they look or feel: *My daddy is really tall. I want more juice than that!* They do this naturally during everyday experiences such as building with blocks, doling out snacks, playing outdoors, and exploring sand, water, and play dough.

Initially, children use terms such as "big" and "small" broadly and imprecisely. Over time, they should have experiences that build familiarity with the specific attributes of length, weight, and capacity, and with terminology that describes each of these characteristics (*long, short, heavy, light, holds more, holds less,* and so on). Children also need varied opportunities to directly compare and order the length, weight, and capacity of objects. All of these experiences lay groundwork for later learning about standard measurement units, tools, and techniques, although you will find many meaningful ways to informally incorporate tools such as rulers, measuring cups, scales, and timers into classroom life.

Time is another aspect of measurement. In Pre-Kindergarten, children's work with time focuses on sequencing familiar events and using terminology such as *first, second, next,* and *last.* Young children are exposed to other time concepts through everyday occurrences, such as "5-minute warnings," but learning to tell time is not an appropriate expectation for Pre-Kindergarten.

Professional Development

See Chapters 12 and 13 of the *Teacher's Reference Manual* for more information about the Measurement and Reference Frames strand.

Choosing Activities

Beginning	Building	Expanding
Beginning activities focus on size in a very general way. In these activities, children	**Building** activities focus on measurement attributes and sequencing. Here, children	**Expanding** activities are more sophisticated. In these activities, children

Beginning

- make and describe gross measurement comparisons, without specific reference to particular measurement attributes such as length and weight;
- use the terms *bigger* and *smaller* to describe various size attributes.

Building

- make direct comparisons of length, weight, and capacity;
- describe length, weight, and capacity with appropriate terminology;
- explore a pan balance, measuring cups, and other measuring tools;
- sequence events in time.

Expanding

- use nonstandard units lined up end-to-end as a concrete introduction to the concept of measurement units;
- compare the size of two or more objects using a third object as a reference.

Activities in Perspective

KEY

 Art

 Dramatic Play

 Manipulatives and Games

 Rug Time

 Sensory

 Core Core Activity

 Books

 Excursion

 Music and Movement

 Science

 Snack

Teaching Resources

Home-School Connection

Family Connections suggest home activities that link to activities children have done at school. The following Measurement activities contain Family Connections: M♦2, The Three Bears; M♦3, Comparing Shoe Lengths; M♦4, Partner Match; M♦8, Ordering the Day; M♦9, Nursery Rhyme Sequencing; M♦10, Exploration of Capacity; M♦13, Classroom Cooking; M♦14, Comparing Heights of Block Buildings. Note that the same Family Connections are suggested with multiple activities, so keep track of which ones you have already sent home.

Mathematics at Home **Books 1–3** provide additional ideas for enjoyable mathematics activities that families can do together, as well as lists of children's books related to the topics in the teacher's guide. Families can do activities from *Mathematics at Home* Books 1–3 throughout the year.

◄*Home Connection Handbook* provides more ideas to communicate effectively with parents.

▼*Resources for the Pre-Kindergarten Classroom* provides additional teaching ideas, including suggestions for bringing mathematics into thematic instruction, as well as using games, literature, technology, songs, and rhymes to support mathematics learning.

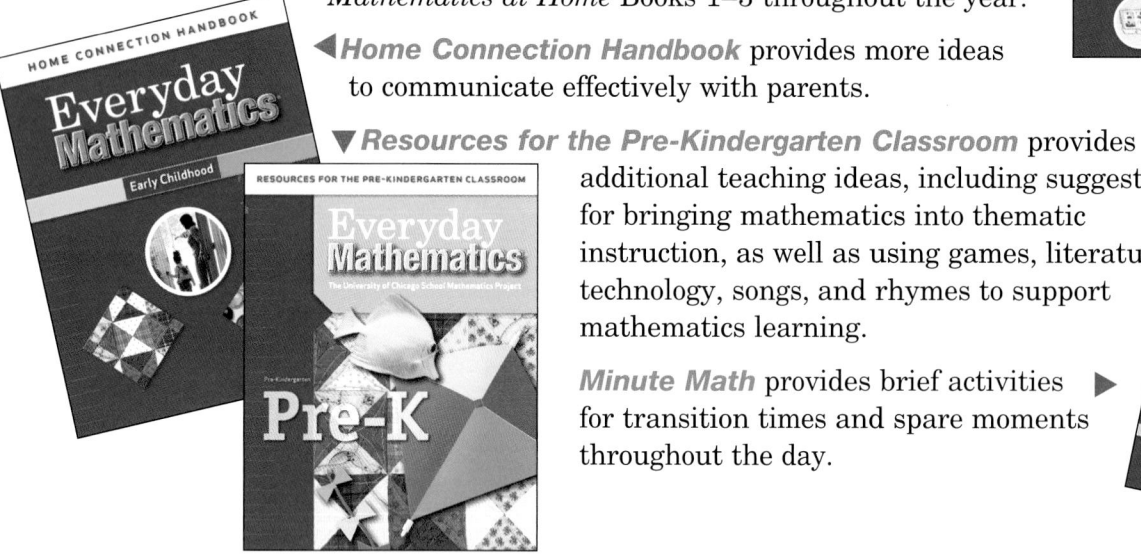

Minute Math provides brief activities ► for transition times and spare moments throughout the day.

Assessment

Ongoing Assessment

 Kid Watching

The following activities in the *Teacher's Guide to Activities* include Ongoing Assessment notes related to measurement. See the *Assessment Handbook* for an expanded table.

Activity	Content Assessed
M◆1, M◆3, M◆4, M◆5, M◆7, M◆10, M◆11, C◆24	Compare sizes of objects (length, weight, and/or capacity). [Measurement and Reference Frames Goal 1]
M◆12	Recognize uses of standard measuring tools. [Measurement and Reference Frames Goal 2]
M◆9	Sequence events in time. [Measurement and Reference Frames Goal 3]

Assessment Handbook

- ◆ Pre-Kindergarten goals, pp. 6–11
- ◆ Measurement Assessment Overview, pp. 32–33
- ◆ Baseline Periodic Assessment Task 5, p. 20
- ◆ End-of-Year Periodic Assessment Tasks 7 and 8, p. 23

ASSESSMENT HANDBOOK

Everyday Mathematics
The University of Chicago School Mathematics Project

Pre-Kindergarten

Pre-K

Differentiated Instruction

Adjusting for Age and Development

Pre-Kindergarten Everyday Mathematics is designed to be flexible enough to adapt to a wide range of preschool classrooms, including classrooms with mixed-age groupings and classrooms with a wide range of developmental levels. Many activities include suggestions to help teachers modify the activity to make it accessible and interesting to children with varying needs, learning styles, or levels of proficiency or understanding.

M◆4 Partner Match

M◆7 Heavier and Lighter

M◆8 Ordering the Day

M◆9 Nursery Rhyme Sequencing

M◆10 Exploration of Capacity

M◆11 In a Row

M◆14 Comparing Heights of Block Buildings

M◆15 Comparing Weights

M◆16 Measuring with Stick-on Notes

Language Support

Everyday Mathematics provides activity-specific suggestions to help all children, including non-native English speakers, develop the language necessary to acquire, process, and express mathematical ideas.

Developing Oral Language

M◆1 Develop language specific to length, weight, and capacity.

M◆5 Develop attribute language specific to length.

M◆7 Develop attribute language specific to weight.

M◆8 Develop sequencing language.

Language & Vocabulary

Informally use these terms that are related to measurement.

recipe	order	length	light
cup	first	weight	lighter
teaspoon	second	same height	heavy
tablespoon	third	same weight	heavier
weigh	last	same length	tall
measure	before	big	taller
compare	after	bigger	short
pan balance	next	biggest	shorter
time	then	small	long
morning	empty	smaller	longer
afternoon	full	smallest	large
early	fill	little	larger
late	height	littler	medium

Activity Connections

The Connections for each activity link the Main Activity to different curricular and classroom areas. They are useful for meeting individual needs and integrating mathematics throughout the day. The following connections are in the Measurement section.

Art

M•1 Bigger and Smaller
M•2 The Three Bears
M•3 Comparing Shoe Lengths
M•8 Ordering the Day
M•14 Comparing Heights of Block Buildings
M•16 Measuring with Stick-on Notes

Blocks

M•4 Partner Match
M•6 Exploration of the Pan Balance
M•11 In a Row

Cooking

M•10 Exploration of Capacity

Dramatic Play

M•2 The Three Bears
M•17 How Long Is a Bus?

Family Connections

See Home-School Connection on page 196.

Field Trip

M•12 Exploration of Standard Measuring Tools

Literacy

M•5 Longer or Shorter
M•8 Ordering the Day
M•9 Nursery Rhyme Sequencing
M•14 Comparing Heights of Block Buildings
M•17 How Long Is a Bus?

Manipulatives

M•4 Partner Match
M•5 Longer or Shorter
M•10 Exploration of Capacity

Mathematics

M•2 The Three Bears
M•8 Ordering the Day
M•11 In a Row
M•14 Comparing Heights of Block Buildings
M•15 Comparing Weights
M•16 Measuring with Stick-on Notes

Outdoors

M•3 Comparing Shoe Lengths
M•6 Exploration of the Pan Balance
M•10 Exploration of Capacity
M•17 How Long Is a Bus?

Science

M•7 Heavier and Lighter
M•9 Nursery Rhyme Sequencing

Sensory Table

M•10 Exploration of Capacity
M•13 Classroom Cooking

Snack

M•1 Bigger and Smaller
M•11 In a Row

Social Studies

M•12 Exploration of Standard Measuring Tools

M·1 Bigger and Smaller

Objective To provide experiences with describing and comparing sizes.

Core Activity

Key Mathematics Concepts and Skills

• Compare objects by size. [Measurement and Reference Frames Goal 1]

• Use size attribute language. [Measurement and Reference Frames Goal 1]

Terms to Use big, bigger, small, smaller, tall, taller, short, shorter, heavy, heavier, light, lighter, little, littler, large, larger, long, longer, various other words that describe size attributes

Materials various items in two sizes (bigger and smaller); trays

Planning Tip Collect several pairs of same-type, but different-size items (a large and small toy car, for example). Possibilities include blocks, buttons, dolls, books, dice, paper clips, index cards, and paper. Label one tray Smaller and the other tray Bigger. You might add simple drawings to illustrate big and small.

▶ Main Activity

☐ Whole Group ✔Small Group ☐ Partners ✔Center

Show children the pairs of materials you collected and the trays labeled Bigger and Smaller. Invite children to describe and compare the sizes of the two items in each pair, and then put each item on the proper tray (the bigger item on the bigger tray and the smaller item on the smaller tray). Leave the trays in a Center and encourage children to find other items in the room that come in two sizes to add to the correct trays. Invite children to share their discoveries with the group.

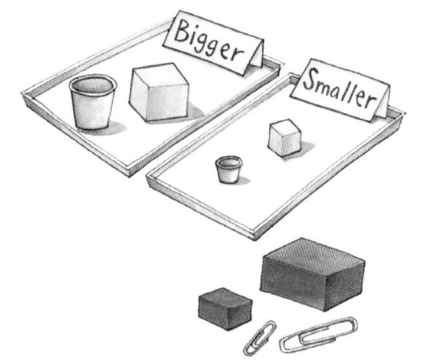

Developing Oral Language ELL

Initially, most children use broad comparison words, such as *big* and *small,* to describe the sizes of objects. Later activities will help children develop language that is specific to length, weight, and capacity (*tall, short, heavy, light, holds more, holds less,* and so on). Begin to model these terms informally during this activity as children describe and sort the objects.

Ongoing Assessment: Kid Watching

You can use this activity to assess whether children can make direct comparisons of size and to note what types of words they understand or use to describe size.

▶ Connections

Art Connection Children can use bubble wrap to print small circles in a big circle. To prepare, cut 4-inch (or larger) circles from bubble wrap. Make a handle by securely attaching a loop of tape on the flat side of the bubble wrap circle. Children dip the bubble wrap circles in a shallow tray of paint and then print them on paper. Alternatively, children could use marker caps or other small circular stamps to make small circle prints on a large paper circle.

Snack Connection Give children pretzel twists (or another food) in mini and regular sizes. Prior to eating, have children sort the pretzels on a plate or napkin according to whether they are little or big.

 Related Books

- *A Pig Is Big* by Douglas Florian (Greenwillow, 2000)
- *Big and Little* by Samantha Berger and Paula Chanko (Scholastic, 1998)
- *Big Little* by Leslie Patricelli (Walker Books, Ltd., 2004)
- *Where's My Teddy?* by Jez Alborough (Candlewick, 1992)
- *Too Big, Too Small, Just Right* by Frances Minters (Harcourt Children's Books, 2001)

M·2 The Three Bears

Objective To provide practice with describing and ordering objects by size in the context of a familiar story.

Key Mathematics Concepts and Skills

• Use one-to-one correspondence in counting and matching objects. [Number and Numeration Goal 2]

• Compare objects by size. [Measurement and Reference Frames Goal 1]

• Use size and comparison language. [Measurement and Reference Frames Goal 1]

Other Skills Listening and Speaking, Reading and Writing

Terms to Use big, bigger, biggest, smaller, smallest, small, medium, large, short, tall

Materials Teaching Masters (*Math Masters*, pp. 7 and 8); flannel board and felt or removable adhesive (optional); book version of *Goldilocks and the Three Bears* (optional; *See* Related Books for suggestions.)

Planning Tip Prepare the figures and objects from *Math Masters* pages 7 and 8 for use on a flannel board by cutting out and applying removable adhesive or felt backing. The pictures can also be used on a chalkboard, wall, or on craft sticks with loops of tape on the back, or on the floor or a table. If possible, laminate the figures to make them more durable. Also choose a book to begin the activity, if desired.

▶ Main Activity

☑ Whole Group ☑ Small Group ☐ Partners ☐ Center

Read or tell the story of *Goldilocks and the Three Bears*. Use the cutout figures and objects from *Math Masters* pages 7 and 8 to enact the story as you share it. After a general discussion of the story, ask questions to encourage discussion and descriptions about relative size. For example: *Who used the big bowl? Who slept in the smallest bed? What size chair did Mama Bear use?*

Invite children to group and arrange the figures and objects from the masters in various ways. For example, they might put all of the objects that belonged to Mama Bear together or all of the bowls together in order from smallest to largest. As children share

Links to the Future

Making direct comparisons between the sizes of objects lays the foundation for learning to measure more precisely later. Using size and comparison vocabulary is another important early measurement skill.

and discuss possible groupings, encourage them to think and talk about size. They might notice that all of Baby Bear's things are small or that there are three sizes of everything in the story. In the course of discussion, model the use of size and comparison language, using the pictures or other objects to demonstrate words as necessary. After children have shared their ideas for groupings, have them work together to order the bears and each type of object by size, if they haven't already done so.

Leave out the figures and objects for children to use for retelling the story and for sorting and grouping.

▶ Connections

Mathematics Connection Put out a variety of objects in three sizes and have children order the objects by size. You might use small, medium, and large cups, buttons, cardboard tubes, books, boxes, or pieces of paper. (See In a Row on page 220 for an activity that focuses on ordering objects by length.)

Dramatic Play Connection Add objects to the Dramatic Play Center to encourage children to use size vocabulary. You might include different-size cups, plates, clothing, purses, or other objects.

 Art and Family Connections Children can color and cut out copies of the Three Bears characters and objects from *Math Masters,* pages 7 and 8. You might have them bring the cutouts home to tell the story to their families. Provide envelopes for storing and carrying the cutouts, or help children make envelopes by folding a sheet of paper in half and taping or stapling three sides.

Math Masters, p. 7

 Related Books

- *Goldie and the Three Bears* by Diane Stanley (HarperCollins, 2003)
- *Goldilocks and the Three Bears* by Jennifer Greenway (Andrews McMeel Publishing, 1991)
- *Goldilocks and the Three Bears* by Candice Ransom (American Education Publishing, 2001)
- *The Three Bears* by Paul Galdone (Clarion Books, 1979)

M·3 Comparing Shoe Lengths

 Objective To introduce direct comparisons of length.

Key Mathematics Concepts and Skills

• Compare objects by length. [Measurement and Reference Frames Goal 1]

• Use terms such as *longer, shorter,* and *same length* to describe length comparisons.
[Measurement and Reference Frames Goal 1]

Terms to Use length, long, short, longer, shorter, same length, compare

Materials children's shoes; classroom objects

▶ **Main Activity**　　　✔Whole Group　✔Small Group　☐ Partners　☐ Center

Ask children to look at their shoes. Have them point to the heel and the toe. Explain
that the length of a shoe goes from the heel to the toe. Have children sit across from a
partner on the floor, extend their legs, and touch their shoes to their partner's shoes,
making sure their heels are touching the floor. Have them compare the length of their
shoes with the length of their partner's shoes. Ask: *Are your shoes the same length?*
If not, whose shoes are longer? (Whose toes stick up higher?) Whose shoes are shorter?
Children can compare shoes with other partners. Or, they might compare the lengths of
other body parts, such as hands.

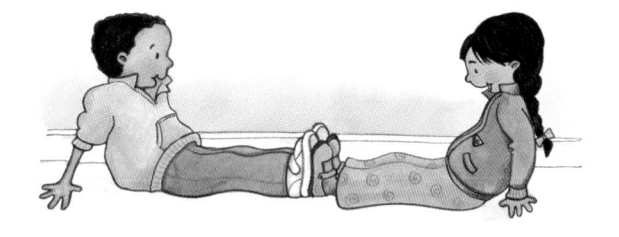

NOTE Having children press
their heels against the floor
helps children line up the ends
of the objects being measured
or compared, an important but
difficult concept for children when
they learn to measure. Reinforce
this idea as children compare the
lengths of various objects and
begin to explore measurement.

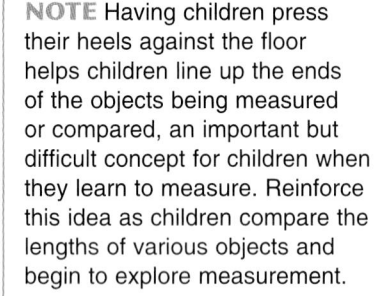

When children are comfortable making direct comparisons, ask them to find an object in the room that is *longer than* (or *shorter than,* or *about the same length* as) their own shoe. Remind them that the heel has to be lined up with the end of the object so they can compare.

 Ongoing Assessment: Kid Watching

You can use this activity to informally assess children's abilities to directly compare the lengths of objects and to use size and comparison terms. Note whether children line up the ends of the objects being compared.

▶ Connections

Outdoors Connection Encourage children to compare objects outside with various body parts. For example, you might ask children to find something taller than they are, something too big to wrap their arms around, or something that fits on their thumb. Children also enjoy standing side by side to compare the lengths of their shadows.

Art Connection Have children work with a partner to trace around each other's shoes. (This will be easiest if children remove a shoe.) Children can cut out the shoes and decorate them. They might use the shoe cutouts for sorting, or children can order shoes by size, which makes a nice display.

 Family Connection You may want to use the Comparing Lengths and Heights Family Connection (*Math Masters,* page 80) to encourage children and families to make measurement comparisons at home.

 **Links to the Future**

Directly comparing the lengths of two objects lays groundwork for learning to use measuring tools to measure lengths, which is a focus in later grades.

Math Masters, p. 80

Building

M·4 Partner Match

 Objective To provide practice with comparing lengths.

Key Mathematics Concepts and Skills

- Compare strips by length. [Measurement and Reference Frames Goal 1]
- Practice measuring techniques. [Measurement and Reference Frames Goal 2]

Other Skills Cooperation

Terms to Use longer, shorter, same length

Materials pairs of paper strips cut from cardstock or heavy paper

---

Planning Tip Cut enough matching-length pairs of heavy paper strips so that each child in the group will have one strip. Sentence strips work well. All strips should be the same color, but each pair should be at least 2 inches different from every other pair. You may want to laminate the strips for durability.

▶ **Main Activity**   ✔Whole Group   ✔Small Group   ✔Partners   ☐Center

Show children the strips that you prepared. Demonstrate how to line up the bottom edges of the strips to compare the lengths. Use a few different pairs of strips to explain and show that when the bottom edges are lined up and the top edges match, the strips are the same length. Also show examples in which the bottom edges are lined up and the top edges do not match; explain that this means that one strip is longer than the other.

Give each child one of the strips you prepared. Each child then finds the other child in the group who has a strip that is exactly the same length. Explain that there are two strips of each length, so each child should find one match. If the group has an uneven number of children, you should be part of the partner match. When children find their matching partner, they should sit down next to that person.

You can repeat the activity by redistributing the strips and inviting children to find new partners. Remind them to match up the ends of their strips when comparing lengths, and provide support as needed.

Save the strips for future use. Once children are familiar with matching lengths, the strips are a good way to pair children for other activities.

 Ongoing Assessment: Kid Watching

You can use this activity to informally assess children's understanding of the need to match ends when comparing length.

 **Adjusting for Age and Development**

You can extend the activity by asking the children to find objects around the classroom that are longer than (or shorter than, or the same length as) their strips. As they compare lengths, remind them to line up ends.

▶ Connections

Blocks Connection Line up three or four blocks to make a "train." Explain that you are building a train for the toy animals, and invite children to build more train cars. Encourage children to make longer train cars for the large animals and shorter train cars for the smaller animals. You might encourage them to experiment with using different-length blocks for their trains.

Manipulatives Connection Encourage children to make a train of connecting cubes that is the same length as a given paper strip.

 Family Connection You may want to use the Comparing Lengths and Heights Family Connection (*Math Masters,* page 80) to encourage children and families to make measurement comparisons at home.

Math Masters, p. 80

Building

M·5 Longer or Shorter

Objective To provide practice with sorting and making direct comparisons of length.

Key Mathematics Concepts and Skills

- Compare objects by length. [Measurement and Reference Frames Goal 1]
- Use terms such as *longer, shorter,* and *same length* to describe length comparisons. [Measurement and Reference Frames Goal 1]
- Sort objects by length. [Patterns, Functions, and Algebra Goal 1]

Terms to Use longer, shorter, same length, compare, sort

Materials classroom objects varying in length from about an inch to 18 inches; trays for sorting; pencil or similar-length object; ruler (optional)

▶ Main Activity

☐ Whole Group ✔ Small Group ☐ Partners ✔ Center

Choose a pencil or similar-length object to use as a reference object. Place the reference object between the 2 trays labeled *Shorter* and *Longer.* Have children sort the materials you collected according to whether they are longer or shorter than the reference object. Model how to line up the end of each object with the end of the reference object and ask children why they think it is important to line up the ends. As children work, encourage them to use the words *longer* and *shorter.* Invite children to find other items in the classroom to add to the appropriate trays.

After awhile, change the reference object so children can sort the items in different ways. Encourage discussion as to why the same materials may now be on different trays. At some point you might use a ruler as the reference object or as part of the collection of

Planning Tip Label one tray *Shorter* and one tray *Longer.* To provide a visual clue, you might draw 2 different-length lines (with their ends lined up on one side) on the label for each tray. Circle the shorter line under the word *Shorter* and circle the longer line under the word *Longer.*

Developing Oral Language ELL

Model and encourage children to use attribute language that is specific to length *(longer, taller, shorter)* during this activity.

items to familiarize children with this tool. Pre-Kindergarten children do not need to use the ruler to measure, though.

Ongoing Assessment: Kid Watching

You can use this activity to informally assess children's abilities to directly compare the lengths of objects and to use size and comparison terms. Note whether children line up the ends of the objects being compared. Also note whether they can re-sort objects correctly when there is a new reference object.

▶ Connections

Manipulatives Connection Use connecting cubes to make a train of 8 cubes and a train of 15 cubes. Ask children to make a train that is *longer* than your short train but *shorter* than your long train. Have children show their trains and talk about all the possible trains that fit the criteria. You might have them put their trains in order, lining up the ends. Repeat with different-size trains as the longest and shortest.

Literacy Connection Use books such as those in Related Books to promote discussion about relative sizes.

Related Books

- *Is It Larger? Is It Smaller?* by Tana Hoban (Greenwillow, 1985)

- *Is the Blue Whale the Biggest Thing There Is?* by Robert E. Wells (Albert Whitman & Company, 1993)

M·6 Exploration of the Pan Balance

 Objective To introduce the pan balance.

Key Mathematics Concepts and Skills

• Explore weight and balance. [Measurement and Reference Frames Goal 1]

• Become familiar with the pan balance as a measuring tool. [Measurement and Reference Frames Goal 2]

Terms to Use pan balance, weigh, weight, heavy, heavier, light, lighter, same weight

Materials pan balance; classroom objects for weighing such as counters, marbles, dice, and inch cubes; paper and drawing tools (optional)

Planning Tip If your pan balance has shallow pans or trays, you may need to tape two matching containers to the pans to hold objects for weighing. Level your balance before the activity.

▶ Main Activity

☐ Whole Group ☐ Small Group ☐ Partners ✔ Center

Children need time to explore and play with a pan balance before they are formally introduced to weighing activities. Allow children to initiate their own explorations. As they become familiar with the pan balance, observe how their play evolves. Do they pile materials into the balance or do they try to compare the weights of fewer objects? Do they seem to know how the pan balance works? Ask questions (and provide explanations) in response to what children are doing, such as: *What do you think the pan balance is for? Why did that side of the pan balance go down? What does that tell you? What do you think will happen if we take this object out (or put this object in)? What does it mean when the two sides are level? What else can we put in the balance?*

Make the pan balance readily available in the Math Center and encourage children to use it frequently, especially when there are real-life opportunities for comparing the weights of objects (two rocks found on the playground or two helpings of snack, for

NOTE Heavier and Lighter, page 212, is a more structured activity involving the pan balance.

example). Model and reinforce correct use of the balance, as needed. If children wish, they can draw pictures to document their explorations and findings.

A level pan balance

▶ Connections

Outdoors Connection If you have a seesaw, children can use it to compare their own weights. Or, in a gym or outdoor space, have children help you create a low seesaw using a beam and large block. Encourage children to explore balance and weight as they place the beam on the block, and as they place objects on each side of the beam. (For safety, do not allow children on the beam.)

Blocks Connection Encourage children to explore weight and balance as they build with blocks. Ask questions to prompt conversations: *Why do you think the roof fell down? Which block can go on top of the tower? Can you find a block that is heavier (or lighter) than that one?*

Related Books

- *You Can Use a Balance* (Rookie Read-About Science) by Linda Bullock (Children's Press (CT), 2004)

- *How Heavy Is It?* (Rookie Read-About Math) by Brian Sargent (Children's Press (CT), 2006)

M·7 Heavier and Lighter

Objective To explore the concept of weight and the use of a pan balance through a direct comparison activity.

Key Mathematics Concepts and Skills

- Compare the weights of objects by feel and with a pan balance. [Measurement and Reference Frames Goals 1 and 2]

- Use terms such as *heavier, lighter,* and *same weight* to describe weight comparisons. [Measurement and Reference Frames Goal 1]

Terms to Use weigh, weight, heavy, light, heavier, lighter, same weight, pan balance

Materials identical, opaque containers that can be sealed, such as half-pint milk cartons; filling material such as sand or pebbles; tape; pan balance

---

Planning Tip See Exploration of the Pan Balance, page 210, for an introduction to the pan balance that should precede this activity. To prepare for this activity, place filling material in several identical containers so the weight of each container is noticeably different. Tape the containers closed.

▶ **Main Activity**   ☐ Whole Group   ✔ Small Group   ☐ Partners   ✔ Center

Show a small group of children two containers that look the same, but have noticeably different weights. Explain that even though the two containers look the same, they are not. Children can take turns investigating this situation by holding a container in each hand. Encourage children to describe what they notice using terms such as *heavier* and *lighter.*

After all children in the group have had a chance to hold and compare the containers, ask whether they can think of another way to test whether one container is heavier than the other. Provide a pan balance for children to compare the containers and review the use of the pan balance as needed. After children compare the containers with the pan balance, discuss their findings.

Developing ELL
Oral Language

Model and encourage children to use attribute language that is specific to weight *(heavier, lighter)* during this activity.

Show children the other containers that you filled and encourage them to compare the weights of the containers, first by hand and then with the pan balance. Place the containers and the pan balance in a Center for continued exploration.

 Adjusting for Age and Development

Provide empty containers and additional filling material for children to make containers of different weights. For an additional challenge, you may want to prompt children to try to match the weight of one of the pre-filled containers. They can hand weigh their containers, and then test them using the pan balance.

▶ Connections

Science Connection Provide a pan balance and an assortment of absorbent materials such as sponges, cotton balls, paper towels, fabric, and so on. Ask: *Which weighs more, wet or dry?* Children can experiment by adding water to the materials and comparing the weight of the wet and dry materials. (Have towels on hand for any spills.) After children have had a chance to explore, ask them why they think the wet materials are heavier and discuss their theories.

 Related Book

- *Mighty Maddie (MathStart 1)* by Stuart J. Murphy (HarperCollins, 2004)

M·8 Ordering the Day

 Objective To provide practice with sequencing using familiar classroom activities.

Key Mathematics Concepts and Skills
- Sequence events. [Measurement and Reference Frames Goal 3]
- Describe the sequence of events using terms such as *first, next, last,* and so on. [Measurement and Reference Frames Goal 3]

Other Skills Cooperation, Listening and Speaking

Terms to Use before, after, first, next, then, last, early, late, morning, afternoon, order

Materials pictures of 3 or 4 typical classroom activities; paper and crayons (optional)

Planning Tip Take photos of 3 or 4 activities that occur during the school day. Show events that predictably occur at the beginning and end of the school day, and 1 or 2 things in the middle, such as snack, lunch, or circle time. If you do not have a camera, you can cut pictures from school-supply catalogs or have children help draw pictures.

 **Main Activity** ✔Whole Group ✔Small Group ☐ Partners ✔Center

To introduce the idea of sequencing by time, have children think through some familiar activities and discuss what usually comes first and next. For example, you might ask children to order the following pairs of activities: tie your shoelaces and put on your shoes; pour the juice and drink the juice; go outside and put on your coat; eat your lunch and get your lunch box; set the table and eat dinner.

Show and discuss your pictures of classroom activities. Make sure children agree which part of the school day each picture depicts (arrival, dismissal, snack time, and so on). Next, ask children to work together to put the pictures in order according to the schedule of their school day. Assist them and prompt discussion with questions such as: *Which activity do we do first thing in the morning? What do we do after snack? Which of these activities do we do last, right before we go home?* You might extend their thinking

NOTE Graphing Favorite Activities, page 182, is another mathematics activity based on classroom activities. Nursery Rhyme Sequencing, page 216, is another sequencing activity.

beyond the school day with questions such as: *What do you do in the morning before you come to school? What do you do in the afternoon after you leave?* In the course of discussion, model and encourage children to use time and sequencing words (*before, after, morning, afternoon, first, next, last,* and so on).

Put the pictures in a Center for children to work with independently.

Adjusting for Age and Development

Include additional pictures for children to sequence.

▶ Connections

Literacy Connection Read *If You Take a Mouse to School* by Laura Numeroff (Laura Geringer, 2002) and talk with the class about how the mouse's antics lead from one to the other. This book reinforces sequencing vocabulary, especially the use of the word *then*.

Art and Mathematics Connection Ask children to draw a picture of something they like to do at school. Make a large chart divided vertically. Label the sections according to a familiar middle point in the school day, such as lunch, snack, or outside time (Before Lunch and After Lunch or Before Recess and After Recess, for example). Have children put their pictures in the correct section on the chart. If children draw the activity that you chose as the middle point, you might attach their pictures to the dividing line or ask them for ideas about where to put those pictures.

 Family Connection You may want to use the Ordering Daily Events Family Connection (*Math Masters,* page 82) to encourage families to talk about the sequence of daily events.

Math Masters, p. 82

M·9 Nursery Rhyme Sequencing

Objective To provide practice with sequencing using a nursery rhyme.

Planning Tip Copy and cut apart a set of sequence cards for each child. Recite "Humpty Dumpty" with the class a number of times over several days before doing the sequencing activity.

Key Mathematics Concepts and Skills

• Sequence events. [Measurement and Reference Frames Goal 3]

• Describe the sequence of events using terms such as *first, next, last,* and so on.
[Measurement and Reference Frames Goal 3]

Other Skills Listening and Speaking, Pretending and Role Play, Reading and Writing

Terms to Use order, first, second, third, last, before, after, next, then

Materials Teaching Masters (*Math Masters,* pp. 9–11); scissors; crayons, glue, and paper (optional); Mother Goose book (optional)

▶ Main Activity

☑ Whole Group ☑ Small Group ☐ Partners ☐ Center

Recite the nursery rhyme "Humpty Dumpty" with the group and invite children to act it out. (They should have had many prior opportunities to become familiar with the rhyme.)

> *Humpty Dumpty sat on a wall,*
> *Humpty Dumpty had a great fall,*
> *All the king's horses and all the king's men*
> *Couldn't put Humpty together again.*

Give each child a set of the three "Humpty Dumpty" sequence cards (*Math Masters,* page 9) and ask them to put their cards in order according to the rhyme. Ask children to explain why they ordered the cards the way they did. Encourage children to use words such as

Math Masters, p. 9

first, second, next, and *last.* If children need help putting the cards in sequence, prompt them with questions such as: *What happened first? Second? What happened last? What happened before Humpty Dumpty fell? What happened after he fell?* You might provide crayons, glue, and paper for children to color the pictures and glue them in order.

Adjusting for Age and Development

To simplify the task, you might begin by using only two "Humpty Dumpty" pictures—the first and the last.

At a later time, use *Math Masters* pages 10 and 11 to sequence "Itsy-Bitsy Spider" (3 cards) and "Jack and Jill" (4 cards). You can also create your own cards.

▶ Connections

Literacy Connection Gather a collection of nursery rhyme books for your classroom library and read aloud from them frequently. Encourage children to compare how different illustrators depict the same nursery rhymes. If you have a Listening Center, you may want to play a recording of nursery rhymes.

Science Connection Soak an egg in a cup of vinegar and watch what happens to the shell after a few days. (The shell gradually dissolves.) You can also experiment with eggs in cola or sports drinks.

Family Connection You may want to use the Ordering Daily Events Family Connection (*Math Masters,* page 82) to encourage families to talk about the sequence of daily events.

Math Masters, p. 82

Related Books

- *My Very First Mother Goose* by Iona Opie (Candlewick, 1996)
- *Mother Goose: A Collection of Classic Nursery Rhymes* by Michael Hague (Henry Holt & Co., 1984)
- *Humpty Dumpty* by Kin Eagle (Charlesbridge Publishing, 1999)
- *The True Story of Humpty Dumpty* by Sarah Hayes (Candlewick, 1999)

M·10 Exploration of Capacity

Objective To promote exploration of capacity using sensory materials.

Key Mathematics Concepts and Skills

• Explore capacity using a variety of materials and containers. [Measurement and Reference Frames Goal 1]

• Make direct comparisons of amounts of materials in containers. [Measurement and Reference Frames Goal 1]

Other Skills Fine Motor

Terms to Use fill, full, empty

Materials water, sand, dried beans, or other pourable materials; sensory table or trays; containers of various capacities, sizes, and shapes; measuring cups and spoons

Planning Tip Disposable aluminum roasting pans can serve as trays if your classroom does not have a sensory table.

▶ **Main Activity**   ☐ Whole Group   ☐ Small Group   ☐ Partners   ✔ Center

As children pour materials such as water, sand, and dried beans into and between containers of different sizes and shapes, they naturally begin to make comparisons of capacity. Observe children during their free play with materials in the sensory table (or in trays). Do children pour contents from one container into another to see which holds more? Do they try to fit one container inside another? Promote exploration, thinking, and discovery by commenting on what children are doing. For example: *I see you filled two containers. Which do you think holds more? How could you find out? What happened when you poured the water from the big cup into the little cup? Why do you think some of it spilled?* Encourage children to share their discoveries with one another.

Adjusting for Age and Development

After children have had time for free exploration, provide several 1-cup measuring scoops and ask children to count how many scoops it takes to fill each container. Encourage children to find the containers that hold the most and the least number of scoops. They will probably not fill the scoop precisely each time, so the number of scoops may vary. Also include other standard measuring cups and spoons for exploration.

▶ Connections

Cooking Connection A good way for children to explore capacity is to measure ingredients while preparing simple recipes. You may want to make cookie or muffin dough, or see Classroom Cooking, page 224, for easy recipes to use in the classroom.

Outdoors or Sensory Table Connection Children may enjoy making sand cakes. You might use pictures from *Math Masters,* pages 12–14, to create a simple "recipe" (sand, water, and rocks are good ingredients). Also provide measuring cups and spoons, bowls, muffin tins or loaf pans, and mixing spoons. You can scent the sand with a bit of spice, such as cinnamon, for added interest.

Manipulatives Connection Provide nesting puzzles such as nesting cups, nesting blocks, and nesting dolls. Encourage children to compare sizes to fit the pieces together.

 Family Connection You may want to use the Bath Time Math Family Connection (*Math Masters,* page 81) to encourage families to promote exploration of capacity at home.

Ongoing Assessment: Kid Watching

Talk with children during their explorations to informally assess their understanding of capacity (the amount a container can hold). Can children think and talk about how much a container holds separate from how tall it is or how heavy it is? Can they compare the capacities of two containers by pouring materials between them?

Math Masters, p. 81

M·11 In a Row

 Objective To provide practice with ordering three or more objects by length.

Key Mathematics Concepts and Skills

• Compare objects by length. [Measurement and Reference Frames Goal 1]

• Use appropriate language to describe and compare length. [Measurement and Reference Frames Goal 1]

Other Skills Cooperation, Fine Motor

Terms to Use length, short, shorter, shortest, long, longer, longest, order

Materials material that can be cut into graduated lengths, such as straws, cardboard tubes, or narrow strips of cardboard; masking tape (optional)

Planning Tip Cut your material into 6–8 pieces that differ in length by at least an inch. Keep the pieces ready, but do not plan to use all of them initially.

▶ Main Activity

☐ Whole Group ✔ Small Group ☐ Partners ✔ Center

Before introducing this activity, which focuses on comparing the lengths of three or more objects, make sure children have had ample practice comparing the lengths of two objects. (See Comparing Shoe Lengths, page 204, Partner Match, page 206, and Longer or Shorter, page 208, for activities that focus on comparing the lengths of two objects.)

Show a small group of children 3 straws (or other material you selected) of different lengths and ask them to work together to put them in order from shortest to longest. Remind children that they need to line up the ends of the objects when they are comparing their lengths. Model this as needed. As children work, encourage them to use words such as *short, shorter, shortest,* and *long, longer, longest* to describe the objects.

Show a new straw of a different length and ask where in the row it would go. Allow ample time for work with the straws and to make comparisons. When children place the straw in the correct position, invite them to explain how they figured out where to put it. Add more straws of different lengths as children are ready.

Place several sets of straws or other materials that children can order by length in the Math Center for continued exploration.

 Ongoing Assessment: Kid Watching

You can use this activity to informally assess children's abilities to order 3 or more objects by length and to use comparison terms such as longer, shorter, longest, and shortest.

▶ Connections

Blocks Connection Invite children to build a row of block towers that vary in height from short to tall. (*Tall* and *long* are both words associated with length. *Tall* generally refers to height. Help children become familiar with both words.)

Mathematics Connection If you have plastic connecting links, have children make chains of different lengths. Each child can hang his or her chains on a wire coat hanger in order by length. Display the coat hangers. Children can also do this activity with paper chains.

Snack Connection Serve pretzel sticks or rods for snack. Invite children to nibble their pretzels to different lengths and then order them from shortest to longest.

 **Adjusting for Age and Development**

For children who need help lining up the ends, put a long strip of masking tape on the table to use as a base. Model how children should align the ends of each object with the tape.

 Related Book

• *Much Bigger Than Martin* by Steven Kellogg (Puffin, 1992)

M·12 Exploration of Standard Measuring Tools

 Objective To provide informal exposure to standard measuring tools.

Key Mathematics Concepts and Skills

- Distinguish size attributes, including length, weight, and capacity. [Measurement and Reference Frames Goal 1]

- Use measurement language to describe size attributes. [Measurement and Reference Frames Goal 1]

- Explore standard measuring tools and their uses. [Measurement and Reference Frames Goal 2]

Other Skills Fine Motor, Pretending and Role Play

Terms to Use measure, length, weight, time, names of standard measuring tools

Materials tools to measure length such as rulers, yardsticks, and tape measures; tools to measure weight such as kitchen or bathroom scales; tools to measure capacity such as measuring cups and spoons; tools to measure time such as timers, clocks, and watches

---

Planning Tip This activity takes place in a variety of centers around the classroom over an extended period of time.

Links to the Future

Do not expect children to master the techniques of standard measurement or to understand the concept of measurement units yet. These are goals for Kindergarten and First Grade and beyond. The focus of this activity is to expose children to measuring tools and begin to gradually build understanding of their uses.

▶ Main Activity

☐ Whole Group ☐ Small Group ☐ Partners ✔ Center

Children need time to explore with standard measuring tools before they are formally taught how to use them. Include standard measuring tools in your classroom centers. For example, tools to measure length will have many uses in the Block Center. Tools to measure weight and capacity can be integrated into the sensory table and Dramatic Play Center. Children may find uses for timers while playing games or completing puzzles. Tell children the names of the tools and describe where in the classroom they can find them. Expect children to find many uses for the tools—maybe even some you haven't thought of!

Observe children as they experiment with the tools. Do they seem to know how the tools work? Do they understand possible uses of the tools? Ask questions such as: *What do you think a ruler (scale, measuring cup, clock, and so on) is for? Have you ever seen someone using one? What else can you do with it?*

Look for real-life opportunities to use standard measuring tools with children. For example, you may need to measure the length of a table when rearranging the classroom, measure 2 cups of flour to make play dough, or use a timer to give children turns at the computer. Model how to use the tools and invite children to assist as much as possible.

▶ Connections

Social Studies Connection When you discuss community helpers, ask children to consider what types of measuring tools are needed to perform each role. For example, bakers use measuring cups to measure ingredients, grocers use scales to weigh produce, and construction workers use tape measures to measure windows and doors. Ask children to share examples of measuring tools that their family members use at home or work.

Field Trip Connection When you go on field trips, look for opportunities for children to see measuring tools being used in the real world. For example, on a trip to the post office, children might see packages being weighed. If possible, ask for a demonstration.

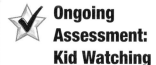

Ongoing Assessment: Kid Watching

Use this activity to informally observe children's familiarity with standard measuring tools and their uses. Do not expect children to know how to use the tools correctly yet.

M·13 Classroom Cooking

 Objective To provide practice with measuring and counting through cooking.

Key Mathematics Concepts and Skills

• Count out ingredients according to a recipe. [Number and Numeration Goal 2]

• Explore standard measuring tools and their uses. [Measurement and Reference Frames Goal 2]

• Practice measuring techniques. [Measurement and Reference Frames Goal 2]

• Sequence steps in a recipe. [Measurement and Reference Frames Goal 3]

Other Skills Fine Motor, Reading and Writing

Terms to Use measure, cup, teaspoon, tablespoon, recipe, first, next, last

Materials Teaching Masters (*Math Masters*, pp. 12–14); recipe; bowls; measuring cups and spoons; stirring spoon; ingredients and cookware based on the recipe you choose; timer (optional)

Planning Tip Use one or more of the recipes provided here or choose another kid-friendly recipe. Use the pictures of measuring tools on *Math Masters* pages 12–14 to create a pictorial version of your recipe. Work with a group small enough so that all children get a turn to measure and mix. Cook often so all children eventually get a turn.

▶ **Main Activity**   ☐ Whole Group ✔Small Group ☐ Partners ☐ Center

Cooking is a wonderful mathematics activity, regardless of the recipe. The recipes below make good class cooking projects, but any recipe will provide meaningful opportunities for counting, measuring, and working together.

Before you begin, read through your recipe with the group. Talk about what a recipe is and what kinds of things you can make with a recipe. Explain that recipes tell what ingredients you need, how much to use, and the order to follow. Demonstrate how to measure by leveling off for dry ingredients, or by carefully looking at the measuring line for liquids.

No-Cook Play Dough
(makes enough for 4–6 children)

1 cup salt

2 cups flour

2 Tablespoons oil

$\frac{1}{2}$ cup water (adjust as necessary
for desired consistency)

food coloring (optional)

Mix and knead together. Store in a tight
container or resealable bag.

Cooked Play Dough (a longer lasting version, also for 4–6 children)

1 cup salt

2 cups flour

$\frac{1}{4}$ cup oil

2 teaspoons cream of tartar

2 cups water

food coloring (optional)

Mix together and cook over low heat, stirring
constantly until dough pulls away from the
sides of the pan. Knead the mixture when cool.
Store in a tight container or resealable bag.

Goop (for one child)

$\frac{1}{2}$ cup cornstarch

$\frac{1}{4}$ cup water

food coloring (optional)

Mix the cornstarch and water together with
fingers in a small bowl or pie tin.

No-Cook Play Dough

Salt

1 cup

Flour

1 cup   1 cup

Oil

1 tablespoon   1 tablespoon

Water

$\frac{1}{2}$ cup

Draw a pictorial recipe on chart paper.

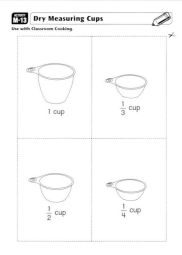

ACTIVITY M-13 Dry Measuring Cups
Use with Classroom Cooking.

1 cup

$\frac{1}{3}$ cup

$\frac{1}{2}$ cup

$\frac{1}{4}$ cup

Math Masters, p. 12

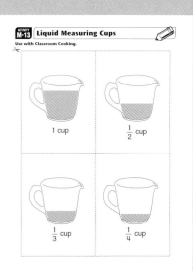

ACTIVITY M-13 Liquid Measuring Cups
Use with Classroom Cooking.

1 cup

$\frac{1}{2}$ cup

$\frac{1}{3}$ cup

$\frac{1}{4}$ cup

Math Masters, p. 13

Building

Pizza Dough (makes about 10–12 small pizzas)

1 cup warm water

1 teaspoon sugar

1 packet active dry yeast ($\frac{1}{4}$ oz)

3 Tablespoons olive oil (or other oil)

$2\frac{1}{2}$ cups all purpose flour

1 teaspoon salt

In a small bowl, place $\frac{1}{4}$ cup warm water and stir in the sugar until dissolved. Sprinkle the yeast on top of the water and let it float there for 1 minute. Stir it in the water and let it "proof" for 10 minutes. (Use a kitchen timer.) It should bubble a bit.

Pour the yeast mixture into a large bowl and stir in the remaining $\frac{3}{4}$ cup water and the oil, flour, and salt. Mix until the dough forms a ball. With hands dusted in flour, knead the dough on a lightly floured surface until it is smooth and elastic.

Lightly oil the inside of a large bowl. Roll the ball of dough in the bowl to coat it with oil. Cover the bowl with plastic wrap and place it in a warm place until it has doubled in bulk (about 1 hour).

Punch the dough down. Give each child a piece of foil with his or her initials in the corner and a piece of dough. Show how to stretch the dough by putting one hand on the middle and gently pulling and turning the dough into the desired shape. If needed roll the edge up a bit.

Brush the top of the flattened dough with tomato sauce, cheese, and any other desired toppings. Pizzas can be put directly in the oven on the foil or the foil can be placed on a baking sheet. Bake at 450° for about 10 minutes.

ACTIVITY M·13 **Measuring Spoons**
Use with Classroom Cooking.

1 tablespoon

1 teaspoon

$\frac{1}{2}$ teaspoon

$\frac{1}{4}$ teaspoon

Math Masters, p. 14

Applesauce Oatmeal Muffins (makes 12 muffins)

1 cup flour

$\frac{1}{2}$ teaspoon cinnamon

$\frac{1}{4}$ teaspoon nutmeg

$\frac{1}{4}$ cup brown sugar

3 teaspoons baking powder

$\frac{1}{2}$ teaspoon salt

$\frac{3}{4}$ cup rolled oats

1 egg

$\frac{1}{4}$ cup oil

$\frac{1}{3}$ cup milk

$\frac{2}{3}$ cup applesauce

Preheat oven to 375° and grease muffin tins or use cupcake liners. Mix dry ingredients well with a fork. In separate bowl, beat egg, then add oil, milk, and applesauce. Add the dry mix to the wet mix until just combined. Spoon into tin and bake for 20 minutes.

NOTE Children may enjoy making the applesauce for this recipe. Give each child one apple to help wash, cut, and pare. Cook the apples in a small amount of water over low heat until soft. You can use a crock pot if desired. Mash apples into sauce. Add sugar and cinnamon to taste.

▶ Connections

Sensory Table Connection Encourage children to measure and compare quantities using measuring spoons and cups as they explore sand or other sensory materials.

Family Connection You may want to use the Cooking at Home Family Connection (*Math Masters*, page 83) to encourage families to use mathematics as they cook together. You might also want to send home copies of the recipes you use in class.

NOTE See the Healthful Foods Theme in *Resources for the Pre-Kindergarten Classroom* for other activity suggestions related to cooking and eating.

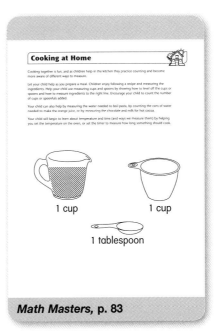

Math Masters, p. 83

Related Books

- *Mudluscious: Stories and Activities Featuring Food for Preschool Children* by Jan Irving and Robin Currie (Libraries Unlimited, 1986)

- *The Kids' Multicultural Cookbook: Food & Fun Around the World* by Deanna F. Cook (Williamson, 1995)

Building

M·14 Comparing Heights of Block Buildings

Objective To introduce the use of paper strips to measure and compare heights.

Key Mathematics Concepts and Skills

• Compare heights of buildings and describe as *taller, shorter,* and *same height.*
[Measurement and Reference Frames Goal 1]

• Practice measuring techniques. [Measurement and Reference Frames Goal 2]

Other Skills Cooperation, Fine Motor

Terms to Use height, taller, shorter, same height, compare, measure

Materials blocks; long, narrow strips of paper; writing tools; scissors; tape; date stamp (optional); paper clips and a box or basket (optional)

Planning Tip Cut lengths of 3 or 4 feet from adding machine tape or cut long paper into narrow strips. Sentence strips or other stiff paper are easiest for children to handle. Tape multiple sentence strips together to make longer strips.

▶ Main Activity

☐ Whole Group ☐ Small Group ☑ Partners ☑ Center

Provide paper strips for children to use to measure and keep track of the heights of their block buildings. Show children how to use a paper strip to record the height of a building. One child holds the bottom of the strip next to the bottom of the structure while another child holds the top of the strip and draws a line to mark the height of the structure on the paper. Then they cut the paper at the mark. The builders can write their names on the strip and may stamp it with the date. They might also record how many blocks high their structure is. If there is room in the Block Center, display the strips with the bottom of the strips touching the floor so children can see and compare

the heights of various buildings. Or, children can roll the strips up, secure them with a paper clip, and put them in a box or basket to have available for comparing. Children might enjoy ordering a group of strips by height.

Once this measuring technique is introduced, encourage children to use it often to record and compare the heights of their buildings. Use the strips to promote discussion about the relative heights of buildings, the number of blocks used, and strategies for building tall buildings.

▶ Connections

Literacy Connection Take pictures of children's buildings and put them in a class book. Frequent builders might enjoy having their own book of buildings. Take dictation from children about their buildings and help them add other information to their pages, such as the number of blocks they used.

Mathematics Connection Allow children to use rulers or meter sticks to measure their buildings. Children will enjoy experimenting with the measuring tools, even if they don't yet understand standard measurement units or techniques. Children might also like measuring with nonstandard units, such as connecting cubes.

Art Connection On lightweight cardboard or old file folders, trace around the largest face of several common blocks in your class block set. Cut out the shapes and put them in the Art or Blocks Center with large sheets of paper. Children can trace around the shapes to create pictures of structures. They may build the structures they draw.

 Family Connection You may want to use the Comparing Lengths and Heights Family Connection (*Math Masters*, page 80) to encourage families to do measuring activities at home.

NOTE Some children may need assistance holding the strips and marking off the heights of their buildings.

 **Adjusting for Age and Development**

Provide strips of paper cut to various lengths. Invite children to choose a strip and build a structure to that height.

Math Masters, p. 80

Expanding

M·15 Comparing Weights

◎ **Objective** To extend children's use of the pan balance and their understanding of weight.

Key Mathematics Concepts and Skills

• Compare objects by weight and describe as *heavier, lighter* and *same weight.*
  [Measurement and Reference Frames Goal 1]

• Sort objects according to whether they are heavier or lighter than a reference.
  [Patterns, Functions, and Algebra Goal 1]

Terms to Use heavier, lighter, same weight, pan balance

Materials Teaching Master (*Math Masters*, p. 27); pan balance; sand; collection of objects varying in weight that will fit in the pan balance; trays; resealable plastic bag (optional)

Planning Tip Fill one side of the pan balance about $\frac{1}{2}$ full of sand or use a sealed plastic bag of sand on one side of the balance. Use the pictorial labels on *Math Masters,* page 27 to label two trays, one for Heavier and one for Lighter.

▶ Main Activity

☐ Whole Group ✔ Small Group ☐ Partners ✔ Center

Review the pan balance by inviting children to use their outstretched arms to act as a pan balance. Place an object in one child's hand and ask him or her to show what happens to that side. (The child should move that arm down and the other arm up.) Continue with other objects and children, as needed.

Direct children's attention to a real pan balance with sand in one pan. Explain that they will use the pan balance to figure out whether various objects are heavier or lighter than the sand. Have children put one object at a time in the empty side of the pan balance. They should then place objects that are heavier than the sand on the tray labeled Heavier and objects that are lighter than the sand on the tray labeled Lighter.

NOTE See Exploration of the Pan Balance, page 210, and Heavier and Lighter, page 212, for pan-balance activities that should precede this activity.

Encourage children to make predictions about whether the objects will be heavier or lighter than the sand before using the pan balance.

After sorting, talk with children about the relative weights of the objects on the Heavier and Lighter trays. Ask: *Are all the objects on the Heavier tray heavier than all the objects on the Lighter tray? How do you know? How can you check?*

Place the objects, pan balance, and trays in a Center for continued exploration. Encourage children to find other objects to weigh.

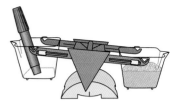

The marker is lighter than the sand in the pan.

Adjusting for Age and Development

To simplify the activity, use only one tray at a time (Heavier or Lighter) so children can focus on finding just heavier or lighter objects relative to the sand.

▶ Connections

Mathematics Connection You can use a pan balance to compare voting results. Label one side of a pan balance Yes and the other side No. Have children respond to a yes/no question by placing a connecting cube on the correct side of the pan balance. The side most weighted down shows the answer given by the most children. Children can predict the results by looking at the pan balance, then remove the cubes and stack them in two towers to count and compare.

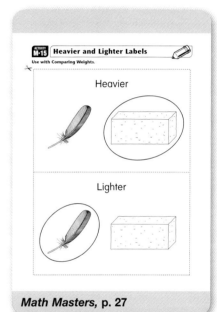

Math Masters, p. 27

Expanding

M·16 Measuring with Stick-on Notes

Objective To provide experience with nonstandard units of measure.

Key Mathematics Concepts and Skills

• Count nonstandard units of measure. [Number and Numeration Goal 2]

• Practice measuring techniques. [Measurement and Reference Frames Goal 2]

• Measure heights using nonstandard units. [Measurement and Reference Frames Goal 2]

Terms to Use measure, height, tall

Materials stick-on note squares or comparable-sized paper squares (preferably two colors); tape; clothespin or other clip; list of children's names with space for recording heights; posterboard or chart paper (optional)

> **Planning Tip** Make a vertical line of same-size stick-on notes on an accessible classroom wall. The lower edge of the bottom note should touch the floor; the rest of the notes should be lined up so their top and bottom edges are touching, up to about 4 feet tall. Use tape to secure the stick-on notes to the wall. You can preserve your stick-on-note line for future use by attaching the stick-on notes to a long strip of posterboard or chart paper.

▶ Main Activity

☐ Whole Group ✔ Small Group ☐ Partners ☐ Center

Show children the line of stick-on notes that you created and ask them what they think it might be for. After children share their ideas, invite each child to measure how tall he or she is by standing against the stick-on strip. You or another child can then mark the student's height with a clothespin or clip. Help the child count the number of stick-on notes underneath the clothespin, then record the height on the class list as *about _____ stick-on notes*. (Help children figure out whether to use the next larger or next smaller number if their heights don't exactly align with the top of a stick-on note.) Work with children in small groups so they will not need to wait too long for a turn and so they can help measure each other.

If you have stick-on notes in two colors, arrange them in an alternating color pattern to make measuring easier.

Keep the stick-on-note strip posted in the classroom for several days and encourage children to use it to measure other items. Model how to include the units (stick-on notes) when children record or report their measurement results.

Adjusting for Age and Development

You might want to create another line of stick-on notes using smaller (or larger) notes. Ask children to predict how many stick-on notes tall they will be using the second strip. Discuss their responses. Then help children measure their heights using the second strip and record their heights on a separate class list as *about _____ small (or large) stick-on notes.* Discuss why the numbers are not the same.

▶ Connections

Art Connections Provide short strips of cardboard and colored squares or small stick-on notes for children to use to make their own measuring sticks. Encourage children to use the squares to make patterns on their sticks. Children can use the sticks to measure objects in the classroom.

You might also put stick-on notes in the Art Center for children to use with other collage materials.

Mathematics Connection Children can use other nonstandard units, such as connecting cubes or plastic links, to measure each other's heights or the heights of other objects.

Related Book

- *The Line Up Book* by Marisabina Russo (Greenwillow, 1986)

M·17 How Long Is a Bus?

Objective To provide experience with measurement using children as a nonstandard unit of measure.

Key Mathematics Concepts and Skills

• Count children. [Number and Numeration Goal 2]

• Practice measuring techniques. [Measurement and Reference Frames Goal 2]

• Measure length using nonstandard units. [Measurement and Reference Frames Goal 2]

Other Skills Cooperation

Terms to Use measure, length, long

Materials a school bus or large paper, markers, and tape; book about school buses (*See* Related Books for suggestions.)

Planning Tip This activity is most meaningful if children can measure a real bus. However, if this is not practical, you can measure out the length of a bus in a hallway or gym and mark with tape where the front and the back of the bus would be. To help children visualize, you might want to use large paper to draw headlights for the front and taillights for the rear. A typical school bus is 40 feet long. Minibuses are about 27 feet long.

▶ Main Activity

✔ Whole Group ✔ Small Group ☐ Partners ☐ Center

Read and discuss a book about school buses. Ask children questions such as: *Have you ever ridden a school bus? How many people do you think can fit on a bus? Where do buses go?* After general discussion, ask children how long they think a school bus is. Children's responses will vary. For example, they might say things like "very long," "as big as a house," "big enough to fit our whole class inside," or "100." Encourage discussion as children share their ideas. Tell children that today they will use their bodies to measure a school bus. Have a few children stand side-by-side with their arms stretched out, touching each other's fingers. Ask the class to estimate how many children standing like this would match the length of a bus. Record their responses.

Next, go to the bus you will measure, or show children where you have marked off the front and rear of the bus and explain that this shows the length of a real school bus. Beginning at the front of the bus, have children stand side-by-side with arms outstretched and fingers touching until the line stretches to the rear of the bus. Together, count the number of children. Say the result, including the units. For example: *The bus is about 14 children long.*

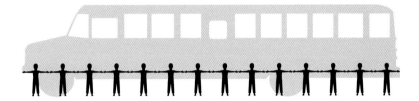

If other vehicles are available, children may be interested in measuring them with outstretched arms and comparing the results. You might mark off other lengths for children to measure: A bicycle is about 70 inches and an average car is about 15 feet.

▶ Connections

Outdoors Connection Use children's arm spans to measure equipment on the playground, such as the slide, climbing bars, or a fence. Record the measurements.

Dramatic Play Connection Children can use chairs and/or large hollow blocks to make a bus. Encourage them to think about how long to make the bus, how many seats they need, how many children can ride the bus, and where the doors should be.

Literacy Connection Read *How Big Were the Dinosaurs?* by Bernard Most (Harcourt Children's Books, 1994) and talk about size comparisons.

Related Books

- *School Bus* by Donald Crews (Greenwillow, 1984)
- *Big Cindy's School Bus* by Lisa Findlay and Cindy Moran (Random House Books for Young Readers, 2004)

Expanding

Shapes

Overview

Shapes Goals

In Pre-K, children should have experiences that help them:

- Recognize and describe basic 2-dimensional geometric shapes. [Geometry Goal 1]

- Explore the relationships between basic 2-dimensional and 3-dimensional shapes. Geometry Goal 1]

Young children have a great deal of informal, experiential knowledge of shapes, though they may initially lack the vocabulary to name and describe them. When children begin to identify and label shapes, they focus on the overall appearance of the shapes, rather than specific attributes. For example, they are more likely to say, *That is a square because it looks like my window* than *That is a square because it has 4 sides.*

Children's earliest learning about shapes should be through tactile, kinesthetic, and visual experiences that allow them to handle, manipulate, and represent shapes in various ways. Through these types of activities, children can gradually be encouraged to notice and describe attributes, such as whether a shape has straight or curved lines, or its number of sides or corners. Gradually children develop their understanding of categories of shapes (triangles, circles, rectangles, and so on) and the idea that the same shape can look different in particular ways: *I see a big circle and a small circle. Those are both triangles, even though one is skinny and one is fat.* Children's shape explorations also develop their understanding of other important ideas in geometry: that changing the position of a shape or object does not change its shape, and that shapes can be put together and taken apart to make other shapes.

As children explore real objects, they naturally explore the relationships between 2-dimensional and 3-dimensional shapes. They may call 3-dimensional shapes by 2-dimensional shape names: *This basketball is a circle. Pass me the rectangle block.* It is useful for children to see these similarities, and their understanding can be deepened through activities that highlight the 2-dimensional shapes that make up 3-dimensional objects: *The die has lots of square sides. This part of the ramp block looks like a triangle.* It is not necessary for young children to use the correct names for 3-dimensional shapes, though they will gradually learn these terms if they are used consistently.

 ## Professional Development

See Chapter 11 of the *Teacher's Reference Manual* for more information about the Geometry strand.

Choosing Activities

Beginning	Building	Expanding
Beginning activities provide a hands-on introduction to the names and attributes of basic 2-dimensional shapes (circles, squares, triangles, and rectangles). In these activities, children	**Building** activities reinforce shape names and deepen children's understanding of shapes and their attributes. In these activities, children	The **Expanding** activity focuses on 3-dimensional shapes. In this activity, children

Beginning activities provide a hands-on introduction to the names and attributes of basic 2-dimensional shapes (circles, squares, triangles, and rectangles). In these activities, children

- explore basic 2-dimensional shapes through tactile and kinesthetic activities;
- identify shapes in their environment.

Building activities reinforce shape names and deepen children's understanding of shapes and their attributes. In these activities, children

- identify and describe attributes of basic 2-dimensional shapes;
- match, compare, group, and sort shapes;
- manipulate and combine shapes;
- notice 2-dimensional shapes in 3-dimensional objects.

The **Expanding** activity focuses on 3-dimensional shapes. In this activity, children

- build 3-dimensional shapes using various media;
- work with familiar objects that are 3-dimensional geometric shapes.

Activities in Perspective

Activity	Objective	Core	Usage	Page
Beginning				
S·1	**Floor Shapes** To increase children's familiarity with basic 2-dimensional shapes through a variety of activities.	Core		244
S·2	**Tactile Shapes** To promote shape exploration through tactile experiences.	Core		246
S·3	**Play Dough Shapes** To promote exploration and discussion of shapes using play dough.			248
S·4	**Shape Walk** To provide opportunities to identify and explore shapes in the environment.	Core		250
Building				
S·5	**"Hokey Pokey" with Shapes** To review shape names and spatial relationships through a movement activity.			252
S·6	**Shape Printing** To provide an opportunity to explore shapes through an art activity.			254
S·7	**Shapes by Feel** To reinforce shape names and attributes through a sensory activity.	Core		256
S·8	***Shape Concentration* Game** To reinforce matching, naming, and describing shapes using a memory game.			258
S·9	**Sorting Shapes** To deepen children's understanding of shapes through a sorting activity.	Core		260
S·10	**Shape Garden** To incorporate shape exploration in a literature-based art activity.			262

Expanding

 S·11 **Creating 3-Dimensional Shapes**
To provide tactile experiences with 3-dimensional shapes.

264

KEY

 Art
 Dramatic Play
 Manipulatives and Games
 Rug Time
 Sensory
Core Core Activity

 Books
 Excursion
 Music and Movement
 Science
 Snack

Teaching Resources

Home-School Connection

Family Connections suggest home activities that link to activities children have done at school. The following Shapes activities contain Family Connections: S♦7, Shapes by Feel; S♦9, Sorting Shapes; S♦10, Shape Garden; S♦11, Creating 3-Dimensional Shapes. Note that the same Family Connections are suggested with multiple activities, so keep track of which ones you have already sent home.

Mathematics at Home **Books 1–3** provide additional ideas for enjoyable mathematics activities that families can do together, as well as lists of children's books related to the topics in the teacher's guide. Families can do activities from *Mathematics at Home* Books 1–3 throughout the year.

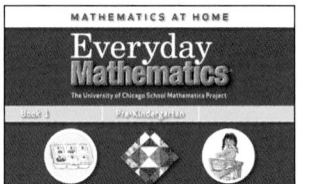

◀*Home Connection Handbook* provides more ideas to communicate effectively with parents.

▼*Resources for the Pre-Kindergarten Classroom* provides additional teaching ideas, including suggestions for bringing mathematics into thematic instruction, as well as using games, literature, technology, songs, and rhymes to support mathematics learning.

Minute Math provides brief activities ▶ for transition times and spare moments throughout the day.

Assessment

Ongoing Assessment

Kid Watching

The following activities in the *Teacher's Guide to Activities* include Ongoing Assessment notes related to shapes. See the *Assessment Handbook* for an expanded table.

Activity	Content Assessed
S♦2, S♦3, S♦4, S♦5, S♦7, S♦9, S♦10	Recognize and name shapes. [Geometry Goal 1]
S♦7, S♦9	Describe shape attributes. [Geometry Goal 1]
S♦4	See 2-dimensional shapes in 3-dimensional objects. [Geometry Goal 1]

Assessment Handbook

- Pre-Kindergarten goals, pp. 6–11
- Shapes Assessment Overview, p. 34
- Baseline Periodic Assessment Task 6, p. 20
- End-of-Year Periodic Assessment Task 9, p. 23

Differentiated Instruction

Adjusting for Age and Development

Pre-Kindergarten Everyday Mathematics is designed to be flexible enough to adapt to a wide range of preschool classrooms, including classrooms with mixed-age groupings and classrooms with a wide range of developmental levels. Many activities include suggestions to help teachers modify the activity to make it accessible and interesting to children with varying needs, learning styles, or levels of proficiency or understanding.

S♦3	Play Dough Shapes	**S♦6**	Shape Printing
S♦4	Shape Walk	**S♦7**	Shapes by Feel
S♦5	"Hokey Pokey" with Shapes	**S♦8**	*Shape Concentration* Game

Language Support

Everyday Mathematics provides activity-specific suggestions to help all children, including non-native English speakers, develop the language necessary to acquire, process, and express mathematical ideas.

Developing Oral Language

S♦2   Develop context for the words *corner* and *side*.

S♦4   Develop familiarity with 3-dimensional geometric shape names.

Language & Vocabulary

Informally use these terms that are related to shapes.

shape	ball	round
circle	box	curved
oval	can	straight
rectangle	cone	side
rhombus	cube	corner
square	cylinder	match
trapezoid	rectangular prism	
triangle		
	sphere	

Activity Connections

The Connections for each activity link the Main Activity to different curricular and classroom areas. They are useful for meeting individual needs and integrating mathematics throughout the day. The following connections are in the Shapes section.

Art

S♦3 Play Dough Shapes
S♦4 Shape Walk
S♦5 "Hokey Pokey" with Shapes
S♦6 Shape Printing
S♦9 Sorting Shapes
S♦11 Creating 3-Dimensional Shapes

Blocks

S♦4 Shape Walk
S♦8 *Shape Concentration* Game

Dramatic Play

S♦8 *Shape Concentration* Game

Family Connections

See Home-School Connection on page 240.

Games

S♦1 Floor Shapes
S♦5 "Hokey Pokey" with Shapes
S♦7 Shapes by Feel

Literacy

S♦1 Floor Shapes
S♦4 Shape Walk
S♦5 "Hokey Pokey" with Shapes
S♦10 Shape Garden

Manipulatives

S♦9 Sorting Shapes
S♦10 Shape Garden

Mathematics

S♦9 Sorting Shapes

Movement

S♦2 Tactile Shapes

Outdoors

S♦10 Shape Garden

Science

S♦6 Shape Printing

Sensory Table

S♦7 Shapes by Feel
S♦11 Creating 3-Dimensional Shapes

Snack

S♦3 Play Dough Shapes

Writing

S♦2 Tactile Shapes

S·1 Floor Shapes

 Objective To increase children's familiarity with basic 2-dimensional shapes through a variety of activities.

Key Mathematics Concepts and Skills

- Recognize and name triangles, circles, squares, and rectangles. [Geometry Goal 1]
- Describe and compare attributes of triangles, circles, squares, and rectangles. [Geometry Goal 1]
- Develop awareness of geometric shapes in the environment. [Geometry Goal 1]

Other Skills Gross Motor

Terms to Use shape, triangle, square, rectangle, circle, straight, curved, corner, side, round

Materials masking or duct tape (If using tape on the floor is a concern, you can make shapes by drawing on a rug with chalk or using yarn or string.)

Planning Tip These activities should extend over several days. Focus on one or two shapes at a time for a few days, then repeat the activities for other shapes.

▶ Main Activity

✔ Whole Group ✔ Small Group ☐ Partners ☐ Center

Use tape or other material to create a large outline of a shape (triangle, square, rectangle, or circle) on the carpet or floor in your classroom meeting area. Have children do some or all of the following activities over the course of several days. The activities should be quick and playful.

▷ **Walk around the edge of the shape.** Help children identify and count things like straight or curved lines and corners (or turns).

▷ **Draw the shape in the air using large arm motions.**

▷ **Use their fingers to draw the shape on the back of a partner.** After they are familiar with multiple shapes, children can guess what shape their partner has drawn.

▷ **Find objects that match the shape and place them inside the shape outline.**

▷ **Think of objects that remind them of, or look like, the shape.** If children need prompts, you might suggest a clock for a circle, or a wedge or ramp block for a triangle. Help children see how 2-dimensional shapes are part of 3-dimensional objects.

Leave the shape outline on the carpet or floor for several days and encourage children to sit on it, use it as a balance beam, and play games such as Duck, Duck, Goose on it. Informally refer to the name of the shape and its properties, such as number of sides and corners, in the context of children's play and exploration.

Repeat for other shapes. After children have worked with several shapes, ask them to describe similarities and differences among the shapes. Children should have tape outlines or other models of the shapes to look at as they make comparisons.

▶ Connections

Game Connection Play I Spy with a small group of children. Give a clue such as, *I spy a red circle,* and ask children to guess what you see. When they are ready, let children choose the objects and give the clues.

Literacy Connection Read shape books with the class. Invite children to point out the shapes in the pictures and talk about their discoveries. See *Resources for the Pre-Kindergarten Classroom* for suggestions of shape books.

Links to the Future

The floor shapes in this activity are 2-dimensional. As children identify shapes in the environment, they will find many 3-dimensional objects. You can help children make connections between 2- and 3-dimensional shapes (and recognize differences between them) with observations and questions such as: *Each side of this cube is a square. Can you find the sides of this block that are triangles? What shapes are the other sides of the block?* These informal explorations of the relationships between 2- and 3-dimensional shapes will lay groundwork for more formalized geometry learning in later grades.

Related Books

- *The Wing on a Flea* by Ed Emberley (Little, Brown, 2001)
- *Shapes, Shapes, Shapes* by Tana Hoban (HarperTrophy, 1986)

S·2 Tactile Shapes

 Objective To promote shape exploration through tactile experiences.

Key Mathematics Concepts and Skills

• Identify basic 2-dimensional geometric shapes (triangles, circles, squares, and rectangles). [Geometry Goal 1]

• Explore, describe, and compare attributes of basic geometric shapes. [Geometry Goal 1]

Other Skills Creative Expression, Fine Motor

Terms to Use shape, square, rectangle, circle, triangle, side, straight, curved, round, corner

Materials Teaching Aid Masters (*Math Masters*, pp. 44 and 45); shaving cream; sand and/or salt; fingerpaint; trays; resealable plastic bags (optional)

> **Planning Tip** Different children will be drawn to different media, so try to provide each of the suggested media at some point for both free exploration and shape exploration. Make copies of *Math Masters*, pages 44 and 45 to display at the Center.

▶ Main Activity

☐ Whole Group ✔ Small Group ☐ Partners ✔ Center

Choose a medium from the list below and set it out in the Math or Art Center. Give children time to experiment with the material independently before focusing on shapes. They may make designs or pictures, or simply enjoy the feel of the material.

▷ Shaving cream on trays
▷ Sand (and/or salt) on trays
▷ Fingerpaint on trays or paper
▷ Fingerpaint in sealed bags with air removed
▷ Other tactile materials

> **NOTE** The purpose of this activity is to provide a tactile way to help children attend to the properties of shapes and the differences between shapes. The focus is **not** on drawing or writing shapes on paper.

Once children have had ample time for free exploration, encourage them to try making shapes in the chosen media. Display large models of the shapes, such as the ones on *Math Masters,* pages 44 and 45, for children to look at as they work. Talk with children as they explore. Help them focus on the properties of shapes with questions such as: *Is the shape you just made round? Does it have corners? Which other shapes have corners? Do you want to try making one of those? How many sides does your shape have? How are the square and rectangle alike? How are they different?*

You might help children "feel" the shapes by holding their hands and moving their fingers to create the shapes. Some children will benefit from hearing you say the motions out loud: for example; *straight across, straight down, straight across, straight up* to make a square or rectangle.

 Ongoing Assessment: Kid Watching

As you interact with children during this activity, you can informally assess their knowledge of shape names and attributes. Children may be able to recognize and name shapes holistically before they can isolate or describe shape attributes.

▶ Connections

Writing Connection Some children may enjoy trying to form letters or numbers, or draw pictures, in the various tactile media.

Movement Connection Have children trace shapes in the air using large arm motions. As they do, model with your own arm and say the motions out loud. Children can also take turns tracing shapes on a partner's back, while the partner tries to guess the shape by feel. (See Floor Shapes, page 244, for other kinesthetic activities related to shapes.)

Related Books

- *Circus Shapes* by Stuart J. Murphy (Sagebrush, 1999)
- *Color Zoo* and *Color Farm* by Lois Ehlert (HarperCollins, 1989; 1990)

Beginning

S·3 Play Dough Shapes

Objective To promote exploration and discussion of shapes using play dough.

Key Mathematics Concepts and Skills

- Identify and create basic geometric shapes (triangles, circles, squares, and rectangles). [Geometry Goal 1]
- Explore, describe, and compare attributes of basic geometric shapes. [Geometry Goal 1]

Other Skills Creative Expression, Fine Motor

Terms to Use shape, circle, square, triangle, rectangle, side, corner, straight, curved, round

Materials laminated paper shape mats; tools such as rolling pins and plastic knives; play dough (*See* Classroom Cooking, page 224 if you want to make play dough with children.)

Planning Tip Cut out large paper circles, squares, triangles, and rectangles to make mats for rolling out play dough. You might use the shapes on *Math Masters*, pages 44 and 45. Laminate the mats so the dough won't stick to them and so they can be reused throughout the year. Alternatively, you can prepare shape outlines by applying masking tape directly to the table. (This will not work for circles.)

▶ Main Activity

☐ Whole Group ✔ Small Group ☐ Partners ✔ Center

After children have had ample time for free exploration with the play dough, invite them to use it to make shapes. As children work, model how to use the mats, or outlines, and tools. Demonstrate how children can make shapes by filling in the shape on the table or mat, or by outlining the shape with play dough "snakes." Encourage children to make shapes in many ways and to experiment with different sizes. In addition to using the shape outlines or shape mats, children can roll out play dough and cut out shapes, make shapes within shapes, or put different shapes together to make play dough pictures or designs.

Adjusting for Age and Development

Some children may benefit from working with just one or two shape mats or outlines at a time. For children who are ready, you can add outlines or mats for other shapes, such as ovals, hexagons, or rhombuses.

As children work, talk with them about the names and properties of the shapes they are making, such as number of sides and corners. It is useful to have shape models displayed so children can see the shapes even when the table or mat is covered with bits of dough. You can display copies of *Math Masters,* pages 44 and 45.

 Ongoing Assessment: Kid Watching

As you interact with children during this activity, you can informally assess their knowledge of shape names and attributes. Children may be able to recognize and name shapes holistically before they can isolate or describe shape attributes.

▶ Connections

Art Connection Children can use circle, square, triangle, and rectangle cookie cutters dipped in paint to explore shape stamping. You might also provide fine-tipped writing tools and items shaped liked circles and squares, such as CDs, CD cases, lids, blocks, and so on, for children to trace around. Some children might enjoy using the shape prints or tracings as the basis for other pictures and designs.

Snack Connection Have a shape snack. For example, you might provide square cheese slices, triangular crackers, and circular cookies on rectangular napkins.

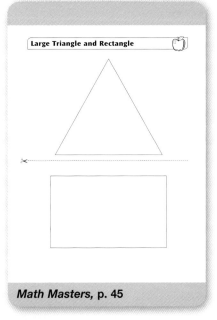

Math Masters, p. 45

 Related Books

- *So Many Circles, So Many Squares* by Tana Hoban (Greenwillow, 1998)
- *Bear in a Square* by Stella Blackstone (Barefoot Books, 2000)

S·4 Shape Walk

 Objective To provide opportunities to identify and explore shapes in the environment.

Key Mathematics Concepts and Skills

- Recognize and name geometric shapes in the environment. [Geometry Goal 1]
- Describe attributes of shapes. [Geometry Goal 1]

Other Skills Listening and Speaking

Terms to Use shape, rectangle, square, circle, triangle, cube, ball, box, can, sphere, rectangular prism, cylinder, cone

Materials shape book or picture (*See* Related Books for suggestions.); pencil, paper, camera (optional)

Planning Tip This walk can take place in the school building or outside. Plan to do this activity after children have been exposed to shape names and attributes. Taking shape walks in small groups provides more opportunity for interaction and discussion.

▶ Main Activity

✔Whole Group   ✔Small Group   ☐ Partners   ☐ Center

Share and discuss a shape book, such as one listed in Related Books below. Or, show a picture of something children are familiar with, such as a house or a playground, and talk about the shapes they see. As children name a shape you might invite them to trace around the shape in the picture with their fingers.

Take a walk and encourage children to look for shapes all around them. Before you leave the classroom, you might have children brainstorm some of the things they could look for, such as signs, buildings, vehicles, and furniture or equipment. During the walk, ask questions that will promote observation and encourage discussion. For example: *What shapes are we walking on? What shape do you see on the top of that house?*

 **Adjusting for Age and Development**

You might have children focus on just one or two shapes as they walk. For example, you could go on a Circle Walk. Take along pictures of the shapes to help children focus on them.

What shapes are the windows? The door? Where do you see a rectangle? A square? A cube?
If you have a camera, take pictures of some of the shapes children notice on the walk.

NOTE Most children will probably focus on 2-dimensional shapes, but it is a good idea to also incorporate informal observation and discussion of 3-dimensional shapes. Children often point out 2-dimensional shapes that are part of 3-dimensional shapes; you might draw their attention to the larger 3-dimensional shape when it seems appropriate.

ELL

Developing Oral Language

Children may not be familiar with 3-dimensional shape names, though they are likely to know names of common 3-dimensional objects such as *ball, box,* and *can.* Allow children to use these everyday names as you introduce and model the use of their geometric names: *sphere, rectangular prism,* and *cylinder.*

▶ Connections

Literacy Connection You might encourage children to draw what they saw on the Shape Walk. Help them label some of the shapes. If you took pictures, display them along with the children's drawings. The pictures can also be used to make a class book about the walk. Have children dictate captions for the pictures.

Art Connection Provide an assortment of pre-cut shapes—squares, rectangles, triangles, and circles—for children to use in making pictures. Encourage children to manipulate the shapes and try different combinations before gluing them down on paper.

Blocks Connection Add traffic signs to the Block Area by using a purchased set or helping children make their own. Encourage children to notice the shapes of different signs.

Ongoing Assessment Kid Watching

You can use this activity to informally observe children's shape recognition skills. Note whether children can see shapes in larger objects, which can be difficult.

Related Books

- *Cubes, Cones, Cylinders, & Spheres* by Tana Hoban (Greenwillow, 2000)
- *Round Is a Mooncake: A Book of Shapes* by Roseanne Thong (Chronicle Books, 2000)
- *Shapes, Shapes, Shapes* by Tana Hoban (HarperTrophy, 1986)
- *The Shape of Things* by Dayle Ann Dodds (Candlewick, 1994)

Beginning

S·5 "Hokey Pokey" with Shapes

🎯 **Objective** To review shape names and spatial relationships through a movement activity.

Key Mathematics Concepts and Skills

• Recognize triangles, circles, squares, and rectangles. [Geometry Goal 1]
• Follow movement directions using position words. [Geometry Goal 2]

Other Skills Gross Motor, Singing and Rhythmic Movement

Terms to Use triangle, circle, square, rectangle, in, out, turn around

Materials Teaching Aid Masters (*Math Masters,* pp. 44 and 45)

▶ **Main Activity**   ☑ Whole Group ☑ Small Group ☐ Partners ☐ Center

Once children know the "Hokey Pokey" song and dance, you can incorporate shapes. Give each child a paper shape. Review shape names and make sure each child can identify his or her shape. Then sing the song, substituting shape names for body parts: *You put your circle in, you put your circle out,* and so on. You can use the version on the Sing Everyday! CD, if desired. Children should do the motions when their shape is called. (You might occasionally invite all children to do the movements at once by saying the word *shape* instead of naming a specific shape.) After several times through the song, have children exchange shapes and then repeat the song.

Planning Tip Prepare large paper shapes (triangles, circles, squares, and rectangles) by cutting around the shape outlines on *Math Masters,* pages 44 and 45. Make 1 or 2 shapes per child. Familiarize children with the "Hokey Pokey" song before doing this activity.

Adjusting for Age and Development

Begin with fewer shapes if this is more appropriate for your group. If children are ready for more challenge, give children two different paper shapes to hold at a time, one in each hand.

✔ Ongoing Assessment: Kid Watching

You can use this activity to informally assess children's shape identification skills. Note whether there are particular shapes they confuse or cannot yet recognize.

▶ Connections

Art Connection Allow children to use their paper shapes as the basis for an art project. They might decorate their shapes with crayons, markers, glitter, buttons, yarn, or other collage materials. Or they might glue the shapes on paper to use as the basis for drawings or collages. A circle might become part of a snowman, or a triangle might become a tent, for example.

Literacy Connection Gather a collection of shape books for your classroom library. Give each child a paper shape and ask him or her to search the books for that shape.

Game Connection Children may enjoy playing *Shape Switch,* an active game that reinforces shape identification. Children stand in a circle, each child holding a paper shape. When you call out a shape, each child holding that shape changes places with another child who has the same shape. You can also call out properties of the shape instead of the shape name. For example, *If you have a shape with 3 sides, switch places.*

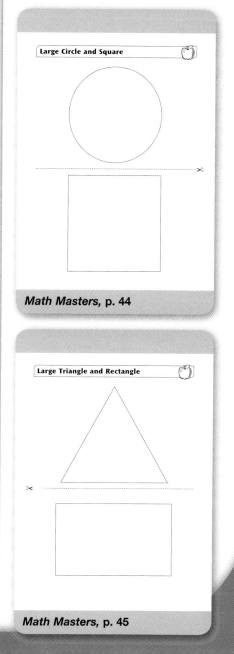

Math Masters, p. 44

Math Masters, p. 45

Building

S·6 Shape Printing

Objective To provide an opportunity to explore shapes through an art activity.

Key Mathematics Concepts and Skills

- Identify and create basic geometric shapes (triangles, circles, squares, and rectangles). [Geometry Goal 1]
- Explore, describe, and compare attributes of basic geometric shapes. [Geometry Goal 1]

Other Skills Creative Expression, Fine Motor

Terms to Use shape names, pattern

Materials geometric shape stamps (*See* Planning Tip.); stamp pads or tempera paint on trays; paper

Planning Tip Cut sponges or vegetables into geometric shapes to use for printing. Make the shape stamps large enough for children to hold easily without dipping their fingers in the paint or ink. Carrots and zucchini work well for circles; potatoes can be easily cut into any shape. Shape cookie cutters, pattern blocks, and other classroom objects, such as marker tops, cups, box lids, and dice, can also be used.

▶ Main Activity

☐ Whole Group ☐ Small Group ☐ Partners ✔ Center

Show children how to dip the shape stamps into a thin layer of paint on a tray (or onto a stamp pad) and press the stamp onto paper to create a print. Children can use the stamps and different colors of paint or ink to print patterns, pictures, or designs.

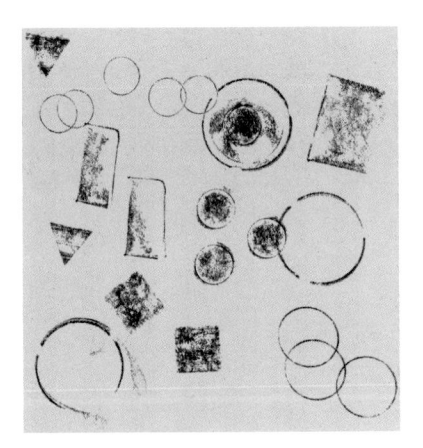

As children work, talk with them about the shapes they are using. You might ask them to name and count various shapes on their pictures. If they make patterns, ask them to describe their patterns.

After children have had a chance to explore with the shape stamps, encourage them to combine the shapes to make other shapes. Can they use the square stamp to make a larger square? What shapes can they make using the triangle stamp?

▶ Connections

Science Connection Children can also print with natural objects, such as shells, pinecones, or leaves, the same way they printed with the shape stamps. Encourage children to dip different parts of these objects in the paint or ink to get a variety of interesting effects.

Art Connection Include the book *Picture Pie 2: A Drawing Book and Stencil* by Ed Emberly (Little, Brown, 1996) in the Art Center. Invite interested children to trace circles, squares, and triangles to make animals, flowers, and machines like those in the book.

S·7 Shapes by Feel

 Objective **To reinforce shape names and attributes through a sensory activity.**

Key Mathematics Concepts and Skills

• Recognize and name basic geometric shapes. [Geometry Goal 1]

• Describe and compare attributes of geometric shapes. [Geometry Goal 1]

Other Skills Fine Motor

Terms to Use circle, triangle, square, rectangle, other shape names, side, corner

Materials "feely" bag or box; pattern blocks (or attribute blocks); circular objects such as chip counters, jar lids, or buttons

---

Planning Tip Use an opaque bag or sock for a "feely bag." Or, make a "feely box" by cutting a hole in a box with a top. Be sure the bag or box is large enough for a hand to reach in and freely feel the objects.

▶ Main Activity   ☐ Whole Group   ✔ Small Group   ☐ Partners   ✔ Center

Play a guessing game with pattern or attribute blocks. Add a circular object if you use pattern blocks. Put an assortment of blocks in the middle of the group. Tell the children you are thinking of one of the blocks, and give clues to help them identify the block. Begin with simple color and shape clues, such as *I'm thinking of a yellow block* or *I'm thinking of a triangle.* Gradually, you might use more difficult clues, such as *I'm thinking of a shape with four sides.* After playing a few times, explain to the group that now they are going to play a guessing game that uses feeling rather than seeing.

Put between 2 and 4 different shapes in a Feely Bag or Box. Collect a duplicate set of shapes to show the group. Hold up and name a shape and ask: *Can you find a shape like this one?* Have children take turns, without looking, to find shapes in the bag or box

NOTE Although they may not know the names of some pattern-block shapes, such as hexagons or trapezoids, many children will be able to find matches for these shapes and describe them. They may also be interested in hearing the names of these shapes.

by feel. Prompt children to describe and try to identify the shapes with questions such as: *Why did you pick that one? What is it called? How do you know it is a triangle? How many sides (or corners) does it have?* Distinguishing between a square and a rectangle is difficult. You can provide practice by using only squares and rectangles in the Feely Bag or Box. After introducing this activity, place the materials in a Center for children to use.

Ongoing Assessment: Kid Watching

You can use this activity to informally assess children's abilities to recognize and name shapes. Also note whether children are able to describe attributes of a particular shape.

▶ Connections

Game Connection Play a guessing game with a Feely Bag or Box to develop tactile discrimination. Use familiar objects such as a hairbrush, toy car, key ring, plastic cup, or sponge. Without looking, children try to guess the object by feel. As needed, give clues about the object's size, shape, color, and function.

Sensory Table Connection Bury pattern blocks or other small objects in the sand table or sandbox. Children can dig in the sand with their hands to discover the buried shapes.

Family Connection You may want to use the Eating Shapes Family Connection (*Math Masters,* page 84) to encourage families to talk about shapes at home.

Adjusting for Age and Development

Add challenge by giving clues about a shape's attributes (without showing the shape) and having children find the shape and name it. For example: *Can you find a shape with four corners? Can you find a shape with three straight sides?*

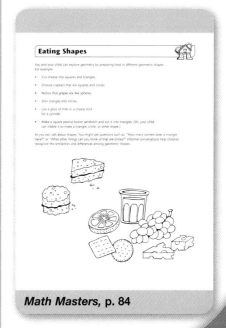

Math Masters, p. 84

257

Building

S·8 *Shape Concentration Game*

Objective To reinforce matching, naming, and describing shapes using a memory game.

Key Mathematics Concepts and Skills

- Identify and name basic geometric shapes. [Geometry Goal 1]
- Describe attributes of geometric shapes. [Geometry Goal 1]
- Recognize and match attributes of geometric shapes. [Patterns, Functions, and Algebra Goal 1]

Other Skills Cooperation

Terms to Use circle, square, rectangle, triangle, side, corner, match

Materials Teaching Aid Masters (*Math Masters,* pp. 46–48); index cards (optional)

Planning Tip Make two copies of the shape cards on *Math Masters,* pages 46–48 and cut apart the cards. Laminate and/or mount the shape cards on index cards for durability.

▶ Main Activity

☐ Whole Group   ✔ Small Group   ✔ Partners   ✔ Center

Show children how to use the shape cards to play *Shape Concentration.* Begin with 4 matching pairs: 2 identical triangles, 2 identical squares, 2 identical circles, and 2 identical rectangles. Arrange the cards facedown in rows and have children turn over two cards at a time to try to find matching shapes. When children find a match, they name the shape and keep the cards. Encourage children to talk about the attributes of the shapes and to explain how they know whether the cards match (for example, the number or size of the sides or the number of corners).

As children become familiar with the game, use more of the shape cards and talk about the variations children notice in each type of shape. You might also create shape cards for other shapes, such as ovals or rhombuses (diamonds).

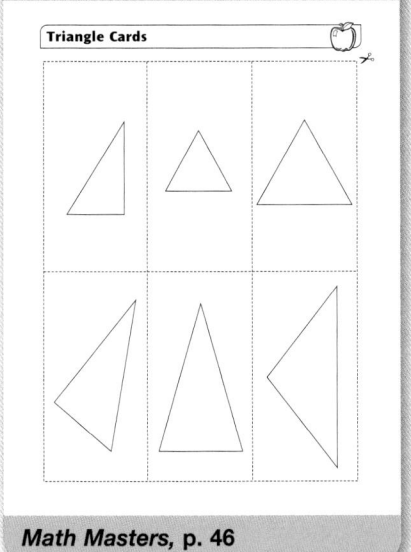

Math Masters, p. 46

Adjusting for Age and Development

Some children might benefit by playing with the cards faceup at first.

▶ Connections

Dramatic Play Connection Provide construction paper, markers or crayons, and scissors for children to make and decorate "shape crackers" for the Dramatic Play Center. Provide a small empty food box for storing the pretend crackers.

Blocks Connection Show children an assortment of 5–10 different blocks. Have them find matches for the blocks and then build a structure using the blocks.

NOTE Although blocks are 3-dimensional, children and adults often refer to them by the size and shape of their largest face (long rectangular block, small square block, and so on). It is useful for children to begin to recognize the 2-dimensional shapes that make up 3-dimensional objects. Informally begin to use 3-dimensional shape names, too.

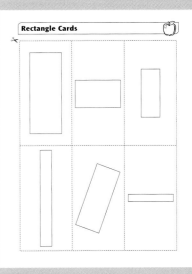

Math Masters, p. 47

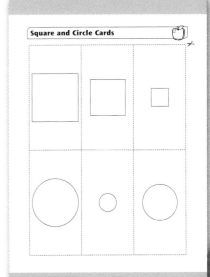

Math Masters, p. 48

Building

S·9 Sorting Shapes

(◎) **Objective** To deepen children's understanding of shapes through a sorting activity.

Planning Tip Use the shapes on *Math Masters,* pages 46–48 to prepare several sets of shapes. (See pages 258 and 259 for pictures of the *Math Masters* pages.) Cut around the outlines of the shapes. Label four sorting trays: one with a circle, one with a square, one with two different rectangles, and one with two different triangles.

Key Mathematics Concepts and Skills

• Identify and name basic geometric shapes. [Geometry Goal 1]

• Describe and compare attributes of geometric shapes, and recognize variations of each type of shape. [Geometry Goal 1]

• Sort shapes by type. [Patterns, Functions, and Algebra Goal 1]

Other Skills Listening and Speaking

Terms to Use side, corner, straight, round, shape names

Materials Teaching Aid Masters (*Math Masters,* pp. 46–48); sorting trays

▶ Main Activity

☐ Whole Group ✔ Small Group ☐ Partners ✔ Center

Invite children to sort the paper shapes onto the trays. Initially, children may sort intuitively, without understanding why. Build children's understanding by promoting discussion about why they put particular shapes together and what is similar and different about the shapes on a tray. Ask questions such as: *Why did you put all of these on the triangle tray? How many sides do they each have? Why are these both rectangles, even though one is skinny and one is fat? Are these both squares even though one is bigger? What do you notice about the sides on each square?*

Encourage children to look for objects to place on the trays. Flat objects, such as a rectangular sheet of paper, a pattern block square, or a circular lid, will probably be fairly straightforward for sorting. Other objects, such as a wedge-shaped block or a coffee mug

Ongoing Assessment: Kid Watching

You can use this activity to informally assess whether children can identify and name basic geometric shapes. Note whether they recognize shared attributes of a particular shape (e.g., 3 sides and corners for triangles), but also understand that shapes can differ in size, orientation, and other characteristics.

might spark interesting discussions. Children may place the wedge-shaped block on the "triangle" tray or the "rectangle" tray depending on which face they are looking at. Or, they might place the coffee mug on the "circle" tray, but realize that it isn't really a circle like the others. Talk with children about their observations and their sorting ideas.

▶ Connections

Manipulatives Connection If you have them, put out geoboards and rubber bands. Encourage children to make different shapes. You might ask: *How many different kinds of triangles can you make? How many squares?*

Mathematics Connection After children have sorted 2-dimensional shapes, you can label trays with 3-dimensional shapes such as sphere, cube, rectangular prism, cone, and cylinder. Encourage children to find and sort 3-dimensional objects onto the trays. Informally use 3-dimensional shape names to build children's familiarity with them and to help children distinguish them from 2-dimensional shapes. (See Creating 3-Dimensional Shapes, page 264 for an activity that focuses on 3-dimensional shapes.)

Art Connection Children can make paper quilts using 2-inch square stick-on notes in a variety of colors. Cut or fold some of the squares to make triangles and rectangles. Provide 6- or 8-inch square paper so the stick-on note "quilt pieces" will fit evenly on the page. Children can fit the different-shape pieces right next to each other to create quilt designs. Glue down children's finished designs and display them.

 Family Connection You may want to use the I Spy with Shapes Family Connection (*Math Masters,* page 85) to encourage families to play a shapes game at home.

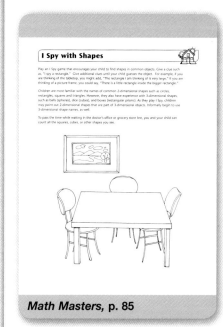

Math Masters, p. 85

S·10 Shape Garden

 Objective To incorporate shape exploration in a literature-based art activity.

Key Mathematics Concepts and Skills

- Count and compare numbers of shapes. [Number and Numeration Goals 2 and 4]
- Identify and name basic geometric shapes. [Geometry Goal 1]
- Combine shapes to make a picture. [Geometry Goal 2]

Other Skills Creative Expression, Fine Motor, Reading and Writing

Terms to Use circle, square, triangle, rectangle (other geometric shape names if they are used)

Materials Teaching Aid Masters (*Math Masters,* pp. 46–48; optional); pre-cut circles, squares, triangles, and rectangles; large sheets of white paper; glue; markers or crayons; a book with collage illustrations (*See* Related Books for suggestions.); scissors and colored paper (optional)

Planning Tip Choose the book you will read, and pre-cut the shapes. Different colors and sizes will be more interesting for children. You may want to use the shapes on *Math Masters,* pages 46–48, to create shape templates to trace and cut. You can also ask parent volunteers to pre-cut shapes.

▶ Main Activity

✔Whole Group ✔Small Group ☐ Partners ✔Center

Begin by reading a collage book. Draw children's attention to the illustrations by asking questions such as: *How do you think the pictures were created? What shapes do you notice? How did the artist combine shapes to make the pictures?*

Show children the pre-cut shapes and explain that they can use them to make pictures like those in the story. Allow children to explore with the shapes to create plants, animals, or other objects. (Not all children will create representational pictures; some may use the shapes to create designs.) After children have had time to experiment with the shapes, invite them to glue the shapes on paper to make a picture to save. Children can use crayons or markers to add details to their pictures. Some children may enjoy cutting additional shapes out of colored paper.

As children work, talk with them about the shapes they are using. You might also encourage children to count the number of each shape and to use comparison words, such as *more, less, equal,* and *same* to describe what they've done. For instance: *Did you use more circles or more squares?* Display the pictures in the classroom, perhaps with captions that children dictate about their work.

Ongoing Assessment: Kid Watching

You can use this activity to informally observe children's shape identification skills. You might also note whether they are able to manipulate and combine shapes to make pictures.

▶ Connections

Outdoors Connection Children can take a walk in a garden and look for shapes.

Manipulatives Connection Encourage children to create pictures using pattern blocks. You might also cut out felt shapes for children to use to create pictures on a flannel board.

Literacy Connection Gather several books by authors and illustrators who use collage, such as Leo Lionni, Ezra Jack Keats, and Eric Carle. Read them aloud and place them in your book corner for children to enjoy.

Family Connection You may want to use the Eating Shapes Family Connection (*Math Masters,* page 84) to encourage families to notice and discuss the shapes of different foods.

Building

Related Books

- *Planting a Rainbow* by Lois Ehlert (Harcourt Children's Books, 1988)
- *Growing Vegetable Soup* by Lois Ehlert (Harcourt Children's Books, 1987)
- *Feathers For Lunch* by Lois Ehlert (Harcourt Children's Books, 1990)

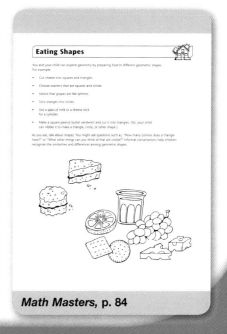

Math Masters, p. 84

S·11 Creating 3-Dimensional Shapes

Objective To provide tactile experiences with 3-dimensional shapes.

Key Mathematics Concepts and Skills

- Build, transform, and manipulate 3-dimensional shapes with clay. [Geometry Goal 1]
- Explore the relationship between basic 2-dimensional and 3-dimensional shapes. [Geometry Goal 1]

Other Skills Fine Motor

Terms to Use cube, sphere, cylinder, cone, rectangular prism, square, triangle, circle, rectangle

Materials clay or synthetic modeling material; plastic knives; familiar objects that are 3-dimensional geometric shapes, such as a ball (sphere), die (cube), party hat (cone), can (cylinder), rectangular block (rectangular prism)

▶ Main Activity

☐ Whole Group   ✔ Small Group   ☐ Partners   ☐ Center

Invite children to look at and hold the objects you collected. Encourage children to comment on what they notice about the shapes. Prompt them to describe how the shapes of the various objects are similar to and different from each other.

Give each child a piece of clay and ask him or her to use the clay to make a model of one of the objects. As children work, encourage them to look at and hold the objects they are making. Talk with the children about what they are making and informally use the proper shape names. For example: *That looks like a ball; it's called a sphere and it's round all over. You made a shape with straight sides. How many squares do you see on your cube? See the circles on the ends of this cylinder?*

Planning Tip Clay and synthetic modeling material work better for this activity than play dough because they hold a shape better.

NOTE It is not important for children to create accurately formed shapes but rather to experience working in three dimensions.

Engage children in conversation to help them think about and describe how 2- and 3-dimensional shapes are alike and different from each other.

You might give the children tips as they work. Children can roll clay in their hands to make a sphere or on a table to make a cylinder. They can make flat surfaces by tapping the clay on the table. Children can turn the clay and tap again to make an edge. After they make one shape, encourage children to look at and hold the other objects and to try making other geometric shapes.

NOTE Refer to 3-dimensional shapes by their names to build children's familiarity with these labels and to distinguish them from 2-dimensional shapes. Although children enjoy hearing the words, do not expect them to use 3-dimensional shape names consistently. Some children may use informal labels, such as *ball* or *box,* which is fine.

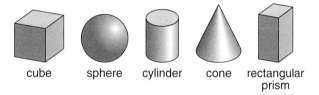

cube   sphere   cylinder   cone   rectangular prism

▶ Connections

Art Connection Provide chenille stems, straw pieces, buttons and beads with large holes, and clay for children to use to create 3-dimensional sculptures. Children may also enjoy creating sculptures with marshmallows and toothpicks. They often use these materials to make both 2- and 3-dimensional shapes.

Sensory Table Connection Hide small geometric shapes, such as beads, marbles, cubes, or dominoes in sand or another sensory material for children to find and sort.

Family Connection You may want to use the I Spy with Shapes Family Connection (*Math Masters,* page 85) to encourage families to play a shapes game at home.

Math Masters, p. 85

Expanding

Position and Spatial Relationships

Overview

> **Position and Spatial Relationships Goals**
>
> In Pre-K, children should have experiences that help them:
>
> • Recognize and describe the position and location of objects. [Geometry Goal 2]
>
> • Use spatial reasoning in concrete tasks, such as putting together puzzles and creating collages and block structures. [Geometry Goal 2]

Spatial reasoning is an important part of mathematics, and one that is often neglected. It involves manipulating shapes and objects and visualizing them in various positions and orientations. For young children, learning concepts and language related to position is an important part of developing their spatial sense.

Children's earliest understanding of position is likely to be in the context of their own needs: *I want to sit on the chair next to you. Pick me up. Mommy is over there.* As children develop their sense of spatial relationships, they will begin to think about and describe the position of one object in relation to another: *The swings are next to the tree. Your eyes are above your nose.* Young children may understand concepts related to position and spatial relationships before they have the language to describe them. For instance, children may be able to follow directions based on position words, but confuse them in their own speech. Children will develop their abilities to express these ideas through natural usage in familiar contexts: taking a walk, playing outdoors, riding in the car, or setting the table.

As they manipulate blocks, puzzle pieces, collage materials, and other objects, children come to understand that the shape of an object remains the same even if its position or orientation is changed. Through these experiences, children also develop their abilities to visualize what will happen as they manipulate shapes and objects in various ways. These "flips," "turns," and "slides" are formally called *transformations*, but young children can describe their actions and effects with any language that makes sense to them.

Some young children are able to use and even create simple maps. Maps are 2-dimensional representations of 3-dimensional space, so they involve more abstract spatial reasoning than describing the position of objects or manipulating objects directly.

 ## Professional Development

See Chapter 11 of the *Teacher's Reference Manual* for more information about spatial reasoning and other aspects of the Geometry strand.

Choosing Activities

Beginning	Building	Expanding
Beginning activities introduce simple position concepts and terminology. In these activities, children ◆ position objects using both visual and verbal cues.	**Building** activities focus on applying position words in a variety of contexts and developing children's sense of spatial relationships. In these activities, children ◆ manipulate pattern blocks to complete puzzles; ◆ follow and give directions using position words.	**Expanding** activities further develop children's spatial sense. In these activities, children ◆ manipulate pattern blocks to complete more difficult puzzles; ◆ use spatial reasoning to follow the route on a simple map.

Activities in Perspective

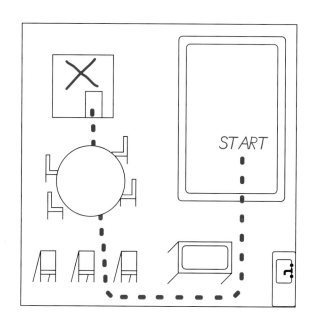

START

gym door

Gym

down the hall

Preschool class

Pictures in the hall

railing

railing

stairs

our class door

M + a h

KEY

 Art

 Books

 Dramatic Play

 Excursion

 Manipulatives and Games

Music and Movement

 Rug Time

 Science

Sensory

 Snack

 Core Core Activity

Position and Spatial Relations

Teaching Resources

Home-School Connection

Family Connections suggest home activities that link to activities children have done at school. The following Position and Spatial Relationships activities contain Family Connections: R♦3, Pattern-Block Puzzles I; R♦4, Where, Oh Where Has My Little Dog Gone?; R♦5, Obstacle Course; R♦6, Pattern-Block Puzzles II. Note that the same Family Connections are suggested with multiple activities, so keep track of which ones you have already sent home.

Mathematics at Home Books 1–3 provide additional ideas for enjoyable mathematics activities that families can do together, as well as lists of children's books related to the topics in the teacher's guide. Families can do activities from *Mathematics at Home* Books 1–3 throughout the year.

◀ *Home Connection Handbook* provides more ideas to communicate effectively with parents.

◀ *Resources for the Pre-Kindergarten Classroom* provides additional teaching ideas, including suggestions for bringing mathematics into thematic instruction, as well as using games, literature, technology, songs, and rhymes to support mathematics learning.

Minute Math provides brief activities for transition times and spare moments throughout the day. ▶

Assessment

Ongoing Assessment

 Kid Watching

The following activities in the *Teacher's Guide to Activities* include Ongoing Assessment notes related to position and spatial relationships. See the *Assessment Handbook* for an expanded table.

Activity	Content Assessed
R♦1, R♦4, R♦5	Understand position and location words. [Geometry Goal 2]
S♦10, R♦3	Use spatial reasoning. [Geometry Goal 2]

Assessment Handbook

- Pre-Kindergarten goals, pp. 6–11
- Position and Spatial Relationships Assessment Overview, p. 35
- Baseline Periodic Assessment Task 7, p. 20
- End-of-Year Periodic Assessment Tasks 10 and 11, p. 24

Differentiated Instruction

Adjusting for Age and Development

Pre-Kindergarten Everyday Mathematics is designed to be flexible enough to adapt to a wide range of preschool classrooms, including classrooms with mixed-age groupings and classrooms with a wide range of developmental levels. Many activities include suggestions to help teachers modify the activity to make it accessible and interesting to children with varying needs, learning styles, or levels of proficiency or understanding.

R◆1   Teddy Bear Positions   **R◆6**   Pattern-Block Puzzles II

R◆5   Obstacle Course   **R◆7**   Treasure Map

Language Support

Everyday Mathematics provides activity-specific suggestions to help all children, including non-native English speakers, develop the language necessary to acquire, process, and express mathematical ideas.

Developing Oral Language

R◆1   Develop context for position words.

R◆4   Develop context for position words and practice giving position clues.

Language & Vocabulary

Informally use these terms that are related to position and spatial relationships.

above	under	straight
below	in front of	through
behind	on	across
between	up	backward
beside	down	forward
in	high	shape
inside	low	side
out	top	corner
outside	bottom	flip
next to	middle	turn
over	center	map

Activity Connections

The Connections for each activity link the Main Activity to different curricular and classroom areas. They are useful for meeting individual needs and integrating mathematics throughout the day. The following connections are in the Position and Spatial Relationships section.

Art
R♦2 Face Collage
R♦5 Obstacle Course

Blocks
R♦6 Pattern-Block Puzzles II
R♦7 Treasure Map

Computer
R♦6 Pattern-Block Puzzles II

Family Connections
See Home-School Connection on page 270.

Games
R♦2 Face Collage
R♦4 Where, Oh Where Has My Little Dog Gone?

Literacy
R♦1 Teddy Bear Positions
R♦2 Face Collage
R♦4 Where, Oh Where Has My Little Dog Gone?
R♦5 Obstacle Course
R♦7 Treasure Map

Manipulatives
R♦3 Pattern-Block Puzzles I

Mathematics
R♦1 Teddy Bear Positions

Music and Movement
R♦5 Obstacle Course

Science
R♦1 Teddy Bear Positions

Snack
R♦2 Face Collage

R·1 Teddy Bear Positions

 **Objective** To provide practice with position words through a song and movement activity.

Key Mathematics Concepts and Skills
• Use position words to describe the location of an object. [Geometry Goal 2]

Other Skills Singing and Rhythmic Movement

Terms to Use on, under, behind, beside, over, next to, in

Materials teddy bears or other stuffed animals (or paper teddy bear cutouts or bear counters); chairs

Planning Tip Each child will need his or her own bear (or other animal) for this activity. The activity can coincide with a Teddy Bear Day. In advance, inform families of the date and request that children bring a favorite teddy bear or stuffed animal to school.

▶ Main Activity

✔Whole Group ✔Small Group ☐ Partners ☐ Center

Have children sit on chairs, holding their teddy bears. Practice and model position words by asking children to place their teddy bears in various places such as *on* their heads, *under* their chairs, and so on. Next, explain that you will sing a song, and they will listen and follow the directions. Sing and act out the following song, which is featured on the Sing Everyday! CD. Sing to the tune of "The Farmer in the Dell."

> *My teddy's on my chair.*
> *My teddy's on my chair.*
> *Oh, dear, my silly bear,*
> *My teddy's on my chair.*

Continue with verse 2 using *behind*, verse 3 with *under*, verse 4 with *beside*, and verse 5 with *over my chair* … .

 **Developing Oral Language** ELL

Because position words are highly contextual, they are often challenging for young children. Position words are best learned in context and with plenty of practice. Children will gain experience at clean-up time (*Put the blocks* on *the shelf.*) and during transitions. (*Line up* next to *the door.*) See *Minute Math®* for other quick activities to practice position words.

Final verse (Have children sit.):

> *My teddy's in my lap.*
> *My teddy's in my lap.*
> *It must be time for a nap.*
> *My teddy's in my lap.*

Sing the song with children often.

 Links to the Future

Learning concepts and language related to position helps children develop their spatial sense. Spatial reasoning is an important part of geometry.

▶ **Connections**

Literacy Connection Read a variety of teddy bear stories such as *Corduroy* by Don Freeman (Viking Juvenile, 1968) or a book version of the song "Teddy Bear's Picnic."

Mathematics Connection Children can sort the teddy bears in various ways, such as old, new, smooth fur, rough fur, wearing clothes, no clothes, and so on.

Science Connection Together with children, open up an old stuffed animal along a seam line and look at what is inside. Take out the stuffing and try re-stuffing with different materials, such as crumbled paper, cotton, small blocks, or beans. Discuss how the different stuffings feel. Re-stuff the animal with the material children choose, perhaps by a class vote, then close the seam. If you use reclosable fabric tape, it will be easy to open and close the seam.

 **Adjusting for Age and Development**

Initially, you may want to focus on one or two verses of the song at a time. Once children are proficient with the verses, you or children can make up verses that incorporate other position words.

 Ongoing Assessment: Kid Watching

You can use this activity to observe children's understanding of various position and location words.

 Related Book

• *Over, Under and Through* by Tana Hoban (Simon & Schuster Children's Publishing, 1973)

R·2 Face Collage

Objective To incorporate position and spatial relationship concepts into an art activity.

Key Mathematics Concepts and Skills

• Explore spatial relationships in the context of a collage. [Geometry Goal 2]

• Use position and location words to describe facial features. [Geometry Goal 2]

Other Skills Creative Expression, Fine Motor

Terms to Use above, below, bottom, middle, between, top, center, next to, beside

Materials assorted pictures of eyes, noses, mouths, and ears cut from magazines (or collage materials such as googly eyes, buttons, yarn, etc.); paper plates; glue; markers

---

Planning Tip Look for large face pictures so the pieces will be easy for children to manipulate. Provide lots of different pieces and sort the pieces by feature onto paper plates or trays (all eyes together, all ears together, and so on).

▶ Main Activity

☐ Whole Group ✔ Small Group ☐ Partners ✔ Center

Invite children to use the cutout facial features or collage materials to create faces on paper plates. Encourage them to mix and match facial features until they are satisfied with their faces. Then have children glue the pieces onto the plates. Invite children to color or draw skin, hair, or glasses onto their faces. As children work, talk with them about the position of various facial features. You may want to ask questions such as: *Are the eyes* above *or* below *the nose? What did you draw* above *the eyes? What is on the* bottom *of your face collage? What is in the* middle *of your face collage?*

▶ Connections

Literacy Connection Make a face book with photographs of children in your class. Take a close-up photo of each child's face. If possible, laminate the photos or glue them to cardstock. Use metal rings to compile the photos into a book. Cut each photo, or page, in half. Invite children to mix and match the faces in the book by turning the pages and trying to figure out which top photo goes with which bottom photo. They will also enjoy creating mismatched faces.

Snack Connection Children can create faces with rice cakes, cream cheese, raisins, shredded carrots, and other food items. Observe and listen as children converse about where they position various facial features.

Art Connection Show and display art books or prints of famous portraits such as DaVinci's *Mona Lisa* or Renoir's *A Girl with a Watering Can.* Encourage children to compare the different works. Children may enjoy painting portraits of friends or family members.

Games Connection Children explore position and spatial relationships as they play with toys or games that place facial features or body parts onto a base.

Music and Movement Connection The class can sing and act out the version of "The Wheels on the Bus" from the Sing Everyday! CD to reinforce position words. Also invite children to include their own ideas for verses and actions.

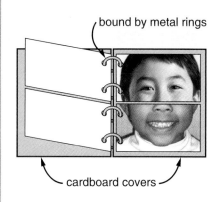

bound by metal rings

cardboard covers

Related Books

- *Two Eyes, a Nose, and a Mouth* by Roberta Grobel Intrater (Cartwheel Books, 1995)

- *Find a Face* by Francois Robert, Jean Robert, and Jane Gittings (Chronicle Books, 2004)

- *Animal Faces* by Akira Satoh and Kyoko Toda (Kane/Miller Book Publishers, 1996)

R·3 Pattern-Block Puzzles I

 Objective To provide experiences with manipulating shapes using puzzles.

Key Mathematics Concepts and Skills

- Explore spatial relationships by manipulating pattern blocks to solve puzzles. [Geometry Goal 2]
- Build pictures, designs, and other shapes from geometric shapes. [Geometry Goal 2]
- Match pieces using size and shape. [Patterns, Functions, and Algebra Goal 1]

Other Skills Fine Motor

Terms to Use turn, flip, corner, side, shape, pattern-block shape names

Materials Teaching Masters (*Math Masters,* pp. 15–22); pattern blocks

---

Planning Tip If possible, laminate the puzzles on *Math Masters,* pages 15–22, or mount them on cardboard to make them more durable. Store the puzzles in a folder or on a tray near your pattern blocks. If your class hasn't had an opportunity for free exploration with pattern blocks, use Exploration of Pattern Blocks, page 308, before doing this activity.

▶ Main Activity

☐ Whole Group ☐ Small Group ☐ Partners ✔ Center

After children have had ample opportunity for free exploration with pattern blocks, add a few pattern-block puzzles (*Math Masters,* pages 15–22; see next page for one of eight masters.) to the Math Center. Include multiple copies of each puzzle so several children can work on the same puzzle at once. Add new puzzles as children are ready.

As children work, talk with them about the shapes they are using. (Children may enjoy hearing names such as *hexagon, trapezoid,* and *rhombus,* but do not expect them to consistently use or remember these names.) Encourage children to manipulate the shapes, and help them notice relationships between the blocks. You might use prompts such as the following: *Try turning it a little. What happens if you flip it over? Does that one fit under this one? Can you use different blocks to fill the same space?*

NOTE The black-and-white puzzle outlines encourage children to attend to the shape of the pattern block pieces. Puzzles that are colored to match the pattern blocks are also engaging for children, but children often use color, more than shape, to complete these puzzles.

After children have completed a puzzle, they might use pattern blocks to copy the picture next to the master. Children may also want to create their own pictures and designs. You can turn children's pictures and designs into puzzles by tracing around the shapes on paper.

NOTE Also see Pattern-Block Puzzles II, page 284, and *Math Masters,* pages 28–36. The puzzle pages for this later activity are more complicated and are missing one or more internal lines. Children will be ready for these more difficult puzzles at different times, so make them available as you see fit.

 Ongoing Assessment: Kid Watching

Watch how children approach pattern-block puzzles and other puzzles. Do they use trial and error? Can they see places where a particular shape might fit? Are they comfortable manipulating pieces to make them fit? Do they notice edges and corner pieces? As you help children extend their strategies, you will also help them develop their spatial reasoning skills.

▶ Connections

Manipulatives Connection Make various types of puzzles available in the classroom (small, large, wooden, cardboard, and so on). Children can assemble large puzzles on heavy cardboard or a tray over an extended period of time.

 Family Connection You may want to use the Puzzles Family Connection (*Math Masters,* page 86) to encourage families to help children develop spatial reasoning through puzzles.

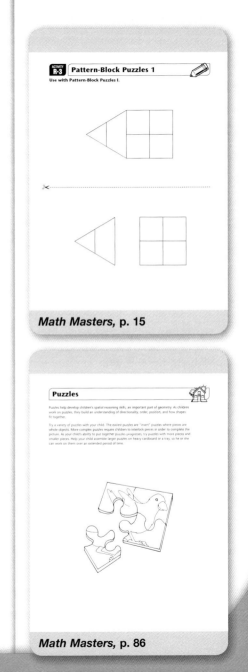

Math Masters, p. 15

Math Masters, p. 86

R·4 Where, Oh Where Has My Little Dog Gone?

 Objective To provide practice with using position and spatial relationship words.

Key Mathematics Concepts and Skills

- Use position words to describe the location of an object. [Geometry Goal 2]

Other Skills Cooperation, Listening and Speaking, Singing and Rhythmic Movement

Terms to Use next to, between, behind, in front of, over, under, on, above, below, in, out, high, low

Materials small toy dog

> **Planning Tip** Initially, you may want to play this game with small groups of children so you can help them give clues, and so they don't need to wait long to be the Seeker. Once children know the game, it is a good whole-group activity.

▶ Main Activity

✔Whole Group ✔Small Group ☐ Partners ☐ Center

Begin by hiding the stuffed dog as children watch, then having them describe the hiding place using position words (*behind the chair, under the box,* and so on). When they seem comfortable describing the location with position words, rather than pointing or simply naming a location, introduce the song and game.

Identify a child to be the "Seeker" and have that child close his or her eyes. (Remind others that they will get a turn, too.) With the other children's help, hide the toy dog somewhere in the room. After the dog has been hidden, the Seeker opens his or her eyes while the group sings "Where, Oh Where Has My Little Dog Gone?"

  **Developing Oral Language** ELL

When children give clues using position words, they may need help finding the right words to express what they mean. Model position words with actions to support children's acquisition of these terms. See Teddy Bear Positions, page 274, for a good activity to practice position words.

Where, oh where has my little dog gone?
Where, oh where can he be?
With his tail cut short and his ears cut long,
Oh where, oh where can he be?

Call on children to use position words as clues to help the Seeker find the dog. For example: *Look behind the bookcase, on the block shelf, under the water table, higher, or lower.* Prompt volunteers to give one clue at a time. When the Seeker finds the dog, he or she can hide it for the next round.

 Ongoing Assessment: Kid Watching

You can use this activity to informally assess children's understanding of position and location words and concepts. Some children may be able to respond to position and location words, but may not yet use them on their own.

▶ Connections

Literacy Connection Make a class book called *Where Has My Little Dog Gone?* Have each child draw a picture of a hiding dog, then dictate words for you to write on his or her page that describe where the dog is hidden (*under the bed, on the roof, next to the car,* and so on). Assemble the pages into a class book.

Game Connection Children can play Hide and Seek on the playground and describe their hiding places using position words. They also enjoy playing hot/cold games, in which they are told if they are getting warmer or colder as they get closer or farther away from a hidden object.

 Family Connection You may wish to use the Playing a Finding Game Family Connection (*Math Masters,* page 87) to encourage families to reinforce position words and concepts.

 Related Books

- *Oh Where, Oh Where Has My Little Dog Gone?* by Iza Trapani (Charlesbridge Publishing, 1995)
- *Harry the Dirty Dog* by Gene Zion (HarperCollins, 1956)

Math Masters, p. 87

R·5 Obstacle Course

Objective To provide kinesthetic experiences with spatial reasoning and position and location concepts.

Key Mathematics Concepts and Skills

• Follow a sequence of steps to complete an obstacle course. [Measurement and Reference Frames Goal 3]

• Follow directions using position words. [Geometry Goal 2]

• Use spatial reasoning to move through an obstacle course. [Geometry Goal 2]

Other Skills Gross Motor, Listening and Speaking

Terms to Use inside, outside, under, over, between, next to, through, beside, forward, backward, up, down, across

Materials classroom furniture or outdoor equipment

Planning Tip This activity can be done indoors or outdoors. Plan ample time for all children to have a turn; you may want to repeat the activity over several days, perhaps with small groups during outdoors time.

▶ Main Activity

✔Whole Group ✔Small Group ☐ Partners ☐ Center

Use classroom furniture or outdoor equipment to create a short obstacle course. Give children directions that they must follow to complete the course. For example:

▷ *Go* around *the chair.* *Crawl* under *the table.* *Stop* next to *the water table and count to three.*

▷ *Slide* down *the slide.* *Hide* under *the climber while you count to five.* *Run* across *the field.*

Some teachers use this as a transition activity: Children complete the course and then move on to the next activity.

Adjusting for Age and Development

You may need to start with one prompt at a time, then add more steps as children seem ready. Younger children may be most successful with 2- or 3-step courses.

Ongoing Assessment: Kid Watching

Use this activity to assess children's understanding of position and location words. You can also assess their abilities to follow multi-step directions.

▶ Connections

Literacy Connection Read and act out *Rosie's Walk* by Pat Hutchins (Aladdin, 2005). The class might work together to make a poster or map that shows where Rosie went. Children might also generate and illustrate a list of the position words from the story.

Art Connection Children can draw and explain a map that shows the obstacle course. See Treasure Map, page 286 for more mapping ideas.

Music and Movement Connection Sing and act out the chant "We're Going on a Bear Hunt." You can find a version of it on the Sing Everyday! CD.

 Family Connection You may wish to use the Playing a "Finding" Game Family Connection (*Math Masters,* page 87) to help families reinforce position words and concepts at home.

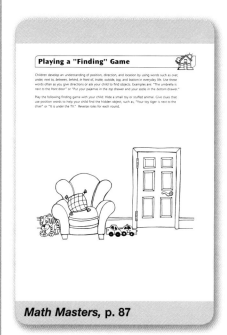

Math Masters, p. 87

R·6 Pattern-Block Puzzles II

Objective To extend children's spatial reasoning through complex pattern-block puzzles.

Key Mathematics Concepts and Skills

• Build pictures, designs, and other shapes from geometric shapes. [Geometry Goal 2]

• Explore spatial relationships by manipulating pattern blocks to solve puzzles. [Geometry Goal 2]

• Match pieces using size and shape. [Patterns, Functions and Algebra Goal 1]

Other Skills Fine Motor

Terms to Use turn, flip, corner, side, shape, pattern-block shape names

Materials Teaching Masters (*Math Masters,* pp. 28–36); pattern blocks

---

▶ **Main Activity** ☐ Whole Group ✔ Small Group ☐ Partners ✔ Center

For children who seem ready for new puzzle challenges, put out pattern blocks and the pattern-block puzzles from *Math Masters,* pages 28–36. These puzzles are more challenging than the first set of pattern-block puzzles because one or more internal lines are missing. Begin by putting out the puzzles that have only a few lines missing; gradually add puzzles that have more lines left out. As children work, encourage them to manipulate the pattern blocks by sliding them, rotating them, and flipping them over. Often, a good strategy is to try to place a hexagon first, or to put in the pieces that are clearly identifiable and then add the rest.

Several of the pattern-block puzzles in this set promote exploration of symmetry. Half of the puzzle is shown with lines for the block shapes and the other half does not show

Planning Tip Make several copies of *Math Masters,* pages 28–36. Cut along the dashed lines so there will be one puzzle per sheet. If possible, laminate the puzzles or mount them on cardboard to make them more durable. Store the puzzles in a folder or on a tray near your pattern blocks.

NOTE Be sure children are comfortable with Pattern-Block Puzzles I, page 278, before they try the new puzzles. It is important not to frustrate children with puzzles they are not ready for. You can add novelty to both sets of puzzles by suggesting that children try a variety of ways to complete the puzzles.

lines. Children can complete the puzzle symmetrically, by putting block shapes on the blank side to match the shapes on the filled-in side. However, many children will prefer to complete the puzzles in other ways. You might encourage children to complete the puzzles in more than one way and compare the differences. (In their own free play with pattern blocks, children often make symmetrical designs, so you can also informally talk about the idea of symmetry in this context.)

Adjusting for Age and Development

For additional variety and skill levels, you can adapt puzzles by whiting out lines or adding more lines when you make copies. To help children see different possibilities for completing puzzles, you might suggest they find different ways to cover the hexagon with pattern blocks. Ask: *How many different ways can you find?*

▶ Connections

Computer Connection Use a pattern-block program and encourage children to make designs on the computer. Children also might like to replicate a design that they make with real blocks on the computer. There are also several basic sites on the Internet that children can use to make pattern-block designs. Go to NCTM.org and search for *pattern-block program* to find sites.

Blocks Connection Encourage children to use symmetry in their block buildings and to incorporate pattern blocks into their block structures.

Family Connection You may want to use the Puzzles Family Connection (*Math Masters*, page 86) to encourage families to help children develop spatial reasoning through puzzles.

Related Book

- *Woof! Woof!* by David A. Carter (Little Simon, 2006)

Math Masters, p. 86

R·7 Treasure Map

Objective **To provide experience using spatial reasoning to follow a simple map.**

Key Mathematics Concepts and Skills

• Describe the position and location of objects. [Geometry Goal 2]

• Use spatial reasoning to follow the route on a simple map. [Geometry Goal 2]

Other Skills Cooperation, Pretending and Role Play

Terms to Use map, before, after, next to, turn, first, next, after, straight, up, down

Materials paper; pencils or markers; costume jewelry or play money for "treasure"; stick-on notes and posterboard (optional)

▶ Main Activity

☐ Whole Group ✔ Small Group ✔ Partners ✔ Center

Show the classroom map to a small group of children. Ask them whether they can tell what the map is showing. Help children recognize the landmarks represented on the map and discuss their location in the room. For example: *The sink is* near *the door. The bookshelf is* next to *the rug.* Ask whether children would like to add anything to the map and have them tell you where it should go.

Tell children that you have hidden a "treasure" for them to find using the map. Have them watch carefully as you draw a route on the map from one place in the classroom to the treasure, using footprints or a line to mark the route. Draw a large *X* where the treasure is hidden. Give the map to children and see whether they can follow the map to the treasure. If children need more guidance, help them use the map to describe the route: *Go* around *the sensory table. Next, go* between *the art easels. Then go* under *the circular table...* .

Planning Tip Draw a simple map of your classroom using easily identifiable landmarks such as the rug, art easels, tables, and so on. (Or, make a classroom map with children. See Adjusting for Age and Development.) Make copies of the map. Hide the "treasure(s)" somewhere in the classroom. You may want to introduce treasure maps to a small group of 2–3 children. If you work with a larger group, divide the group in half and use two maps and two treasures.

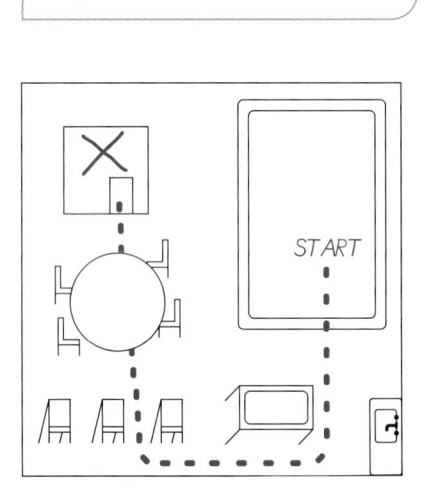

Use copies of the classroom map to make treasure maps for other groups of children. Vary the route and the treasure's location each time, though it's helpful to keep the same starting point—the rug, for example. Once all the treasures have been found, invite children to hide a treasure and use the classroom map to draw a treasure map for other children to follow. Children can switch maps and look for the treasures.

Leave blank paper in the Writing or Math Center to encourage children to make their own maps. Often, treasure hunts become a popular dramatic play theme and children create highly imaginative maps. You can leave out extra copies of the classroom map, as well. You may want to repeat this activity in a gross motor room or on the playground, using the equipment as landmarks for mapmaking.

NOTE Making maps involves representing spatial relationships in two dimensions. Do not expect children to make accurate maps yet; the goal is for them to explore the concept of a map.

A child's treasure map

Adjusting for Age and Development

You might create the classroom map with children prior to the treasure hunt activity. Have children draw different classroom landmarks on stick-on notes, and help them arrange the pictures on posterboard. Then draw and make copies of a smaller version of the class-made map to use for treasure maps.

▶ Connections

Literacy Connections Read and discuss books about going to new places, such as *Dylan's Day Out* by Peter Catalanotto (Scholastic, 1993) or *How to Make an Apple Pie and See the World* by Marjorie Priceman (Knopf Books for Young Readers, 1994).

If children make their own maps, help them add labels. Children can dictate a story about where they started and where they are going.

Blocks Connection Children may make a map of their block cities. You can also include road maps in the block corner to encourage exploration.

Related Books

- *The Secret Birthday Message* by Eric Carle (HarperCollins, 1972)

- *Oliver Finds His Way* by Phyllis Root (Candlewick, 2002)

- *My Map Book* by Sara Fanelli (HarperCollins, 1995)

Patterns and Sorting

Overview

Patterns and Sorting Goals

In Pre-K children should have a variety of experiences that help them:

- Recognize and match attributes of objects, such as size, shape, and color. [Patterns, Functions, and Algebra Goal 1]
- Use rules to sort objects. [Patterns, Functions, and Algebra Goal 1]
- Use rules to create and extend repeating patterns. [Patterns, Functions, and Algebra Goal 1]

Patterning and sorting are both governed by "rules" that describe relationships. For example, a sorting rule may involve grouping a collection by size, and a patterning rule may involve alternating colors on a striped shirt. Since many of children's early patterning and sorting activities are based on attributes of size or shape, measurement and geometry concepts are often embedded in their work. Patterning and sorting activities lay groundwork for developing algebraic thinking, which focuses on numeric patterns and relationships and the rules that govern those patterns and relationships.

In children's initial, often spontaneous, sorting efforts, they generally do not apply a single rule. Rather, they may put a group of red items together, a group of small items together, and leave the remaining items unsorted. With modeling and practice, young children can sort an entire collection of objects by the same attribute, such as shape or color. It is quite a bit more advanced to be able to sort by multiple attributes at once (color and shape, for example), and most Pre-K children are not ready for this. Pre-K children should have experience sorting the same collection in different ways. Once they have had many sorting experiences, they can try to figure out the sorting rule for a sorted collection.

Children's initial experiences with patterning should include visual patterns, sound patterns, and movement patterns. Children's earliest patterning activities involve copying someone else's pattern. Extending someone else's pattern is more difficult, as it requires understanding what a pattern is and also figuring out the patterning rule. Describing a pattern with words can help children extend patterns and identify the repeating part. Over time, children are able to create their own patterns and often become very perceptive about patterns in their environment.

 ## Professional Development

See Chapter 15 of the *Teacher's Reference Manual* for more information about patterns and sorting and other aspects of the Patterns, Functions, and Algebra strand.

Choosing Activities

Beginning	Building	Expanding
Beginning activities develop a basic understanding of attributes. They also introduce the concepts of patterning and sorting. In these activities, children	**Building** activities introduce new materials for patterning and sorting and encourage children to be more independent and flexible. In these activities, children	**Expanding** activities add challenge in various ways. In these activities, children

Beginning

- identify and match attributes;
- sort familiar objects by a single attribute;
- extend and create movement and color patterns;
- explore pattern blocks.

Building

- sort and re-sort collections;
- create and extend patterns with various materials;
- describe patterns and sorting schemes.

Expanding

- determine sorting rules based on a sorted collection;
- notice patterns in their environment;
- identify missing elements in patterns.

Activities in Perspective

Activity	Objective	Core	Usage	Page
P·1	**Attribute Match** — To lay groundwork for sorting through an activity that involves matching and describing attributes.	Core		296
P·2	**Movement Patterns** — To provide kinesthetic experiences with patterns through a movement activity.	Core		298
P·3	**Officer, Officer Game** — To provide practice with identifying and describing attributes through a game.	Core		300
P·4	**Color Patterns** — To introduce and provide practice with making and extending color patterns.	Core		302
P·5	**Sorting Objects** — To introduce and provide experiences with sorting common objects by their attributes.	Core		304
P·6	**Sorting Leaves** — To provide experiences with sorting using natural objects.			306
P·7	**Exploration of Pattern Blocks** — To provide an opportunity for children to explore and play with pattern blocks.	Core		308
P·8	**Sorting Pasta** — To reinforce sorting skills through a sensory activity.			310
P·9	**Pasta Patterns** — To provide practice with creating and extending repeating patterns through an art project.			312
P·10	**Making Jewelry** — To provide opportunities to explore and create patterns through an art project.			314
P·11	**Child Patterns** — To provide practice with making and identifying patterns using children's bodies.	Core		316

Beginning: P·1–P·7
Building: P·8–P·11

Building

Expanding

KEY   Art   Dramatic Play   Manipulatives and Games   Rug Time   Sensory   Core Core Activity

 Books   Excursion   Music and Movement   Science   Snack

Patterns and Sorting

Teaching Resources

Home-School Connection

Family Connections suggest home activities that link to activities children have done at school. The following Patterns and Sorting activities contain Family Connections: P◆5, Sorting Objects; P◆8, Sorting Pasta; P◆10 Making Jewelry; P◆14, Sorting Vehicles; P◆16, *"What's My Rule?"* Game. Note that the same Family Connections are suggested with multiple activities, so keep track of which ones you have already sent home.

Mathematics at Home Books 1–3 provide additional ideas for enjoyable mathematics activities that families can do together, as well as lists of children's books related to the topics in the teacher's guide. Families can do activities from *Mathematics at Home* Books 1–3 throughout the year.

◀ *Home Connection Handbook* provides more ideas to communicate effectively with parents.

◀ *Resources for the Pre-Kindergarten Classroom* provides additional teaching ideas, including suggestions for bringing mathematics into thematic instruction, as well as using games, literature, technology, songs, and rhymes to support mathematics learning.

Minute Math provides brief activities ▶ for transition times and spare moments throughout the day.

Assessment

Ongoing Assessment

Kid Watching

The following activities in the *Teacher's Guide to Activities* include Ongoing Assessment notes related to patterns and sorting. See the *Assessment Handbook* for an expanded table

Activity	Content Assessed
P✦1, P✦3	Recognize and describe attributes. [Patterns, Functions, and Algebra Goal 1]
P✦2, P✦4, P✦9, P✦10, P✦11, P✦12	Copy, extend, and/or create repeating patterns. [Patterns, Functions, and Algebra Goal 1]
G✦3, P✦5, P✦8, P✦14	Sort objects. [Patterns, Functions, and Algebra Goal 1]

Assessment Handbook

- Pre-Kindergarten goals, pp. 6–11
- Patterns and Sorting Assessment Overview, pp. 36–37
- Baseline Periodic Assessment Tasks 8 and 9, p. 20
- End-of-Year Periodic Assessment Tasks 12 and 13, p. 24

Differentiated Instruction

Adjusting for Age and Development

Pre-Kindergarten Everyday Mathematics is designed to be flexible enough to adapt to a wide range of preschool classrooms, including classrooms with mixed age groupings and classrooms with a wide range of developmental levels. Many activities include suggestions to help teachers modify the activity to make it accessible and interesting to children with varying needs, learning styles, or levels of proficiency or understanding.

P♦9   Pasta Patterns

P♦10 Making Jewelry

P♦13 Sorting Children

P♦14 Sorting Vehicles

P♦15 Weaving Outdoors

P♦16 *"What's My Rule?"* Game

P♦18 What's Missing?

Language Support

Everyday Mathematics provides activity-specific suggestions to help all children, including non-native English speakers, develop the language necessary to acquire, process, and express mathematical ideas.

Developing Oral Language

P♦1   Develop vocabulary to describe how objects are alike and different.

P♦8   Develop descriptive language.

Language & Vocabulary

Informally use these terms that are related to patterns and sorting.

pattern	sort	through
rule	group	weave
repeat	groups	pattern blocks
match	over	shape names
missing	under	words to describe size, shape, and color
same	in	
different	out	

Activity Connections

The Connections for each activity link the Main Activity to different curricular and classroom areas. They are useful for meeting individual needs and integrating mathematics throughout the day. The following connections are in the Patterns and Sorting section.

Art

P◆4 Color Patterns
P◆6 Sorting Leaves
P◆7 Exploration of Pattern Blocks
P◆9 Pasta Patterns
P◆12 Snake Patterns
P◆14 Sorting Vehicles
P◆15 Weaving Outdoors
P◆16 *"What's My Rule?"* Game
P◆17 Pattern Search

Blocks

P◆17 Pattern Search

Cooking

P◆9 Pasta Patterns

Dramatic Play

P◆10 Making Jewelry

Family Connections

See Home-School Connection on page 292.

Games

P◆1 Attribute Match

Group Time

P◆3 *Officer, Officer* Game
P◆10 Making Jewelry

Language

P◆1 Attribute Match

Literacy

P◆6 Sorting Leaves
P◆11 Child Patterns
P◆12 Snake Patterns
P◆13 Sorting Children
P◆16 *"What's My Rule?"* Game
P◆17 Pattern Search

Manipulatives

P◆14 Sorting Vehicles

Mathematics

P◆7 Exploration of Pattern Blocks
P◆8 Sorting Pasta
P◆11 Child Patterns

Music and Movement

P◆2 Movement Patterns
P◆3 *Officer, Officer* Game
P◆9 Pasta Patterns
P◆13 Sorting Children
P◆15 Weaving Outdoors
P◆18 What's Missing?

Outdoors

P◆6 Sorting Leaves
P◆17 Pattern Search

Science

P◆5 Sorting Objects
P◆6 Sorting Leaves
P◆8 Sorting Pasta
P◆9 Pasta Patterns
P◆12 Snake Patterns

Social Studies

P◆3 *Officer, Officer* Game

P·1 Attribute Match

 Objective To lay groundwork for sorting through an activity that involves matching and describing attributes.

Key Mathematics Concepts and Skills

- Find objects with matching attributes. [Patterns, Functions, and Algebra Goal 1]
- Describe attributes such as color, size, and shape. [Patterns, Functions, and Algebra Goal 1]

Other Skills Listening and Speaking

Terms to Use match, same, different, words to describe size, shape, and color

Materials several (5–8) pairs of identical matching objects

Planning Tip Use familiar objects from the classroom, such as markers, bear counters, plastic food or dishes, and blocks.

▶ Main Activity

✔Whole Group ✔Small Group ☐ Partners ✔Center

Show three objects to the group, two that match and one that is different. Ask: *Which of these objects match? How do you know they match?* Most children will respond that they match because they are both the same; for example, they are both bears or both cups. Encourage children to describe other ways they are the same, using attributes such as color, shape, and size. Show all of the objects you collected and have children take turns finding matches and describing the objects. Over time, make the differences between the objects more subtle. For example, you might use 2 large red bear counters and 1 small red bear counter.

 Developing Oral Language ELL

Even for children who find the matching aspect of this activity easy, the activity is useful for helping children describe objects using various attribute words. Developing vocabulary to describe how objects are the same or different lays a foundation for sorting by attributes later.

Put the objects in the Math Center for children to match on their own. Keep the activity fresh by periodically adding new pairs of objects to the Math Center for children to match and describe.

▶ Connections

Language Connection Show a collection of 5–8 objects to a small group of children. Mentally choose an object and describe it using attributes such as color, size, and shape. Invite children to identify the object. Once they understand the game, children can take turns choosing objects and giving attribute clues. (It is a good idea to have children whisper their chosen object to someone else before giving clues.)

Game Connections You can play this self-made game with the whole class or a smaller group. Collect matching pairs of cards from a memory game, or make matching pairs of cards using stickers. You might use stickers related to an upcoming holiday or theme. Give one card to each child; if there is an odd number of children, you should take a card, too. When everyone has a card, children move around to try to find the other child who has the same card as theirs, and then sit with their matching partner. Collect the cards and repeat as often as children are interested. You can leave the cards in the Math Center for children to match on their own.

Many familiar card games, such as Go Fish and Old Maid, are based on matching and also provide practice with social skills, such as turn-taking and following rules. Teach these games to your children as they are ready.

Red, round on bottom and top, small, smooth...

Ongoing Assessment: Kid Watching

You can use this activity to informally assess children's abilities to recognize and describe attributes of color, size, and shape.

Related Books

- *A Pair of Socks* by Stuart J. Murphy (HarperCollins, 1996)
- *I Spy* Books by Jean Marzollo (Cartwheel, various)

P·2 Movement Patterns

Core Activity

 Objective To provide kinesthetic experiences with patterns through a movement activity.

Key Mathematics Concepts and Skills

• Copy and extend movement patterns. [Patterns, Functions, and Algebra Goal 1]

• Create movement patterns. [Patterns, Functions, and Algebra Goal 1]

Other Skills Singing and Rhythmic Movement

Terms to Use pattern, repeat

Materials none

▶ Main Activity

✔ Whole Group   ✔ Small Group   ☐ Partners   ☐ Center

Begin a simple, 2-part movement pattern such as clap, pat lap; clap, pat lap; clap, pat lap; and so on. Invite children to join along with you. After most children are following along, stop and ask them what movement comes next. How do they know? Help children describe the pattern by labeling the two movements. If no one mentions it, tell children that they are making a *pattern* and that patterns *repeat*.

Explain that you will start another pattern, and invite children to join in when they see the pattern. Use a variety of movements (jump, stomp, pat head, pat knees, reach to the sky, touch your toes, and so on) to create repeating patterns for children to copy and extend. Begin with 2-part patterns, then try 3-part patterns as children seem ready.

NOTE Movement and sound patterns entice children to watch and listen, so they are a good way to get children's attention during transitions.

When children become familiar with movement patterns, model a pattern and ask children to repeat it back to you. Give at least three full examples of the repeating element of the pattern. Children may enjoy creating movement patterns for the class to repeat.

 Ongoing Assessment: Kid Watching

You can use this activity to informally assess children's abilities to copy and extend repeating movement patterns.

▶ Connections

Music Connection Give children musical instruments such as rhythm sticks, bells, tambourines, or drums. Play a rhythmic pattern, such as shake, shake, (rest); shake, shake, (rest); shake, shake, (rest). Emphasize the rests with a gesture or by saying *rest* or *shhh*. Have children play the pattern back with their instruments. Invite children to create rhythmic patterns for the group to play.

Movement Connection Sing and do the movements for "Head, Shoulders, Knees and Toes." Talk to children about any movement patterns they notice.

> *Head, shoulders, knees and toes, knees and toes.*
> *Head, shoulders, knees and toes, knees and toes.*
> *Eyes, and ears, and mouth, and nose,*
> *Head, shoulders, knees and toes, knees and toes.*

P·3 *Officer, Officer* Game

 **Objective** To provide practice with identifying and describing attributes through a game.

Key Mathematics Concepts and Skills

• Use attribute-based clues to describe and identify people. [Patterns, Functions and Algebra Goal 1]

Other Skills Listening and Speaking, Pretending and Role Play

Terms to Use clue, descriptive words

Materials none

▶ **Main Activity**   ✔Whole Group   ✔Small Group   ☐ Partners   ☐ Center

Have children sit in a circle and make sure they can easily see each other. Explain that children are going to pretend they are police officers by using clues to help you find your "lost" child.

Choose a child to be the first "Officer" and have that child sit in the middle of the circle. Think of one of the other children to be your missing child, but do not tell who it is. Begin the game by saying: *Officer, Officer, my child is lost. Can you help me? My child is wearing a **red shirt**.* (Use appropriate clue.) Have the Officer make a guess, encouraging him or her to use a child's name, rather than just point to someone. (This game helps children learn each other's names at the beginning of the year.) Respond appropriately to the Officer's guess.

NOTE You may need to talk with children about clues. Clues are like puzzle pieces; they show a little part, not the whole thing. Clues give information, but not the answer. Giving clues is difficult for young children and is a skill that develops with practice and modeling over time.

For example, you might say: *You found my child!* Or: *That's a great guess but my child also has **short pants**.* (Add a second identifying attribute.) Or: *Yes, John has **red pants** but my child is wearing a **red shirt**.* Continue to narrow the Officer's choices with new clues. When the Officer identifies the lost child, that child becomes the Officer and play begins again.

When children have played often and are comfortable responding to clues, they can select the lost child and give the clues.

▶ Connections

Social Studies Connection Use one of the books about police officers in Related Books, or another book of your own choosing, to initiate a discussion on the role of police officers as community helpers. This could be part of a Community Helpers Unit.

Group Time Connection Ask a child to identify someone who has something, such as shirt color, hair length, or shoe type, the same as they have. Then that child finds a different child with whom he or she has something in common (a different attribute than the first child identified). For example, Agnes identifies Kesha because they both have red shoes. Then Kesha identifies Pedro because they are both wearing jeans. Then Pedro identifies George because they both have brown hair. Continue as long as there is interest. Children enjoy finding surprising ways in which they are similar.

Music and Movement Connection Children can sing and act out "If You're Wearing Red" (to the tune of "The Muffin Man"). See *Resources for the Pre-Kindergarten Classroom* for the lyrics and listen to the Sing Everyday! CD for the tune.

Ongoing Assessment: Kid Watching

Over time, you can use this activity to assess whether children can use attribute clues. Also note whether they can keep track of multiple attributes at the same time.

Related Books

- *I Want to Be a Police Officer* by Dan Liebman (Firefly Books, 2000)
- *Policeman Small* by Lois Lenski (Random House Books for Young Readers, 2001)

P·4 Color Patterns

Objective To introduce and provide practice with making and extending color patterns.

Key Mathematics Concepts and Skills

• Copy and extend color patterns. [Patterns, Functions, and Algebra Goal 1]

• Create color patterns. [Patterns, Functions, and Algebra Goal 1]

Terms to Use repeat, pattern, color words

Materials any set of manipulatives of different colors, such as small blocks, plastic animals, connecting cubes, or beads

▶ Main Activity

☐ Whole Group ✔ Small Group ☐ Partners ✔ Center

Create a simple, repeating color pattern with manipulatives: for example, blue, red; blue, red; blue, red … . Ask children what they notice about what you are making. As children share, reinforce comments about *patterns* and *repeating,* or model and explain these terms, as needed. One at a time, invite children to use the manipulatives to extend your pattern.

Next, make a new color pattern. Ask children to describe the new pattern and then add manipulatives to extend the pattern. Repeat several times, making different patterns each time. You will probably want to stick with AB patterns initially.

NOTE Repeating color patterns are easy to see, but may be difficult for children to verbalize. Help children label the colors and identify the pattern's core, or what repeats.

Place the manipulatives in your Math Center and encourage children to use them to make patterns and extend each other's patterns. You may also want to include cards with color patterns that children can copy and extend using the manipulatives. As children become comfortable with patterning, begin to model 3-part patterns or more complicated 2-part patterns, such as red, red, blue; red, red, blue; red, red, blue … .

▶ Connections

Art Connections Children can create color patterns by gluing pre-cut colored squares onto sheets of paper. Suggest that children finish laying out their patterns before they begin gluing them. Have children describe their patterns. You might also show children how to make patterned paper chains using different-color strips of paper. Use the chains to decorate the room for special occasions.

Provide cookie cutters, rolling pins, and plastic knives to use with play dough. Encourage children to roll out the play dough and cut out shapes to use in making patterns. Children can also roll or pat out the play dough and use craft sticks to carve patterns in the dough.

Ongoing Assessment: Kid Watching

You can use this activity to informally assess children's abilities to copy and extend repeating color patterns.

P·5 Sorting Objects

Objective To introduce and provide experiences with sorting common objects by their attributes.

Key Mathematics Concepts and Skills

• Identify and describe attributes of objects, such as size, shape, and color. [Patterns, Functions, and Algebra Goal 1]

• Use rules to sort objects. [Patterns, Functions, and Algebra Goal 1]

Other Skills Listening and Speaking

Terms to Use sort, group, groups

Materials a collection of objects that can be sorted according to various attributes; containers for sorting, such as egg cartons or deli or TV trays; small strips of paper and writing tools to make labels (optional)

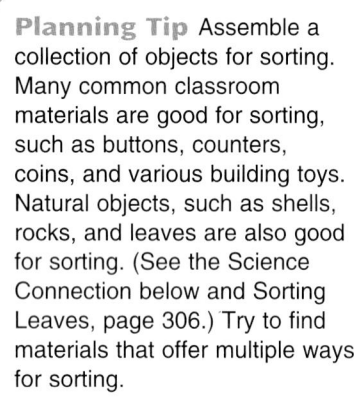

Planning Tip Assemble a collection of objects for sorting. Many common classroom materials are good for sorting, such as buttons, counters, coins, and various building toys. Natural objects, such as shells, rocks, and leaves are also good for sorting. (See the Science Connection below and Sorting Leaves, page 306.) Try to find materials that offer multiple ways for sorting.

▶ Main Activity

☐ Whole Group ✔Small Group ☐ Partners ✔Center

Introduce the idea of sorting to a small group. Choose a collection that lends itself to sorting by color. Show children the objects and sorting containers and invite them to sort the objects by color. You may need to model what you mean by beginning to group the red objects together, the blue objects together, and so on. When the objects have been sorted by color, ask children whether they can think of another way to group—or *sort*—the objects. If needed, prompt with suggestions. Re-sort the objects with the group according to a new rule.

Put the materials in a Center for children to sort. As children work, talk with them about how they are sorting. Help them make labels to describe their categories.

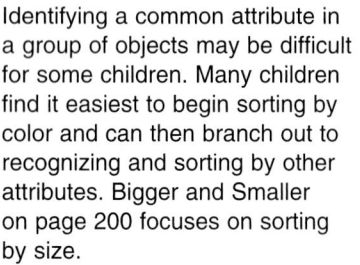

Links to the Future

Identifying a common attribute in a group of objects may be difficult for some children. Many children find it easiest to begin sorting by color and can then branch out to recognizing and sorting by other attributes. Bigger and Smaller on page 200 focuses on sorting by size.

Allow children to share and explain their sorting schemes with the class. They can show the trays with their sorted objects and describe their categories. Some ways of sorting may be personal, such as "Toys I play with" and "Toys I don't play with." These are valid and meaningful ways to sort.

Provide different types and collections of objects for sorting on a regular basis, and encourage children to sort the objects in different ways. Through experience, children will begin to realize that there is more than one way to sort, and that objects can belong to more than one category.

Ongoing Assessment: Kid Watching

You can use this activity to informally assess children's abilities to sort objects according to a rule. You might note whether they are able to sort the same collection in different ways.

▶ Connections

Science Connection Children can sort natural objects, such as leaves, rocks, or shells, in different ways in your Science or Discovery Center. In addition to providing sorting practice, this activity also helps children observe these objects closely and notice details about them. See Sorting Leaves on page 306 for more suggestions about sorting natural objects.

Family Connection You might want to use the Cleaning Up Toys Family Connection (*Math Masters,* page 76) to encourage families to recognize natural opportunities for sorting at home.

Related Books

- *The Button Box* by Margarette S. Reid (Dutton Juvenile, 1990)

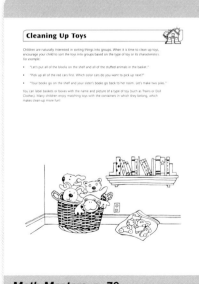

Math Masters, p. 76

Beginning

P·6 Sorting Leaves

 Objective To provide experiences with sorting using natural objects.

Key Mathematics Concepts and Skills

• Identify common attributes of leaves. [Patterns, Functions, and Algebra Goal 1]

• Use rules to sort leaves. [Patterns, Functions, and Algebra Goal 1]

Other Skills Listening and Speaking

Terms to Use sort, group, groups

Materials paper bags; newspaper or butcher paper; yarn, string, paper plates, or trays (optional); small strips of paper and writing tools to make labels (optional)

Planning Tip Plan to do this activity on a nice fall day with lots of leaves on the ground. Bring leaves into the classroom if it isn't possible for children to collect them. The activity will also work well using other natural objects such as rocks, shells, or seeds.

 **Main Activity**   ✔Whole Group   ✔Small Group   ✔Partners   ✔Center

Pass out bags and tell the group that they will be going on a nature walk to collect leaves. Encourage children to collect a variety of leaves in their bags, especially those they find interesting.

After the walk, discuss different ways to sort the leaves. Because dry autumn leaves crumble easily, cover the floor or table with newspaper or butcher paper. Try one or more sorting schemes as a group; children can select one or two leaves from their bags to fit the categories the group decides on. A few possible categories include color, shape, size, long/short stems, or crumbled/whole, but children will likely think of others. You may want to use pieces of yarn or string to mark off the groups. As you sort, add circles as needed for new categories. Label each group.

Children can work alone or with a partner to sort their leaves at a Center. Provide several long pieces of yarn or string and encourage children to create as many circles as they need to accommodate their sorting schemes. If desired, help children make labels for their groupings.

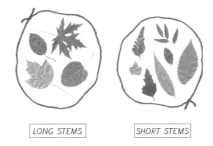

LONG STEMS   SHORT STEMS

One way to sort leaves into yarn circles

▶ Connections

Art Connection Children can make leaf rubbings. Demonstrate how to tape a leaf onto the back of lightweight white paper and rub a peeled crayon lengthwise over the leaf until the design of the leaf appears on the paper. Children can make multiple rubbings on the same sheet of paper.

Literacy and Science Connections Provide leaf books or posters and encourage children to try to match their leaves to ones they see in the pictures. Many children enjoy learning the names of the trees that leaves are from.

Outdoor Connection Children can work together to make a leaf pile (using their hands or rakes) and then have a leaf-jumping party. Remind children to be careful and to jump feet first. Always keep the leaves in large piles to cushion children's jumps.

NOTE See the Nature all Around and the Weather and Seasons themes in *Resources for the Pre-Kindergarten Classroom* for other activity suggestions related to natural objects.

NOTE Children can sort onto paper plates or trays, or simply make distinct piles on the newspaper or butcher paper, but many children enjoy using the yarn. Yarn circles also allow them to easily spread out their leaves and create new categories as needed.

Related Books

- *Fall Leaves Fall!* by Zoe Hall (Scholastic, 2000)
- *Leaf Jumpers* by Carole Gerber (Charlesbridge Publishing, 2004)
- *Red Leaf, Yellow Leaf* by Lois Ehlert (Harcourt Children's Books, 1991)

P·7 Exploration of Pattern Blocks

 Objective To provide an opportunity for children to explore and play with pattern blocks.

Key Mathematics Concepts and Skills

• Explore shapes using manipulatives. [Geometry Goal 1]

• Manipulate geometric shaps to build shapes, pictures, and designs from geometric shapes. [Geometry Goal 2]

• Explore repeating shape and color patterns. [Patterns, Functions, and Algebra Goal 1]

• Explore sorting objects by shape and color. [Patterns, Functions, and Algebra Goal 1]

Other Skills Creative Expression, Fine Motor

Terms to Use pattern blocks, sort, pattern, shape and color names

Materials pattern blocks; trays or black construction paper (optional); camera (optional)

▶ Main Activity

☐ Whole Group   ☐ Small Group   ☐ Partners   ✔ Center

Children need ample time to explore and play with pattern blocks before they are more formally introduced to activities that use them. Put the pattern blocks where children will have easy access to them and ample space to make creations. You might provide large trays or black construction paper to define the work space.

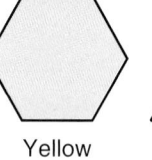 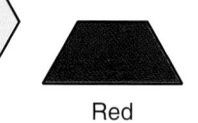 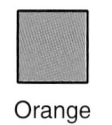   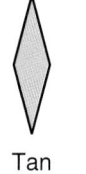

| Yellow Hexagon | Red Trapezoid | Orange Square | Green Triangle | Blue Rhombus | Tan Rhombus |

Observe what children do as they play with the blocks. Children might count, sort, stack, or make designs, pictures, and patterns. Comment on children's activities and creations, without directing children's free exploration or play: *I see you sorted the blocks by color (or shape). That is an interesting pattern you made; you have a triangle after every square. Your design uses all the shapes.* You might ask questions to gently guide children to expand their thinking and exploration: *Can you sort the blocks another way? Is there another way to stack the blocks? Do any of the blocks fit together to make other shapes?* You may want to take photographs of children's designs to display or to put into a class book.

Make pattern blocks available for free play on a regular basis over a period of several weeks or longer. Over time, encourage all children to give them a try. When all children have had time to freely explore and use the pattern blocks, you can begin to introduce other activities that use pattern blocks. (See Pattern-Block Pictures, page 68, Pattern-Block Puzzles I, page 278, and Making Snake Patterns, page 318.)

▶ Connections

Art Connection Children can incorporate pattern-block shapes in their artwork by tracing around pattern blocks or using paper shapes cut from the pattern-block masters (*Math Masters,* pages 38–43). Copy the masters on colored paper to correspond to the colors of the pattern blocks. Later, children might use the shapes to record their pattern-block creations on paper. You will probably also find other uses for the shapes on the masters.

Mathematics Connection Children enjoy using small, unbreakable mirrors with pattern blocks. Their explorations will spark many discoveries, including an informal exposure to symmetry as they notice that they can use the mirrors to create a design with two or more matching sides.

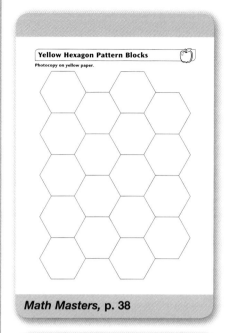

Math Masters, p. 38

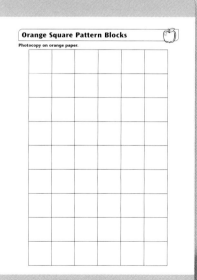

Math Masters, p. 39

P·8 Sorting Pasta

 Objective **To reinforce sorting skills through a sensory activity.**

Key Mathematics Concepts and Skills
- Identify and describe attributes of pasta, such as size, shape, color, and texture. [Patterns, Functions, and Algebra Goal 1]
- Use rules to sort pasta in various ways. [Patterns, Functions, and Algebra Goal 1]

Other Skills Fine Motor, Listening and Speaking

Terms to Use sort, group, groups, words that describe size, words that describe shape

Materials different types of uncooked pasta; large box or tub (or empty sensory table); sorting trays, such as egg cartons or deli or TV trays; food coloring and rubbing alcohol, or liquid watercolors (optional); large jar (optional)

> **Planning Tip** Collect a variety of types of pasta. To incorporate color as a variable, you may include colored pastas from the grocery store or dye some of the pasta by shaking it in a jar with food coloring or liquid watercolors. Add rubbing alcohol to the food coloring for more vivid colors. Then drain and let dry. **It is not safe for children to assist you because of the alcohol fumes.**

▶ Main Activity

☐ Whole Group ✔ Small Group ☐ Partners ✔ Center

Put several kinds of uncooked pasta into a large container or in your sensory table. Provide time for children to explore the pasta. Many will enjoy the sensory experience of feeling, pouring, and stirring the pasta in the container. To avoid the spread of germs, remind them not to eat the pasta.

When children seem ready, provide sorting trays and invite them to sort the pasta in any way they choose. Children may sort by shape, size, color, texture, whether they like to eat it, whether it has a hole, or other characteristics.

After children have had an opportunity to sort the pasta in different ways, begin a discussion by asking questions such as: *What do you notice about the pasta? How did*

> **NOTE** See Pasta Patterns, page 312, for another Main Activity and additional Connections that use pasta.

you sort it? Did anyone sort it a different way? Can you think of any other ways to sort the pasta? Provide opportunities for children to look at others' sorting schemes before clearing the trays for new sorters.

Ongoing Assessment: Kid Watching

Open-ended sorting activities such as this one provide an opportunity for you to observe children as they create categories and classify objects. Note whether children have difficulty finding a sorting scheme. Can they sort in different ways? What attributes do they notice—shape? size? color?

▶ Connections

Science Connection Discuss where pasta comes from and how it is made. You might read an informational book such as *From Wheat to Pasta (Changes)* by Robert Egan (Children's Press [CT], 1997).

Mathematics Connection You might cook several types of pasta. Have children taste them and create a graph showing their favorite pasta. Choose your favorite graphing technique.

 Family Connection You may want to use the Sorting Laundry Family Connection (*Math Masters,* page 89) to encourage families to find natural opportunities to sort at home.

Math Masters, p. 89

 Developing Oral Language ELL

This activity provides an opportunity to develop descriptive language for size, shape, texture, and other attributes. Point out characteristics and model with comments such as: *Feel this one; it is* bumpy. *That one is* straight *and* smooth. *Can you find another* curved *one? Make* a curved *shape with your hand, like this!*

 Related Books

• *Strega Nona* by Tomie dePaola (Editorial Everest, 1999) (There are several other Strega Nona stories that children will enjoy.)

P·9 Pasta Patterns

 Objective To provide practice with creating and extending repeating patterns through an art project.

Key Mathematics Concepts and Skills
- Create repeating patterns using different shapes and/or colors of pasta. [Patterns, Functions, and Algebra Goal 1]
- Describe pasta patterns. [Patterns, Functions, and Algebra Goal 1]

Other Skills Creative Expression, Fine Motor

Terms to Use pattern, repeat

Materials two or more types and/or colors of pasta; strips of tagboard or cardboard (Sentence strips work well.); glue; markers or crayons (optional); food coloring and rubbing alcohol, or liquid watercolors (optional); large jar (optional)

▶ Main Activity

☐ Whole Group ✔ Small Group ☐ Partners ✔ Center

Invite children to use two pasta shapes to make a pasta pattern. Encourage children to describe their patterns. For example: small, big; small, big; small, big…; or twisty, twisty, straight; twisty, twisty, straight; twisty, twisty, straight… . Give children time to use the shapes to explore and create a variety of patterns.

Give children a strip of tagboard or cardboard and have them glue one of their pasta patterns onto the strip. Children may want to decorate the area around the pattern with markers or crayons. Pasta patterns make an interesting display for the classroom.

Planning Tip You may want to use colored pasta. You can get green (spinach) and red (tomato) pasta at the grocery store. Or, you might dye each type of pasta a different color with food coloring or liquid watercolors. (See Sorting Pasta, page 310 for directions.)

NOTE See Sorting Pasta, page 310, for another Main Activity and additional Connections that use pasta.

A pasta pattern

Adjusting for Age and Development

Use more than two kinds of pasta and encourage children to create more complex patterns. You can also provide different colors of the same type of pasta to allow for more variety.

Ongoing Assessment: Kid Watching

You can use this activity to assess children's understanding of patterns and their abilities to create their own patterns. Note whether children stick with AB patterns or branch out to more complicated patterns.

▶ Connections

Science and Cooking Connection Have children compare the differences between cooked and uncooked pasta. Involve children in cooking the pasta, if possible. The class can cook and/or eat a pasta snack, such as pasta salad, macaroni and cheese, or noodle pudding.

Music and Movement Connection Children can do a version of Freeze Dance. When the music is playing, children should dance loosely, like a cooked noodle. When the music stops, children should freeze stiff, like uncooked pasta.

Art Connection Children might enjoy using a variety of pasta to create collages.

Related Book

- *Strega Nona* by Tomie dePaola (Editorial Everest, 1999)

(There are several other Strega Nona stories that children will enjoy.)

Building

P·10 Making Jewelry

 Objective To provide opportunities to explore and create patterns through an art project.

Key Mathematics Concepts and Skills

• Create and describe patterned jewelry. [Patterns, Functions, and Algebra Goal 1]

Other Skills Creative Expression, Fine Motor

Terms to Use pattern, repeat

Materials colored beads, dyed macaroni, colorful loop cereal, or other material for stringing in assorted colors; string, yarn (Dip the ends in glue or wrap them with tape.), pipe cleaners, or lanyard strings; patterned necklaces (optional)

Planning Tip If you plan to use colored macaroni, see Sorting Pasta, page 310, for directions for dyeing pasta. If you'd like children to give the jewelry they make as a gift, plan to do this activity near Mother's Day or another holiday.

▶ Main Activity

☐ Whole Group ✔ Small Group ☐ Partners ✔ Center

Show a small group of children your chosen materials. Invite them to use the materials to make a necklace or bracelet with a color pattern. Remind children that a pattern repeats. You might want to reinforce or review the concept by showing children any patterned jewelry that you have. To help children get started, place a handful of beads or other stringing material on the table and ask children to help you rearrange the items to form a repeating color pattern.

Give each child a string with a large knot or a bead tied to the end. As children begin to string, talk with them about the patterns they are making and encourage them to look at and describe one another's patterns. Assist anyone who is having difficulty. Sometimes it is helpful for children to hear or say the colors in order as they try to

identify or extend a pattern. When they are finished, tie the ends of the string together so children can wear what they made or give it to a family member, if desired.

After everyone has had a chance to make something, place any extra materials in the Math or Art Center and invite children to create additional patterned necklaces or bracelets.

Adjusting for Age and Development

You may want to limit the beads, or other stringing material, to two or three colors. Later, the activity could be repeated with additional materials, so that children can make patterns using different shapes and/or different materials (macaroni, bead; macaroni, bead; macaroni, bead...).

▶ Connections

Dramatic Play Connection Encourage children to wear patterned necklaces and bracelets and other patterned clothing when they dress up. Children may be interested in pretending to buy and sell their jewelry in a jewelry store that they set up in the Dramatic Play Center.

Group Time Connection Invite children to look for patterns on their clothing. Note that these patterns may not be linear. Help children find language to describe these more complicated patterns. *Your pattern seems to go in a circle* or *The red flower is always next to the white one,* for example. Encourage children to wear something to school with a pattern on it. You may want to wear patterned clothes as well.

Family Connection You may want to use the Creating Patterns Family Connection (*Math Masters,* page 88) to encourage families to explore patterns at home.

Ongoing Assessment: Kid Watching

You can use this activity to informally assess whether children can create and describe repeating patterns and to note whether they tend to create AB patterns or more complicated patterns.

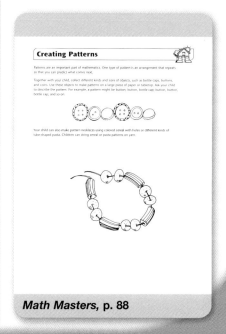

Math Masters, p. 88

Building

P·11 Child Patterns

Objective To provide practice with making and identifying patterns using children's bodies.

Key Mathematics Concepts and Skills
- Use position words to describe "child" patterns. [Geometry Goal 2]
- Extend and describe repeating patterns using children's bodies. [Patterns, Functions, and Algebra Goal 1]
- Create "child" patterns. [Patterns, Functions, and Algebra Goal 1]

Other Skills Cooperation, Listening and Speaking

Terms to Use pattern, repeat

Materials none

▶ Main Activity

☑ Whole Group ☐ Small Group ☐ Partners ☐ Center

Call several children to the front of the group and begin to arrange them in a stand/sit pattern. Continue until the other children discern a pattern. Ask: *What is the pattern? Why is it a pattern?* Engage the class in extending your pattern by calling a couple more children and asking the group how they should be positioned.

NOTE This is a good opportunity for children to practice position words.

Repeat with a different pattern, this time calling on children who weren't part of the previous pattern. You might ask a child to suggest the pattern by whispering it to you or, eventually, by telling his or her classmates how and where to position themselves. Possible body positions might include the following: facing forward, facing backward, holding arms up, holding arms down, tiptoeing, or squatting.

Repeat the activity frequently using children's suggestions. Children will also enjoy creating patterns with other characteristics, such as boy/girl, long hair/short hair, and clothing details (long sleeves/short sleeves, solid colors/stripes, and so on). Begin with 2-part patterns and increase the complexity as children are ready.

▶ Connections

Mathematics Connection As a transition activity, you can call children to line up according to a pattern such as: long pants, short pants; long pants, short pants; long pants, short pants …; or girl, girl, boy; girl, girl, boy; girl, girl, boy … . Encourage them to guess your patterning rule.

Literacy Connection Many popular children's books use patterned language. When you share a book such as *Brown Bear, Brown Bear, What Do You See?* by Bill Martin, Jr. (Henry Holt & Co., 1992) or *I Went Walking* by Sue Williams (Gulliver Books, 1990), help children identify the phrases that repeat. An interesting discussion might emerge if you ask children how these types of patterns in books are similar to, and different from, patterns made with children, movements, sounds, or materials such as pasta or colored beads.

Ongoing Assessment: Kid Watching

You can use this activity to informally assess children's abilities to recognize, extend, and create patterns. Over time, note whether children are comfortable only with AB patterns or whether they can work with more complex patterns as well.

NOTE Recognizing and reciting the language patterns in books is a good pre-reading literacy skill.

P·12 Snake Patterns

(◎) **Objective** To expand children's experiences with patterns.

Key Mathematics Concepts and Skills

• Notice and describe patterns in nature. [Patterns, Functions, and Algebra Goal 1]

• Create repeating patterns with pattern blocks. [Patterns, Functions, and Algebra Goal 1]

Other Skills Creative Expression, Fine Motor

Terms to Use pattern, repeat, shape names

Materials Teaching Aid Masters (*Math Masters,* pp. 38–43) and colored paper (optional); pattern blocks; stick-on notes or small pieces of paper; pencils or markers; pictures of real snakes

---

Planning Tip There are many nonfiction children's books about snakes. Find photographs of snakes from one or two books to show children.

▶ Main Activity

☐ Whole Group ✔ Small Group ☐ Partners ✔ Center

Show children pictures of snakes and encourage children to look at the patterns on the snakes' skin. Reinforce the idea that patterns repeat and ask children to describe the patterns they notice. Tell children they are going to make their own snake patterns. Have each child make a snake head on a small piece of paper or a stick-on note. Children can draw their own snake heads, or you can provide an outline that children can use to trace the head shape and then add details. Place each child's snake head at one end of his or her workspace. Ask them to create their snakes' patterns with pattern blocks. Encourage children to share their patterns with each other as they work.

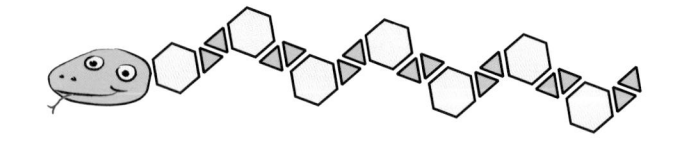

NOTE The patterns on real snakes' skin are often quite complex. Many children will enjoy discovering and describing these patterns. However, when children are ready to make their own patterns, help them understand that they won't be able to exactly replicate real snake-skin patterns. Some teachers wait and show pictures of real snakes *after* children have made their pattern-block snakes.

Some children may want to replicate their snakes on paper by tracing around the pattern blocks they have used or by gluing cutouts of pattern-block shapes from the pattern-block shapes found on *Math Masters,* pages 38–43. You can also take photographs of children's snakes.

 ## Ongoing Assessment: Kid Watching

Observe whether children are able to use the pattern blocks to make patterns, or whether they simply make designs. Pattern blocks are a bit more complex than some of the materials that children have used for patterning so far.

▶ Connections

Literacy Connection Share tongue twisters about snakes and have children move like snakes.

> *Slippery, slimy, snakes slide slowly.*
> *Slippery, slimy, snakes slither smoothly.*

Art Connection Put out play dough or clay for children to make snakes. Encourage children to add patterns to the snakes by pressing small items such as marker tops or pencil points into the play dough or clay.

Science Connection Many children may be interested in learning more about snakes. Provide books, pictures, and other resources for children to explore. You might arrange for someone to bring a snake to the classroom.

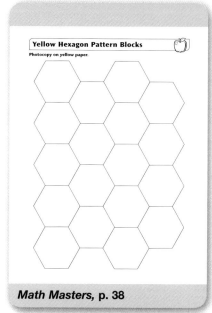

Math Masters, p. 38

One of 6 masters

 ### Related Books

- *Hide and Snake* by Keith Baker (Harcourt Children's Books, 1991)
- *Lots and Lots of Zebra Stripes: Patterns in Nature* by Stephen R. Swinburne (Boyds Mills Press, 1998)

Building

P·13 Sorting Children

 Objective To provide ongoing practice with sorting by attributes.

Key Mathematics Concepts and Skills

• Identify and describe attributes of children and clothing. [Patterns, Functions, and Algebra Goal 1]

• Use rules to sort children in various ways. [Patterns, Functions, and Algebra Goal 1]

Other Skills Cooperation, Listening and Speaking

Terms to Use sort, group, groups

Materials none

▶ **Main Activity**   ✔Whole Group ✔Small Group ☐ Partners ☐ Center

Gather the class or a small group of children together and have them sit in a circle. Remind them of things they have sorted previously; then share, or ask children to share, a few examples of groupings they remember. (Examples might be sorting counters by color, or leaves by size.) Tell them that today they are going to sort children. Explain that you are going to sort them so that all the children with long sleeves are sitting together, and all the children with short sleeves are sitting together. Go around the circle and, one at a time, send each child to the correct group. Invite children to verify that you sorted correctly.

Ask children to suggest other ways they might be sorted and try some of their ideas. For example, if a child mentions sorting by shirt color, have all children with mostly white shirts sit together, all children with mostly red shirts sit together, or all children with striped shirts sit together. Provide this type of sorting practice frequently throughout

Planning Tip Some teachers find it works best to introduce this activity in small groups to help children understand the concept and to minimize the wait-time while sorting. Once children are familiar with it, this is a good whole-group or transition activity.

NOTE You can reinforce these skills during transition times. For example, call all children with red shoes to line up, then children with blue shoes, and so on. Or call all children with long sleeves to get their coats, or children with brown hair to wash their hands.

the year, using a variety of attributes related to children or their clothing (hair color or hair length, clothing color, belt or no belt, and so on). Gradually, allow children to work together to sort themselves according to agreed-upon groupings, and you can check their sorting.

Adjusting for Age and Development

Follow the children's lead. If they are not ready to suggest ways to sort, continue to suggest categories for sorting and stick with obvious attributes, such as those based on clothing color. Once children are very familiar with sorting in this context, you might play *What's My Rule?*— a game in which children try to figure out your sorting rule. (See *What's My Rule?* Game, page 326, for instructions.)

▶ Connections

Literacy Connection Read *How Many Snails? A Counting Book* by Paul Giganti, Jr. (Greenwillow, 1988) and discuss how the objects in the story can be grouped. The prompts in the story are good starting points for discussion and also provide good counting practice.

Music and Movement Connection Many songs involve groups of children doing various movements according to what they are wearing. See the Music and Movement Connection in Officer, Officer, page 300, and *Resources for the Pre-Kindergarten Classroom* for suggestions, in addition to using songs that you already know.

Related Book

- *3 Little Firefighters* by Stuart J. Murphy (HarperCollins Publishers, 2003)

P·14 Sorting Vehicles

 Objective To provide experiences with sorting by a variety of attributes.

Key Mathematics Concepts and Skills

• Identify and describe attributes of toy vehicles. [Patterns, Functions, and Algebra Goal 1]

• Use rules to sort toy vehicles in various ways. [Patterns, Functions, and Algebra Goal 1]

Other Skills Cooperation, Listening and Speaking

Terms to Use sort, group, groups

Materials toy vehicles; paper plates or trays (optional)

Planning Tip Collect a variety of toy vehicles (different types, colors, and sizes).

▶ **Main Activity**   ☐ Whole Group ✔Small Group ☐ Partners ✔Center

Show children your assortment of toy vehicles and allow them to peruse and play with the collection. After some time, ask questions such as: *What do you notice about the vehicles? How can you group them?* Encourage children to think of different ways to sort the vehicles. You might have children sort the vehicles independently, or you might have a small group of children work together to sort them one way, and then a different way. Some children may like to use paper plates or trays to organize their groupings. Leave the materials in a Center for children to continue sorting in different ways. Make time for them to share their sorting schemes with others before cleaning up.

NOTE It is important for children to have sorting experiences with materials that allow them to be creative in their sorting schemes. Toy vehicles are particularly good for sorting because they can differ in a range of attributes. Among other things, children can sort vehicles by color, size, number of wheels, speed, function, or whether they travel on the ground, in air, or in water.

See the Transportation Theme in *Resources for the Pre-Kindergarten Classroom* for other mathematics activities that involve vehicles.

Racing Cars

"Regular" Cars

Emergency Vehicles

Encourage children to sort vehicles by two attributes such as white *and* trucks. Children may want to try sorting using a negative attribute such as ground vehicles and *not* ground vehicles.

 Ongoing Assessment: Kid Watching

You can use this activity to informally assess children's understanding of sorting and their abilities to sort in different ways and describe their groupings.

▶ Connections

Art Connections Children enjoy doing "vehicle printing." Show them how to dip toy vehicles in a thin layer of paint on a tray, and then drive them across their papers to make lines, designs, and patterns.

Children can also create vehicles using scrap materials such as cardboard tubes, boxes, buttons, or paper. Or, they might use collage materials or pre-cut geometric shapes to make pictures of vehicles. Children can sort the vehicles they make.

Manipulatives Connection Children can sort a collection of coins. Although they do not need to know the names or values of coins yet, sorting coins by appearance (size or color, for example) lays groundwork for later learning.

 Family Connection You may want to use the Sorting Laundry Family Connection (*Math Masters*, page 89) to encourage families to find natural opportunities to sort at home.

Math Masters, p. 89

Building

P·15 Weaving Outdoors

Objective To provide kinesthetic patterning experiences in an outdoor setting.

Key Mathematics Concepts and Skills

• Use and describe position and spatial relationships *(in, out, over, under, through)* while weaving. [Geometry Goal 2]

• Use rules to create and extend patterns while weaving. [Patterns, Functions, and Algebra Goal 1]

Other Skills Creative Expression, Cooperation, Fine Motor

Terms to Use weave, in, out, over, under, through, front, back, pattern, repeat

Materials fence; strips of scrap material in different lengths and colors

Planning Tip Find a section of a chain-link or slat fence that children can use for weaving. Cut or tear material into narrow strips and lengths appropriate to the fence you are using. You might ask parents for donations of old sheets or other scrap material (plastic tablecloths, crepe paper, ribbon, or yarn). If a fence is not available, children can weave on laundry baskets, bicycle tires, or berry baskets.

▶ Main Activity

✔Whole Group ✔Small Group ☐ Partners ✔Center

The over/under pattern of weaving provides a concrete and kinesthetic patterning experience for children. The collaborative effort and festive look of a woven fence makes the experience satisfying. A woven fence makes a great decoration for a spring gathering.

Depending on the span of your fence, you may need children to work in small groups, so they won't be too crowded. Show children the weaving materials and demonstrate how to weave on the fence. Ask children whether they notice any pattern in the weaving motion. Emphasize the in/out and over/under pattern of the material going through the slats. You may need to hold children's hands and say the pattern out loud to get some children started. In addition to the movement pattern, some children will be interested in creating a visual pattern with the colors in their weaving.

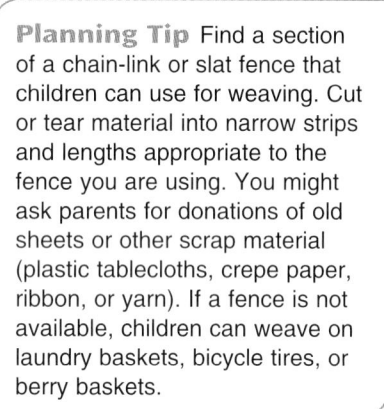

Photo: Julie A. Vogel

For children who have not had previous experience weaving, you might start with a simple paper weaving activity such as the one described in the Art Connection below.

▶ Connections

Art Connection Weave with paper strips on a paper loom. Cut paper strips about 9" × 1". To make a paper loom, fold a 9" × 12" piece of construction paper in half to 9" × 6". With the paper folded, make 5 cuts (3 for younger children) starting from the folded edge to about 1 inch from the top. Make the cuts at least $1\frac{1}{2}$ inches apart. Open the paper to make the loom for children to weave on. Help children weave the strips in and out of the loom. When finished, use glue sticks to tack the edges down.

Alternately, children can weave on looms made with rubber bands on trays from the supermarket. Provide chenille stems for children to weave over and under the rubber bands.

Music and Movement Connection Have children join hands in a circle and sing "Go In and Out the Circle," which is featured on the Sing Everyday! CD. Children can do the motions as the class sings. Select a child, or a train of children, to weave in and out as the group sings.

> Go in and out the circle,
> Go in and out the circle,
> Go in and out the circle,
> As we have done before.

Modify the words and actions to reinforce other position words, such as *Go 'round and 'round the circle, Reach up and touch the sky,* or *Bend down and touch the ground.*

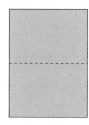

Fold the paper in half.

Cut lines to make slits.

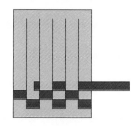

Use paper strips for weaving.

P·16 "What's My Rule?" Game

 Objective To provide practice with identifying and describing attributes and sorting rules through a game.

Key Mathematics Concepts and Skills

• Identify and describe attributes of children and clothing. [Patterns, Functions, and Algebra Goal 1]

• Identify sorting rules. [Patterns, Functions, and Algebra Goal 1]

Other Skills Cooperation

Terms to Use rule, sort, group, groups

Materials none

Planning Tip Before learning to play *"What's My Rule?,"* the class should have many experiences identifying attributes of children and sorting children into groups. See *Officer, Officer* Game, page 300 and Sorting Children, page 320 for activities that provide practice with these skills.

▶ Main Activity

✔Whole Group ✔Small Group ☐ Partners ☐ Center

Introduce the game *"What's My Rule?"* in which children try to figure out your sorting rule. Begin with an easily observable attribute, such as shirt color. Without telling children how you are sorting them, select a group of children according to your rule, such as everyone wearing red shirts. Have the children you select stand up or come to the front of the group, so they are easily distinguished from the other children. When all children who fit the rule are in the group, ask whether anyone knows how you sorted them. You might ask: *How are all the children in this group alike?* Give clues, as needed, to help children identify the attribute. After they describe how you sorted them, explain that they have figured out the "rule."

Play again using a variety of attributes related to children or their clothing, such as children wearing hair ribbons or white sneakers. Each time, ask children to figure out

NOTE *"What's My Rule?"* is a good transition activity. Have children guess the rule you are using as you call them to line up or move to another activity.

your sorting rule. You can also play *"What's My Rule?"* with collections of objects such as buttons, blocks, or toy vehicles.

 Adjusting for Age and Development

For an additional challenge, use two attributes in your sorting rule. For example, select all children wearing red shirts who are also girls. Some children might be ready to think of rules and sort their classmates.

▶ Connections

Art Connection Put out a collection of art materials: construction paper cut into small shapes, markers, crayons, and collage materials such as buttons, beads, bottle caps, and pasta. Invite children to make a collage using only one category of material, such as all round, all red, or all small. Children can take turns guessing the rules for each other's artwork.

Literacy Connection If some of your children are learning letter sounds, you may want to play *"What's My Rule?"* with beginning sounds of words. List words all beginning with the same letter. Children can guess the rule (words beginning with *d*, for example).

Family Connection You may want to use the Sorting Laundry Family Connection (*Math Masters,* page 89) to encourage families to find sorting opportunities at home.

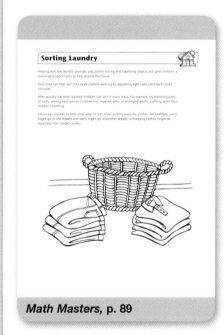

Math Masters, p. 89

P·17 Pattern Search

◎ **Objective** To encourage children to find patterns in their environment.

Key Mathematics Concepts and Skills
- Notice and describe patterns in the environment. [Patterns, Functions, and Algebra Goal 1]

Other Skills Listening and Speaking

Terms to Use pattern, repeat

Materials camera and/or drawing materials (optional)

Planning Tip This activity can take place in the school building or outside. It should be done after children are very familiar with the concept of patterns. Doing the activity in small groups provides more opportunity for interaction and discussion.

▶ Main Activity

☑ Whole Group ☑ Small Group ☐ Partners ☐ Center

Ask children to look around the room and identify patterns. It is often hard for children to see patterns in the environment at first, so you might point out a few, such as patterns on carpeting or floor tiles, clothing, vents, or windows. After a few examples, many children will notice numerous patterns in their surroundings. As they identify patterns, ask children to describe the patterns by naming what they see. For example, they might say "red square, black square, red square, black square, red square, black square, …" to describe the floor tile. Or, children might describe the heating vent as "line, open space, line, open space, line, open space, … ." In each case, ask children how the pattern would continue: *What comes next? What part repeats?*

Continue this activity by taking children on a walk to look for patterns outside or around the school. If you have a camera, take photographs of the patterns to create a display in the classroom or a class book about the walk. Some children may be

Patterned slats in a heating vent

interested in drawing pictures of patterns they see. Point out patterns in the environment frequently. Over time, children will do the same.

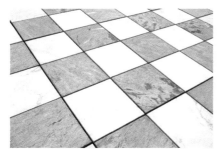

Patterned floor tiles

A patterned picket fence

▶ Connections

Art Connection Children can cut pictures of patterns, such as those on natural objects, buildings, or clothing, from old magazines. Have children glue the pictures onto a large piece of paper or posterboard labeled Patterns All Around and encourage them to add to the group collage over time. You might also add photographs or drawings from your pattern walk(s).

Blocks Connection Encourage children to incorporate patterns in their block buildings. You might display photographs of interesting buildings in your Block Center for inspiration. Postcards are a good source of photographs.

Literacy Connection Invite children to look for patterns in illustrations as you read picture books to the class. You may want to look for books with patterned borders, such as several by Vera Williams or Jan Brett.

Outdoors Connection Invite children to create patterns on the sidewalk with different colors of chalk.

 Related Books

- *Market Day: A Story Told with Folk Art* by Lois Ehlert (Harcourt Books, 2000)
- *Pattern Bugs* by Trudy Harris (Lerner Publishing Group, 2001)
- *Pattern Fish* by Trudy Harris (Lerner Publishing Group, 2000)

Expanding

P·18 What's Missing?

Objective To reinforce and expand children's understanding of patterning through a partner activity.

Key Mathematics Concepts and Skills

• Create and extend patterns. [Patterns, Functions, and Algebra Goal 1]

• Use a pattern's rule to identify a missing element in the pattern. [Patterns, Functions, and Algebra Goal 1]

Other Skills Cooperation, Fine Motor

Terms to Use pattern, repeat, missing

Materials various manipulatives that can be used to make patterns

---

Planning Tip Choose a variety of materials for patterning so children have the opportunity to create patterns that are based on attributes other than just color. Children should have many experiences with patterning prior to doing this activity.

▶ Main Activity

☐ Whole Group ✔ Small Group ✔ Partners ✔ Center

Create a pattern and show it to the children in a small group. To make sure they recognize the pattern, have children help you extend your pattern. Then have children close their eyes while you remove a piece from the middle of the pattern, leaving the space empty. Tell children to open their eyes and try to figure out which piece is missing. After children have guessed, show them the piece and put it back to confirm the pattern. Repeat several times, increasing the complexity of the pattern as children are ready. If children are having difficulty, encourage them to describe the pattern out loud to help them determine the missing piece. Once children understand the activity, they can repeat it several times with a partner. Children should take turns creating patterns and figuring out the missing part. Leave the materials in a Center for children to play together.

NOTE Children tend to expect color and shape patterns. Expand children's thinking by creating new and unexpected patterns. For example, if you are using small cubes you might create your pattern by alternating stacked cubes and side-by-side cubes. Or, if you are using bear counters, you might create a pattern based on the way the bears are facing, such as front, front, back; front, front, back; front, front, back;... .

Adjusting for Age and Development

For a simpler partner patterning activity, have children begin a pattern with manipulatives for their partner to extend. Children can take turns creating the patterns and extending them.

▶ Connections

Music and Movement Connections The following songs incorporate patterned movements:

"Pease Porridge Hot"
Children sit facing a partner. They do the movements together, repeating the pattern for each line. When children are comfortable with the songs, partners might agree to leave out one part of the pattern each time and see whether they can remain synchronized.

> *Pease porridge hot,* (pat thighs, clap hands, clap partner's hands)
> *Pease porridge cold,* (Repeat movements for each line.)
> *Pease porridge in the pot,*
> *Nine days old.*
> *Some like it hot, some like it cold,*
> *Some like it in the pot, nine days old.*

"Head, Shoulders, Knees and Toes"
Children point to each body part as they sing the song. They repeat the song several times, each time omitting the word for the next body part but continuing to do the motions. The last time the song is sung, there are no words, just movements. Speed up as you sing for extra fun and challenge.

> *Head, shoulders, knees and toes, knees and toes,*
> *Head, shoulders, knees and toes, knees and toes,*
> *Eyes and ears and mouth and nose,*
> *Head, shoulders, knees and toes, knees and toes.*

Index

Notes

Notes

Notes

Notes